The *Whitefaced* drift of Dartmoor's '*prapper*' Sheep

C Pearse

Widecombe Fair

14 - 09 - 04.

'Dartmoor Whitefaces' about to be let out at Runnage Gate (circa late 1930s) (Richard Coaker).
(John Hamlyn Collection via Tom Greeves. Courtesy of the Coaker family).

The *Whitefaced* drift of Dartmoor's '*prapper*' Sheep

'A story as olde as them hills'

Commemorating the 50th Anniversary of the Whitefaced Dartmoor Sheep Breeders Association

Colin Pearse

'The Runnage Drift'

Published in 2004 by
Colin Pearse

Copyright © 2004 Colin Pearse

ISBN 0-9548570-0-3

All rights reserved. No part of this publication may be reproduced,
stored in a retrieval system, transmitted or utilized in any form or by any means,
electronic, mechanical, photocopying, recording or otherwise, without
the permission in writing from the publishers.

Every effort has been made to trace all the copyright holders of the
material reprinted herein, but if any have been inadvertently overlooked
the publishers will be pleased to make the necessary arrangements
at the first opportunity.

Printed in Great Britain by
Short Run Press Ltd, Exeter, Devon

Contents

Widecombe Fair at 'Two-Gates' (between the two World Wars) moving out from the village for a while. 'Very strong charactered' Whitefaced Dartmoor Rams.
William Langdon (far right) casting his eye over these sheep. Hamel-Down can be seen on the skyline.
(Courtesy of Pat and Patrick Coaker).

Preface

There is a lot to admire about sheep. It may have something to do with our long history with them, their trust in us, their utility, mothering instincts, variety, and ability to live in a wide range of environments and weathers. They also are pleasing to the eye, and add both to the view and to the quality of our lives. Despite all this, there remains something about them that even those who work with them may find hard to define.

We see and hear them usually in flocks and this has become so much a part of the British countryside scene – iconic not least in the uplands such as Dartmoor. And there is no doubt that lambs have an appeal all of their own – but so too do all sheep. Take a little time to look at the single animal and admire, revere and respect it.

In addition to seeing sheep as flocks that roam these hills, not just as providers of meat and wool but also playing their part as conservation graziers, and as well as seeing them as living entities in their own right, we can look at them as a specific breed or type – a *selective* process reflecting fitness of purpose and place.

In this book we gain a significant insight into the story of one particular breed – the Whitefaced Dartmoor, a descendant of the native heath sheep. Today, some five hundred Dartmoor farms keep sheep, but only a small number of the total 240,000 sheep are Whitefaced Dartmoors. These sheep are now far less common than in the past – their heydays were in the 17th and 18th centuries. Their on-going story reflects the ups and downs of farming and a variety of pressures, internal and external, and changing market demands that can affect a geographical area and its people. Today, efforts are being made to ensure that the breed remains as much a part of Dartmoor as the tors and hill ponies are, and in this respect the Dartmoor National Park Authority greatly appreciates the work of the Whitefaced Dartmoor Sheep Breeders Association and the vigilance of individual farmers who still keep them. Colin Pearse is one of those farmers.

Flocks, individuals and breeds: I like sheep, and particularly that inextricable link between them, working dogs, people and place, and the associated vocabulary that enriches our language and stories that enrich our lives. These aspects are admirably reflected in the following pages. After reading there can be no doubt that Whitefaced Dartmoors are part of our living Dartmoor and national heritage.

John Weir
Head of Communications
Dartmoor National Park Authority

Introduction

(Photo: Chris Chapman).

As I hold this Whitefaced lamb, we exchange palpitations, and my heart begins to quicken as I plot its past in my mind, and ponder that its ancestors were probably the wild and restless creatures of the moor; later to become 'moorwise' in its own survival world, as a truly born thing of its Dartmoor homeland.

My very first memories of Dartmoor were my parents Sunday drives over the moor during my innocent, uncluttered boyhood at Rattery, South Devon, and it initiated something for me that was to become a true story.

I saw rugged wilderness, depicting farmstead isolation, and being envious of its loneliness, and of landscape unspoilt; not *just* through dreamlike eyes!

I was smitten by the tidy stone-walled fields and in particular in July, the White Dutch (clover) flower buds peppering the hayfields aftermath, seen as I peered in between the wooden gates lexes, looking from the back seat of my parents car, as my father crept by, driving down narrow lanes, hoping as he might, to see other farmers crops, sheep, and cattle over the hedge!

My fascination for Dartmoor and its history was rekindled when my parents Leonard and May Pearse, and twin brother Jim and I, moved to near Moretonhampstead in 1966 from Crediton.

Through this strange circle of events, the 'introvert' was to return to the proximity of the moor, but now to live and farm and to confront the experience first hand, its true real atmosphere; its shadowy hills, it sunset splendour, its often unforgiving harshness, and sudden cruelty, and its tranquillity and landscape beauty.

This was to provide the 'touchstone' for my new life, for in 1974 Hazel (nee White) and I were married, linked now to one of Dartmoor's oldest families, that had been rooted at the moors heart at Sherril, *Widecombe-in-the-Moor*, generating insight for me into what being born on the moor could really mean for man and beast, as the permanent inhabitants. 'Some centuries ago, "Widdicombe" *belonged* to Dartmoor', hence no doubt its name. Whitefaced sheep were kept from the beginning and I was also endeared to their lively, hardy moorland character, and important survival value, never failing to excite, and who the family rightly call the 'Mother of all Dartmoors'.

A chance remark and a fortunate one from two officers of the W.F.D.S.B. Association Secretary, John Harris and Paul Vincent in the year 2000, concerning the writing of a millenium book, inspired in me a bigger story than just the important 50th Anniversary of the

Whitefaced Dartmoor Sheep Breeders Association and Flock Book, through my love for Dartmoor too.

It led me to research and incorporate something the Whitefaced sheep meant in Dartmoor's evolution as a prize-grazing area, and the bond that connected its many farming families. Also, how the South Hams together with Dartmoor, its town and villages, moulded the story, and shaped the sheep's history.

A moor with many 'spoken memories', but also with secrets dissolved in its past, that only the imagination can attempt to visualise, but eludes us in evidence today. Snippets of history, however, helps to expand the mind to some of what really happened around the moor.

I felt a sense of emptiness when I was finally about to give up all that I had gathered, and been given to record by the W.F.D.S.B.A. members and other Whitefaced breeders, to Short Run Press Ltd, the printers of the book, but to whom I'm very grateful. I believed it was very important that these many memories and photos should find a common home.

There was a sense of relief that I could 'rest my mind', no longer wondering if the right cup was awarded to a certain breeder in a certain year, or if sheep actually grazed a particular named common, or if it was the correct tor that might be overshadowing a named farm, with Whitefaced Dartmoors grazing nearby; and how many sheep went to the said fair or market, or grazed grass or ate folded roots on a farmer's fields in the South Hams; and did I remember his name correctly, and in which Parish he or his shepherd may have lived. However, I gained satisfaction when we got it right, all in the excitement of 'reliving the past'!

All innocent stuff really and 'the incomer', or as the locals call them, the 'blow-in' (that's me) from outside, must expect his thirst for knowledge to be a patient one, and realise his place, and understand the innocence of others, being where they live, and for how long!

Yet, as I talked to people and read about, and visited many of these wonderful farmsteads that nurture our sheep, I began to 'live this story'.

Metaphorically perhaps, 'looking for the way to Widecombe', was really in essence, the knowing and getting to know more the people of the area that kept Whitefaced sheep, to realise and understand the 'familiar talk' of those who spoke and knew its dialect over generations and to appreciate that 'Bonehill' could also be pronounced and written 'Bunhill', or where 'out au(w)ver' is supposed to be 'out-over', and 'Mister' is actually that Great Mis Tor on the moors western side, but its all been part of this area's deep, deep history and some still uttered in lovely dialect, and long may it remain!

So, this century's old 'jigsaw' that had been turned out of cupboards and pasted into old albums, was seeing many of its pieces fitting together in a fresh light, helped by new knowledge and technology, and rejuvenation of the old, and my quest and persistence to place in a book.

It was stimulated by 'I remember so and so', and how that someone brought a ram home in their first car, from Ashburton Market, and driver and ram nearly became hung around the gear stick by the ram's halter, and both were hanging out of the car door . . . ! Or, I think I've got some photo's and generously bringing them to me to use, feeling as they may, very proud, and myself fascinated by the antiquity of some of the black and white photos, and I worried about their safe return!

I've really enjoyed this long journey through time, and thank my wife for her tolerance, and realising how important it became for me to see it through.

Also for the great encouragement Miss Needham has given me all through as the Association President this Millennium, and at the wonderful age of 90 years her enthusiasm doesn't wane for the Whitefaced Dartmoor sheep, and Dartmoor itself, that she loves too.

She has always been 'spot-on' in what she's had to convey to me.

My thanks too, to the W.F.D.S.B.A.'s members, it presidents, its secretaries, its chairmen, its treasurers, its flock book writers, its tattooers, and to others that contributed to and helped compile this book.

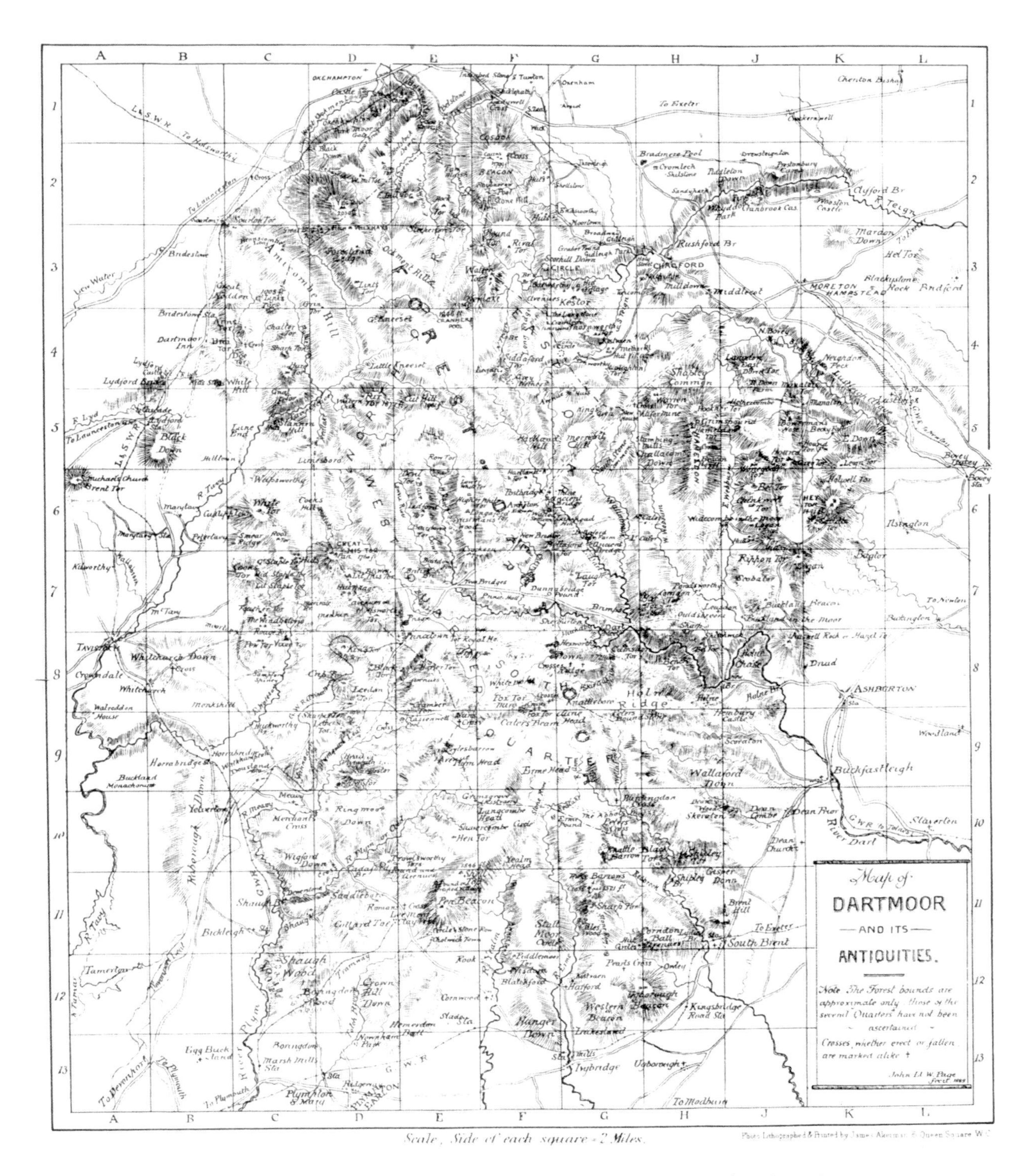

1889 – Map of the 'Forest of Dartmoor' and its north, south, east and west quarters.
Some of its Bronze-age history; 'Hut villages', stone-rows ('avenues'), Cairns and Kistvaens,
Pounds or fortified villages and crosses. Names and height of major tors and birth of rivers.
The Great Western Railway (G.W.R.) and the London and South Western (L. & S. W. R.) railway lines.

(Photo: Chris Chapman).

Letter from the President Miss S. Needham

FOREWORD

It is my great pleasure and privilege as President of the Whitefaced Dartmoor Sheep Breeders Association to write a short Forword to this highly commendable work of Colin Pearse on the story and history of the Whiteface Dartmoor sheep. This is the story of one of the most ancient and interesting long woolled sheep in the South West of the British Isles.

Colin has dedicated his life over the past few years to studying the history of the breed, delving into its past and seriously researching every means possible to learn of the merits of the breed and its many varied aspects.

He has gathered much of his information about the sheep by direct communication with many breeders both old and young, so gaining much first hand knowledge handed down through families long associated with the breed.

The book is greatly enriched by many photographs hitherto unpublished.

We owe a great debt of gratitude to Colin for writing this highly informative history. I hope it will be widely read; I commend it to every type of reader.

Sylvia Needham

Ram Hogg.
Published by the Whitefaced Dartmoor Sheep Breeders and Flock Book Association.

John Harris (holding the Hammer!) selling at the Annual Association Sale of Whitefaced Dartmoors in the field at Whistley Hill, Ashburton.
(Photo: Chris Chapman).

Letter from the Secretary

The Whitefaced Dartmoor Sheep Breeders Association and Flock Book as it was originally known was formed in 1951 and its purpose was to maintain and increase the numbers of the breed coupled with the need to retain their characteristics. This hopefully would be achieved by careful selection of Rams and Ewes.

Prior to the formation of the Association the breed had shown a considerable decline in numbers. The prolificacy and crossing ability of the Suffolk and Border Leicester breeds in particular, and the increased numbers of Scotch Blackface sheep on Dartmoor, were reasons for the Whiteface Dartmoor's decline, along with the displacement of wool by synthetic products.

Additionally, from the 1940's onwards many Dartmoor farms had introduced dairying, which contributed in some way to the decline in sheep numbers.

In view of this and the concern of a small number of dedicated 'Whiteface sheep men', it was decided to form an Association with the help of Cecil Harris of Sawdye and Harris Auctioneers at Ashburton and Newton Abbot, who arranged meetings and co-ordinated procedures leading to the official formation of the Association and its affiliation to the National Sheep Association.

The territory of the Whiteface extended from Widecombe to the Tavistock area, South Devon and the South Hams. Whiteface rams were also used on the Greyface Dartmoor and the South Devon breeds.

A considerable number of Whitefaces were taken to Cornwall. As an exceptional crossing female the Whiteface ewe combined with terminal sires to increase the carcass weight and conformation of the offspring and also produced an excellent first cross breeding ewe, particularly with the Suffolk breed. Whiteface rams were also used on native Cornwall Longwools.

The founder members of the Association were John Savery, Leonard Ball, John Coaker, Hermon French, Cecil Caunter, Sylvester Mann, John Norrish, who farmed respectively at Zeal (South Brent), Axna (Mary Tavy), Sherberton (Princetown), Dockwell Rowden (Widecombe), Weekaborough (Ipplepen), Great Dunstone (Widecombe) and Sherrell (Ivybridge), and my father Cecil Harris of Sawdye and Harris at Ashburton and Newton Abbot was the first Secretary and official Auctioneer of the newly formed Association. The officers and members of the Association comprise and provide a team effort which has proved successful over the years ensuring that everyone is fully informed on all matters. Inspection of rams and ewe lambs are carried out annually on member farms and I have had the pleasure of accompanying the Flock Inspection Committee to inspect approve and tattoo acceptable stock on many occasions since 1962. Sheep that pass the inspector's keen eyes are then eligible for inclusion in the Flock Book.

Registered sheep are eligible for showing at major and local shows. Over the years the Devon County Show has been regularly supported by members, and in addition during the Association's earlier years there were appearances at the Royal, and the Bath and West Shows, when they were still travelling shows.

Whiteface Dartmoor sheep were shown when the Bath and West came to Exeter, Launceston and Plymouth (in the 1950's and early sixties), and when the Royal Show came to Bristol in 1958. In 1952 the Royal Show also came to Newton Abbot, but all livestock classes were cancelled due to Foot and Mouth. However, the Whiteface Dartmoor entries were still catalogued and eight members had entered their sheep.

The over and under fifty flock competition of ewes, and a separate ewe lamb and best ram competition is also judged on the members farms prior to the annual dinner, which is usually held in October, and where cups and prizes won at the August/September show and flock judging competition are presented.

Following the formation of the Association, it was necessary to provide a 'shop window' for the breed and the first official Show and Sale was held at Ashburton Market adjoining Vealenia Terrace. Due to the rapid increase in numbers and other factors, the sale then moved across the A38 to higher up Whistley Hill. Pennage was erected and the Registered Whiteface Sheep were incorporated in the Annual Sheep Sale.

Whiteface sheep were at one time also sold at Widecombe Fair, together with cattle and ponies. In 1975 I was elected Secretary and Official Auctioneer of the Association and took over from my Father. I continued as such until the year 2000. During that time I had the pleasure of meeting and working with some very knowledgeable Flockmasters, many having succeeded to the office of President and Chairman. Both my Father and I had the considerable benefit of continuity as regards the finances of the Association so ably dealt with for over 50 years by Sylvia Needham, as Treasurer. Her allegiance to the Association over the years has been tremendous and much appreciated by all who have had the pleasure of being associated with her.

It is my sincere hope that our breed will continue to flourish, despite the dreadful times the industry has had to contend with in recent times. I am sure that through the co-operation of all concerned and the 'maintenance of the family atmosphere' of the Association, that the Whitefaced Dartmoor sheep's survival will not be a problem and our sheep will always be in demand.

It has been recorded that on the formation of the Association in 1951, 28 Flocks were inspected and some 1204 sheep were passed and tattooed. Numbers fluctuated over the years as new flocks joined and others were dispersed. The present membership stands at 32 with 30 active flocks.

Membership probably peaked during the 1970's, when in 1978 there were 50 members.

Ashburton Market (circa 1930s). Rows of Whitefaced Dartmoor sheep can be seen in the top half of this picture beyond auctioneers John Sawdye and Cecil Harris.

Letter from the Chairman

The fiftieth anniversary of the W.F.D.S.B.A. is a significant milestone for the breeders of White-faced Dartmoor sheep and it is my honour and privilege to be its chairman during this celebration and I am humbled to be writing the Chairman's Letter for this very special occasion.

The Whitefaced breed have enjoyed better times when in the past there were flocks of 2 tooth and older wethers leared on the high moor. They were being kept mainly for their wool. Today's wool price and mutton trade makes this unprofitable. A lot of the in-country farmers used to keep and buy Whitefaced ewes 'off the hills' to cross with terminal sires in order to breed from the first cross ewe lambs. These became good mothers that milked well and held their teeth. The arrival of some breeds producing more lambs and milk has not helped 'the Widdicombe' to remain the favoured sheep of the lowland farmer. A combination of bad udders, defects in feet and teeth has questioned the wisdom of change to other breeds.

Today's members owe a huge debt of gratitude to the founder members that launched the association and kept the breed to its present look and standard.

We must acknowledge the immense achievement of Miss Needham both as a founder member and treasurer during the first 50 years of the association, only retiring in 2001.

Phil with his Devon County Show male and breed champion 1996.

We thank her for the tireless work she has contributed over so many years. We cannot thank her enough and all the founder members for their dedication, hard work and foresight. Many of them have held office over the years to help guide the present members. We recognise too the good work of the present families of founder members in continuing the work of their forefathers and for favouring our wonderful sheep and for the sincerity of all breeders.

Equally we are indebted to the unselfish work of Cecil and John Harris the renowned Sawdye and Harris Auctioneers based at Ashburton in providing a founder member and our association secretaries over 50 years. Cecil and John both completed 25 years each, serving the needs of the association.

My own enthusiasm for these sheep has developed through breeding and showing and the challenge was presented to me through my parents; Eileen and Cyril Abel's success with Whiteface Dartmoor sheep here at Higher Godsworthy.

This book has been compiled to share members and breeders stories and to help keep memories alive before they are lost forever.

Unfortunately we have lost some prominent breeders since we began to research the book but we have the consolation of their recollections in print to savour for the future.

An old saying, 'if it's not broke, why fix it' can relate to why the Whiteface has changed so little since the beginning of time, retaining their main characteristics down the centuries. Maybe today's preference is for less hair on the face and legs but their best attributes have stood the test of time because they are the postive needs of longevity that have courted these lovely sheep right through history. They include good teeth, excellent wool and feet coupled with reliable mothering, milking and handling ability. The rams however retain to this millennium 'fire in their blood' that suggest a very strong link with the past and it is always best to keep aware when the rams are around.

As the harsh memories of Foot and Mouth still linger in our minds it is the hardest time to be upbeat with anything to do with farming, however as an association we were very lucky not to lose many sheep with their irreplaceable bloodlines and hopefully the new rules and regulations will not make it harder to keep them. With few shows in 2002 there was nowhere to promote the breed.

I wish the breeders and association every success for the future and for continued growth and better sheep prices.

Phil Abel
Chairman

National Anthem of the Whiteface Dartmoors

1.
I've travelled all over this country and fine sheep I have seen by the score;
But the only sheep I know worth keeping are the sheep that are bred on Dartmoor.
There are Scottish Blackfaces and Closewools and Cheviots some people keep,
But you and I know that they cannot compare with the Whiteface Dartmoor sheep.

2.
That carpet you keep by your fireside, that fine leg of lamb that you eat,
If it came from a Whiteface Dartmoor, then you know that it cannot be beat,
The Herdwicks and Hampshire and Leicester's will only make good farmers poor,
For you and I know that they cannot compare with the Widecombe Whiteface Dartmoor.

3.
And when men once tried to improve them and invented a new sort of cross,
They called them the Greyface Dartmoors but they're nothing more than a dead loss.
For man shouldn't meddle with nature, and those who keep Greyfaces find
That they've not only got dirty faces, they've also got dirty behinds.

4.
When the cold March weather's upon us and it's freezing and blowing a storm
Up higher side of the field the Whiteface Dartmoor is born.
But good sheep can put up with bad weather be it Winter or Summer or Fall,
And of all the sheep in this country the Whiteface Dartmoor's the best of them all.

Written by Roger Whale

In Their Place

The history of the Whitefaced Dartmoor sheep taken from the breeders and their associates on Dartmoor and the four quarters of Devon.

The photographs, both old and new, tell a story of people's love for these animals and translates a sense of place for this very ancient breed.

'Widecombes' wintering near to the snow-line on Dartmoor.

The granite heaving moorlands, where on we dimly trace
Traditionary footsteps of many a vanished race;
A wildnerness of heather, a paradise of gold,
Where every ancient trackway is strewn with stories old.

Arthur L. Salmon, *Crossings – One Hundred Years on Dartmoor*

'A story as olde as them hills,' where sheep pastured and were agisted and leired (leared) over many centuries.

'Old Widdecombe-in-the-Moor' – *'The Dartmoor Road'*.

Whitefaced Dartmoor Sheep

Characteristics. White Head and Face. Face of Ewe free of wool.
Ears short and thick, with occasional black spots on them.
Nose black, face broad and bold.
Male sheep may be horned.
Neck – strong and massive by shoulder and of medium length.
Breast deep and prominent.
Body of medium length, deep and broad.
Good broad tail.
Ability to withstand either very wet or hard winters, without detriment to subsequent lambing season or to wool.

Wool. Average weight of wool 12–16 lbs from Ewe, 10–16 lbs from Hoggs. Under suitable conditions much heavier fleeces are possible and shears up to 21 lbs have been recorded by Breeders. White of good staple with a fairly strong curl. The wool should be moderately greasy.

Ewes are excellent for crossing, are first class milkers and good mothers.

History of the Breed. The Whitefaced Dartmoor is believed to be one of England's most ancient breeds of sheep, and was probably originally not entirely confined to Dartmoor but spread over the greater part of West Somerset and Devon, however, as more land became enclosed, the breed was finally driven back to Dartmoor, where it became firmly rooted, and continues to flourish as one of Devon's native breeds.

Records show the Whitefaced Dartmoor were recognised as a valuable cross on any Longwool Breed over the last 150 years, more recently they were used successfully on the Welsh Mountain breed increasing wool and carcass output, while maintaining their vigour and hardy characteristics.

Crossed with the Suffolk produces a very attractive finished Lamb for the modern requirement being lean and well muscled.

The Sheep are very hardy and can thrive on the very poorest pasture. Most of the grazing is at an altitude varying from 500–2000 feet above sea level.

'The Mother of all Dartmoors'.

Widecombe Fair 1906. Whitefaced Dartmoor Rams tied to carts awaiting sale, between farmers. This photograph could be said to represent the 'Founder Sheep' or the Foundation Sheep of the moor.
(Courtesy of the Manns Collection, Great Dunstone, Widecombe).

The 1951 Founder Members of The Whitefaced Dartmoor Sheep Breeders Association.
Left to right: John Savery, John Coaker, Hermon French, Cecil Caunter, Leonard Ball,
Cecil Harris, Sylvester Mann and John Norrish.

Inspection Committee for the W.F.D.S.B. Association in 1951 at Cudlipptown,
(Harry Rowse) Peter Tavey.
Left to right: Leonard Ball, G.H. French, H.J. French, John Norrish, Cecil Caunter,
Sylvester Mann, Cecil Harris, Reg Hill and Mr Cleverdon (clerk holding tattooing clippers).

First Association Sale 1951

Left: Cecil Caunter – First prize for Best Old Ram;
Centre: Leonard Ball – Best Pen of Ewes;
Right: Horace Nosworthy – First prize for Ram Hogg.

Best Ram Hogg.

Memorandum of Articles of the Association

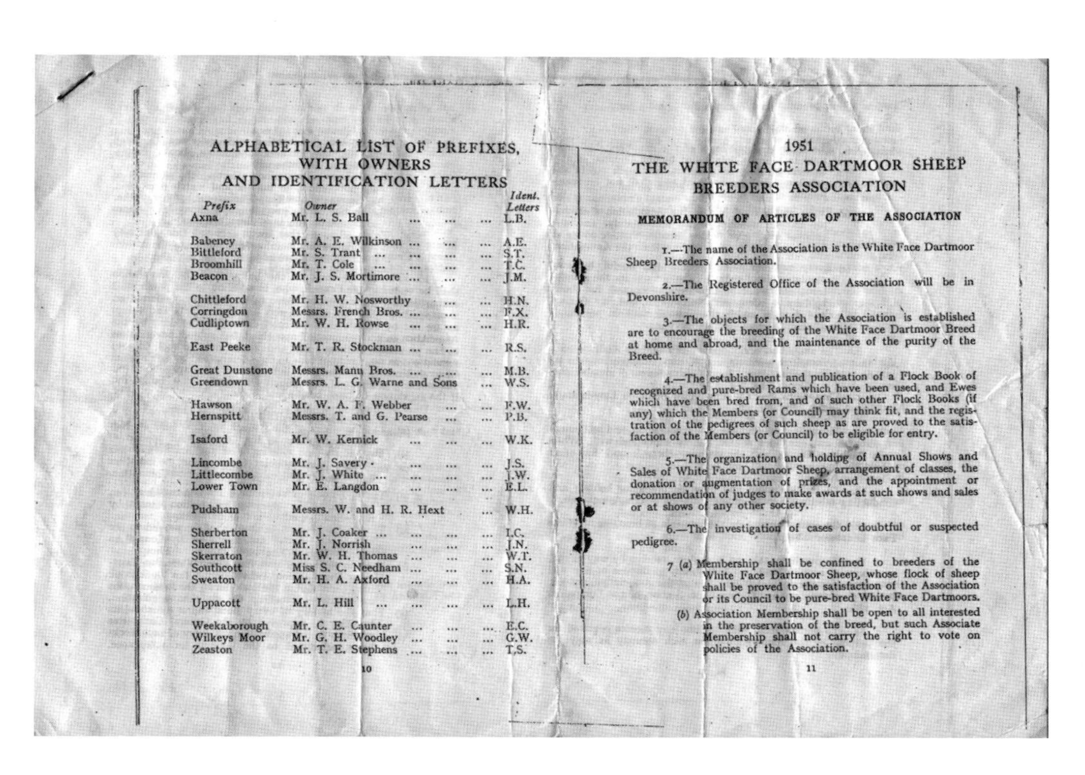

ALPHABETICAL LIST OF PREFIXES, WITH OWNERS AND IDENTIFICATION LETTERS

Prefix	Owner	Ident. Letters
Axna	Mr. L. S. Ball	L.B.
Babeney	Mr. A. E. Wilkinson	A.E.
Bittleford	Mr. S. Trant	S.T.
Broomhill	Mr. T. Cole	T.C.
Beacon	Mr. J. S. Mortimore	J.M.
Chittleford	Mr. H. W. Nosworthy	H.N.
Corringdon	Messrs. French Bros.	F.X.
Cudliptown	Mr. W. H. Rowse	H.R.
East Peeke	Mr. T. R. Stockman	R.S.
Great Dunstone	Messrs. Mann Bros.	M.B.
Greendown	Messrs. L. G. Warne and Sons ...	W.S.
Hawson	Mr. W. A. F. Webber	F.W.
Hernspitt	Messrs. T. and G. Pearse	P.B.
Isaford	Mr. W. Kernick	W.K.
Lincombe	Mr. J. Savery	J.S.
Littlecombe	Mr. J. White	J.W.
Lower Town	Mr. E. Langdon	E.L.
Pudsham	Messrs. W. and H. R. Hext ...	W.H.
Sherberton	Mr. J. Coaker	I.C.
Sherrell	Mr. J. Norrish	J.N.
Skerraton	Mr. W. H. Thomas	W.T.
Southcott	Miss S. C. Needham	S.N.
Sweaton	Mr. H. A. Axford	H.A.
Uppacott	Mr. L. Hill	L.H.
Weekaborough	Mr. C. E. Caunter	E.C.
Wilkeys Moor	Mr. G. H. Woodley	G.W.
Zeaston	Mr. T. E. Stephens	T.S.

10

1951

THE WHITE FACE DARTMOOR SHEEP BREEDERS ASSOCIATION

MEMORANDUM OF ARTICLES OF THE ASSOCIATION

1.—The name of the Association is the White Face Dartmoor Sheep Breeders Association.

2.—The Registered Office of the Association will be in Devonshire.

3.—The objects for which the Association is established are to encourage the breeding of the White Face Dartmoor Breed at home and abroad, and the maintenance of the purity of the Breed.

4.—The establishment and publication of a Flock Book of recognized and pure-bred Rams which have been used, and Ewes which have been bred from, and of such other Flock Books (if any) which the Members (or Council) may think fit, and the registration of the pedigrees of such sheep as are proved to the satisfaction of the Members (or Council) to be eligible for entry.

5.—The organization and holding of Annual Shows and Sales of White Face Dartmoor Sheep, arrangement of classes, the donation or augmentation of prizes, and the appointment or recommendation of judges to make awards at such shows and sales or at shows of any other society.

6.—The investigation of cases of doubtful or suspected pedigree.

7 (a) Membership shall be confined to breeders of the White Face Dartmoor Sheep, whose flock of sheep shall be proved to the satisfaction of the Association or its Council to be pure-bred White Face Dartmoors.

(b) Association Membership shall be open to all interested in the preservation of the breed, but such Associate Membership shall not carry the right to vote on policies of the Association.

11

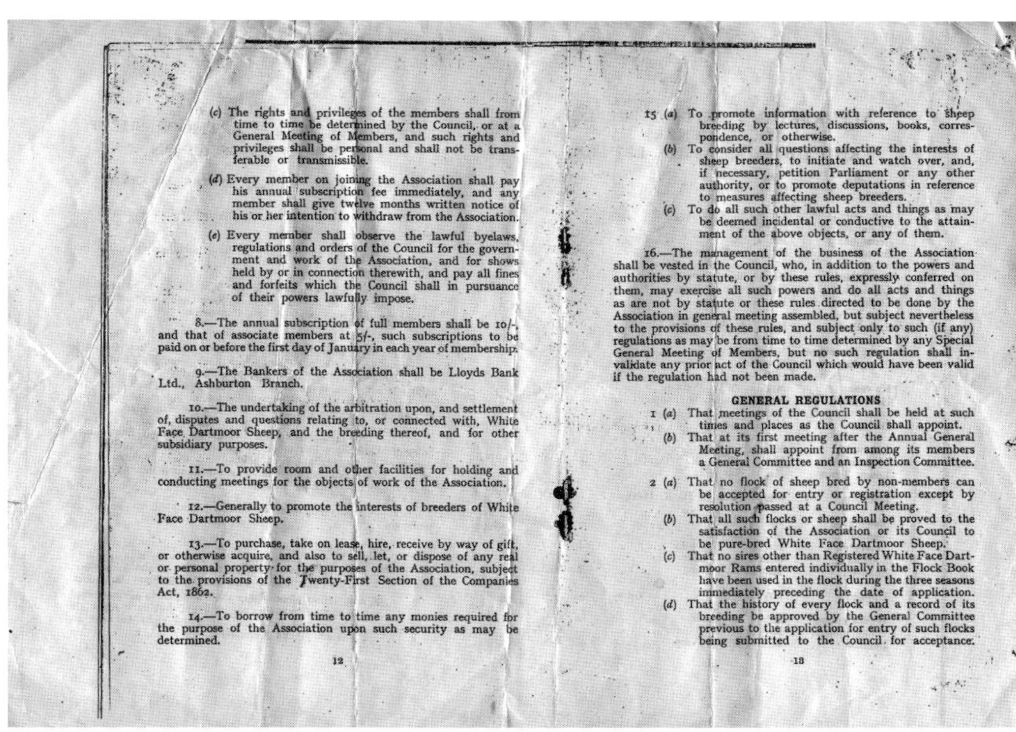

(c) The rights and privileges of the members shall from time to time be determined by the Council, or at a General Meeting of Members, and such rights and privileges shall be personal and shall not be transferable or transmissible.

(d) Every member on joining the Association shall pay his annual subscription fee immediately, and any member shall give twelve months written notice of his or her intention to withdraw from the Association.

(e) Every member shall observe the lawful byelaws, regulations and orders of the Council for the government and work of the Association, and for shows held by or in connection therewith, and pay all fines and forfeits which the Council shall in pursuance of their powers lawfully impose.

8.—The annual subscription of full members shall be 10/-, and that of associate members at 5/-, such subscriptions to be paid on or before the first day of January in each year of membership.

9.—The Bankers of the Association shall be Lloyds Bank Ltd., Ashburton Branch.

10.—The undertaking of the arbitration upon, and settlement of, disputes and questions relating to, or connected with, White Face Dartmoor Sheep, and the breeding thereof, and for other subsidiary purposes.

11.—To provide room and other facilities for holding and conducting meetings for the objects of work of the Association.

12.—Generally to promote the interests of breeders of White Face Dartmoor Sheep.

13.—To purchase, take on lease, hire, receive by way of gift, or otherwise acquire, and also to sell, let, or dispose of any real or personal property for the purposes of the Association, subject to the provisions of the Twenty-First Section of the Companies Act, 1862.

14.—To borrow from time to time any monies required for the purpose of the Association upon such security as may be determined.

12

15 (a) To promote information with reference to sheep breeding by lectures, discussions, books, correspondence, or otherwise.

(b) To consider all questions affecting the interests of sheep breeders, to initiate and watch over, and, if necessary, petition Parliament or any other authority, or to promote deputations in reference to measures affecting sheep breeders.

(c) To do all such other lawful acts and things as may be deemed incidental or conductive to the attainment of the above objects, or any of them.

16.—The management of the business of the Association shall be vested in the Council, who, in addition to the powers and authorities by statute, or by these rules, expressly conferred on them, may exercise all such powers and do all acts and things as are not by statute or these rules directed to be done by the Association in general meeting assembled, but subject nevertheless to the provisions of these rules, and subject only to such (if any) regulations as may be from time to time determined by any Special General Meeting of Members, but no such regulation shall invalidate any prior act of the Council which would have been valid if the regulation had not been made.

GENERAL REGULATIONS

1 (a) That meetings of the Council shall be held at such times and places as the Council shall appoint.

(b) That at its first meeting after the Annual General Meeting, shall appoint from among its members a General Committee and an Inspection Committee.

2 (a) That no flock of sheep bred by non-members can be accepted for entry or registration except by resolution passed at a Council Meeting.

(b) That all such flocks or sheep shall be proved to the satisfaction of the Association or its Council to be pure-bred White Face Dartmoor Sheep.

(c) That no sires other than Registered White Face Dartmoor Rams entered individually in the Flock Book have been used in the flock during the three seasons immediately preceding the date of application.

(d) That the history of every flock and a record of its breeding be approved by the General Committee previous to the application for entry of such flocks being submitted to the Council for acceptance.

13

3.—Before the acceptance of any flock or sheep by the Council for entry and registration becomes operative, all such flocks and sheep must be inspected and passed by the Association's duly-appointed Inspectors, who have full power to accept or reject the whole or any portion of the flock of sheep offered for entry, the expenses of the Inspectors to be paid by the applicant for registration.

4.—That ram lambs shall not be eligible for entry in the Flock Book for three years from the date of the inspection, except from flocks founded with all registered sheep.

5.—That every flock or such portion of it as may be passed by the inspectors shall thereupon be tattooed, at the owner's expense, at a fee of 5/- per score, together with the reasonable travelling expenses of the tattooer.

6.—That every applicant for entry of a flock or sheep agrees to pay the sum of 6d. per head for each sheep passed by the inspectors.

7.—The Council shall have power at any time to inspect any flock or sheep owned by a member of the Association, and in the event of such inspection proving satisfactory, the expenses incurred be paid by the Association, but if not satisfactory to be paid by the owner of the flock or sheep inspected.

8.—That the whole of the ewe lambs born in every year, and all the ram lambs be tattooed by the official tattooer each year, at the fee of 5/- per score and 3/- per flock for expenses, such fees and expenses being payable by the flock owner.

9.—That all ram lambs kept for stud purposes shall be tattooed in their left ear, whilst with their dams, and forthwith entered in the Flock Book. The official tattooer, at the time of tattooing, shall, unless previously done by the owner, individually number the same at the owner's expense, and the owner shall forthwith enter the same upon the entry given him by the official tattooer, with particulars also of the number of ewe lambs marked and forward the said form to the Secretary immediately, together with such fees as are prescribed herein.

10.—That no sire be used in the flock until the same is individually recorded in the Flock Book, and that the Annual Flock Return be properly filled in annually.

11.—That a fee of 2/6 per ram lamb tattooed yearly be paid.

12.—That no sheep, male or female, can be added to, or form part of, a registered flock except the same be duly trade-marked previous to its being added to a registered flock, other than lambs purchased by the side of their dams.

13.—That no sheep, male or female, except it be tattooed with the Association's tattoo, and its breeder's or owner's flock identification, is a registered White Face Dartmoor Sheep.

14.—Applicable for the entry of individual sheep:

(*a*) That all entries for individual registration both of rams and ewes, must be made upon the official form, and such information as is required thereupon, the minimum conditions being:
   (1) Name and address of breeder, name and address of the breeder of the sire and dam, except in the case of original entries, when the General Purposes Committee shall have power to make such minimum conditions as may be deemed by them desirable; and
   (2) That all sheep, male or female, individually recorded in the Flock Book must have in their right ear (*a*) either their owner's private number, or (*b*) their Flock Book number; and
   (3) That all ewes and rams be named in accordance with the system sanctioned by the Council.

(*b*) That the fee for the individual registration of all rams trade-marked shall be 2/6 per head, and that the said fee shall be payable on the certificate of the official tattooer, who shall for that purpose certify to the Secretary the number of ram lambs trade-marked in each flock.

(*c*) That the fee for the individual registration of all ewes and ewe lambs shall be 6d. each.

(*d*) That all ewes bred by non-members, except on the original entry of a flock, shall pay an entrance fee of 5/- per head.

TRADE-MARKING REGULATIONS

15.—That in addition to the foregoing conditions of entry, the owner of every entered flock shall agree to comply with the following additional conditions:

(*a*) That the whole of his flock, as inspected and passed, as well as all sheep added thereto from year to year, must be individually tattooed by the official tattooer, at such fees as may be fixed by the Council, with the registered trade mark of the Association and owner's flock number, and such other sheep as stated hereinbefore.

(*b*) That all ewe lambs and all ram lambs shall be trade-marked in their left ear when with their dams.

(*c*) If required by the Council to give a written undertaking not to add any ewe to, nor use any ram in, his entered flock, unless the same be the produce of registered sires and entered dams, until the same has been inspected by the inspectors and duly trade-marked, and to hold the Association, its officials, etc., free from all or any liability for any loss or damage, by death or in any other manner whatsoever, to any sheep or lamb during the operation of trade-marking, or from any subsequent result traceible, or supposed to be traceable, to such operation.

(*d*) That the official tattooer shall, before commencing to trade-mark any sheep or lamb, if required by the owner of such sheep or lamb, in his presence, and at his expense, thoroughly disinfect the tattooing machine and any numbers required for use.

(*e*) That the near or left ear of every entered sheep is reserved by the Association for the purpose of marking the sheep with the registered trade mark, so far as to the centre of the ear between the large veins.

FLOCK BOOK

16.—The Flock Book shall be published annually, and shall contain a register of White Face Dartmoor Sheep (for this purpose each breeder shall make a complete return of his entered flock in each year on a form supplied, by the date named thereon), a statement of results of the principal Sales and Shows during the year, and any other information which in the opinion of the Council shall be of interest to breeders.

The General Purposes Committee shall be responsible to the Council for the publication of the Flock Book, each member being entitled to one copy of each volume of the Flock Book published after the date of his election free, the price to non-members being not less than 10/6 each volume.

INSPECTION COMMITTEE

The Inspection Committee shall, by direction of the Council, appoint at least two members of the Inspection Committee to inspect any flock or flocks or any sheep the Council may deem necessary, three to form a quorum.

COUNCIL

17.—The Council shall consist of twelve members and the duly elected Officers (four members to retire annually and not to be eligible for re-election). The Council shall have full power to manage the affairs of the Association, to authorize the expenditure of the Association's funds for the proper working of the Association's business (all cheques being signed by the Hon. Treasurer and countersigned by the Secretary); to prepare and publish the Flock Book, and employ such assistance (editorial or otherwise) as they may deem necessary, and to do and perform all such lawful acts as may be entrusted to them by the Council from time to time, three to form a quorum.

STANDING COMMITTEES

18.—Meetings of Committees shall be summoned at such times and places as the Chairman of each Committee shall appoint.

Chairman of Council: JOHN COAKER, Sherberton, Princetown.

Secretary: C. H. HARRIS, F.A.I., 12, Highweek Street, Newton Abbot.

Adopted by the Council at their Meeting held at Ashburton on Saturday, December 16th, 1950

Revival of the Native Dartmoor

EARLY 1950s

The Widecombe Dartmoor, or whitefaced Dartmoor, is one of the indigenous breeds of the moor. It was recently in danger of becoming extinct, but interest in it was revived, and the flock book started in 1951 now contains nearly 50 registered flocks.

A typical flock, with all the breed's character of hardiness, milkiness and fertility, is that of Miss Bodington at Manaton. This flock of two score ewes serves the lowland feeder in two ways: wether lambs go off to grade off roots in the spring, and ewes, after two or three crops, are drafted for down-crossing below.

The flock is kept around the 1,400 ft level on open, unimproved moorland all the year, except in the depth of winter and for lambing, when it comes down on to roots at about 1,150 ft. This breed is probably surpassed only by the Blackface in its capacity to thrive on these barren heights, and it gives a far greater clip – averaging 15 lb and rising to 19 lb. And Miss Bodington's ewes have a lambing percentage of 125 to 150.

Down crosses on the Widecombe give a lamb of fashionable weight. An example is those of Mr S. H. Eva at Cambourne. His Suffolk x Widecombes grade at about 45 lb in June, and, run on till September, at about 53 lb.

Some virtues of the Widecombe or whitefaced Dartmoor for down crossing on the lower hills are well illustrated at Baddaford, Ashburton, a Crown Commissioners' farm by Mortimore Bros. Elevation here is between 400 and 600 ft, and some excellent grass is grown.

The breeding flock is of Widecombe Dartmoors, and the Mortimores have been using a Dorset Down cross on it for about 15 years. Their comment on their choice of ram is that a Dorset with a clean face and leg and a close wool reaults in a neat and small-boned lamb. The Hampshire might give a heavier bone. The Suffolk might be even better than the Dorset at greater heights because of the hardiness of the Suffolk cross lambs.

The Dorset Down–Widecombe Dartmoor lambs born in early January give a 60 lb carcase in July with no keep except good leys; February-born lambs reach about 50 lb by the same time.

The fecundity of the Widecombe Dartmoor persists in the cross. A first-cross Dorset–Dartmoor ewe here which persists in stealing the Dorset ram has had seven lambs in 12 months – two early in 1953, two in August, 1953, and three this last spring.

The Widecombe, or whitefaced, Dartmoor is reviving fast as a hardy competitor to its north-country competitor on the moor, the Scottish Blackface. These Widecombe ewes and lambs, belonging to Miss Bodlington, are on the open moor above Manaton

'Divine commitment'. Mr Harold Mortimore and Mr Tom Mortimore of Baddaford.

The Earliest Officers appointed to the Association in 1951 and those in office in 2001

Since 1951 the sale of registered Whitefaced Dartmoor ewes and rams has been conducted at Ashburton, and as the associations main auction under the auspices of the auctioneers *Sawdye and Harris*. The sheep were not new to John Sawdye and Cecil Harris for they had offered Whitefaces for sale at Ashburton market for many years previous to 1951 in its top and bottom market (built in 1910). John Sawdye and Cecil Harris were the first to sell sheep in the early years of the association and Cecil completed twenty five years as its secretary, at which time in 1976 Cecil's son John became the auctioneer who was to sell the Whitefaced Dartmoor Sheep at the annual association sale in Ashburton. The Sawdye and Harris office is situated in Ashburton. Cecil Harris was an enthusiastic founder of the association as well as its first secretary. Following in his father's footsteps, John became the second secretary and remained in office for twenty-five years until relinquishing the job in 2001, the association's 50th anniversary.

Miss Sylvia Needham of Dipleigh, Widecombe-in-the-Moor is the President during the first few years of the new millenium and the 50th anniversary. She has also been the treasurer since the association inception in 1951. The first President in 1951 was Cecil Caunter of Lower Weekaborough, Ipplepen. His grandsons still farm Whitefaced Dartmoor sheep at the home farm. At this time, John Coaker of Sherberton, Hexworthy, near Princetown was the first Chairman and his family still keep Whitefaced Dartmoor sheep today. Phil Abel of Higher Godworthy Farm, Peter Tavy, Tavistock has been appointed the associations Chairman for the 50th anniversary in 2001, and has shown great skill in showing and farming Whiteface sheep. Paul Vincent of Dittisham Dartmouth is the elected Vice-Chairman. The Office of Secretary is taken by another of the Sawdye and Harris team, Gordon Chambers. The newly elected treasurer is Tissa Haley from Buckfastleigh.

Annual Dinner and Officers

1965

THE WESTERN TIMES & GAZETTE, FRIDAY, DECEMBER

Officers and members of the Whitefaced Dartmooor Sheep Breeders' Flock Book Association at their first annual dinner at Dartmoor Motel, Ashburton, on Tuesday.

The Whitefaced Dartmoor Sheep Breeders Flock Book Association. Officers and members at their first annual dinner at Dartmoor Motel, Ashburton.

Other venues for the Annual Dinner included the Green Cafe, Widecombe-in-the-Moor, 1968 and 1969, and the Golden Lion, Ashburton for the Seventh Annual Dinner of the Association.

The President in 1968 and 1969 was John Savery and J. K. Soper in 1970. The toastmaster for these two years was Roger Whale.

OFFICERS

President	R. A. COAKER, Esq.
Chairman	P. W. COAKER, Esq.
Hon. Treasurer	Miss S. C. NEEDHAM
Hon. Secretary ...	C. H. HARRIS, Esq.

The Teign Press, Printers, Kingsteignton

WHITEFACE DARTMOOR SHEEP BREEDERS
FLOCK BOOK ASSOCIATION

FIRST

ANNUAL DINNER

ON

Tuesday, December 14th 1965

AT THE

Dartmoor Motel, Ashburton

MENU

COUNTRY VEGETABLE SOUP

ROAST LEG OF ENGLISH LAMB
ROAST & DUCHESS POTATOES
BUTTERED CARROTS & GARDEN PEAS

FRUIT SALAD & DEVONSHIRE CREAM

CHEESE AND BISCUITS

COFFEE

TOAST LIST

THE QUEEN
Proposed by : THE PRESIDENT, R. A. COAKER, Esq.

THE ASSOCIATION
Proposed by : F. H. COX, Esq.
Responded to by : C. E. CAUNTER, Esq.

THE JUDGES
Proposed by : J. A. SAWDYE, Esq.
Responded to by : R. KERSWELL, Esq.

Toastmaster—P. W. COAKER, Esq., Chairman.

WFDSB Association, November 1971, celebrated their 21st year of association by cutting twin iced cakes.

Better Quality in Whiteface Sheep

The annual flock judging competition of the Whiteface Dartmoor Sheep Breeders' Association has again shown a great improvement in the quality of the ewes and rams and in the number of flocks now attached to the flock book. Prize-winners were:

Flocks of over 50 ewes – 1. John Savery, Lincombe, South Brent; 2. Messrs. Mann Bros. Widecombe-in-the-Moor; 3. Richard Coaker, Runnage; res. S. Northmores. Kingshead Flock. Flocks of under 50 ewes – 1. D. Webber Hawson; 2. J. S. Mortimore, Shallowford; 3. George Woodley, Ivybridge.

The judges were Miss S. C. Needham and Mr L. S. Ball, the previous flock winners.

Whiteface Sheep

The Whiteface Dartmoor Sheep Breeders' Association 1970 flock judging competition has resulted in the following awards:

Flocks of over 50 ewes – 1. Mr W. R. Norrish, Sherrell, Ivybridge; 2. Mr S. E. Northmore, Widecombe; 3. Capt. Peek, Loddiswell. Ewe lamb compeition – 1. Messrs. E. Caunter and Son; 2. Capt. Peek; 3. Mr W. R. Norrish.

Dartmeet, Badgers Holt. John Harris, John Sawdye and Archie Mortimore (Photo courtesy of Audrey Mortimore).

Sheep breeders' birthday dance

The Whitefaced Dartmoor Sheep Breeders' Association celebrated its 21st anniversay on November 11 with a dinner at the Golden Lion Hotel, Ashburton.

It was the eighth annual dinner held by the association and many of the foundation members were present.

The toast of the association was proposed by Mr J. Coaker, who was its first chairman, and the response was by the first president, Mr C. Caunter.

The judges' toast was proposed by Mr J. Slavery and the response was from Mr W. R. Norrish and Mr H. G. Woodley.

Cups and prizes won at the September show and flock judging competition were presented by Mrs J. K. Soper.

The president, Mr Soper, made presentations to the treasurer, Miss S. C. Needham, and the secretary and auctioneer, Mr C. H. Harris, for their 21 yearss of service.

Mr Harris told members that by forming the association they had benefited and were now reaping the rewards of much improved flocks.

The evening was rounded off with a cabaret and dance.

White Face Dartmoor Sheep Breeders Association

Affiliated to The National Sheep Breeders Association

President: Miss S.C. Needham

Chairman: P. Abel

Hon. Treasurer: Mrs. P. Haley, Mayfields, Oaklands Road, Buckfastleigh 01364 643063
Hon. Secretary: Mr. G.T. Chambers, 13 West Street, Ashburton 01364 652304

GTC/djr

7th October 2002

Dear Member,

re: Annual Dinner
- Friday 25th October : 7.00 pm for 7.30 pm

We are again holding our dinner at Badgers Holt and I am assured by the proprietor that all will be well and an excellent chef will be looking after us. The menu is more extensive than before with Whiteface Lamb as well as South Devon Beef and Dart Salmon!

The cost per person will be the same as last year at £12.50. Please make your reservations as early as possible with Margaret Phipps (01364 631421) or me at the office.

There will again be a draw and any prizes donated will be very much appreciated.

Cups and trophies will be presented on the evening so last years winners please have your cups engraved and return them to me or bring them to the dinner all nicely cleaned - thank you.

Yours sincerely,

pp G.T. Chambers
Hon. Secretary

SAWDYE & HARRIS

Wednesday 30th August
Newton Abbot Livestock Market
Usual Weekly Sale of Primestock
Prime Cattle, Beef Bulls & Calves
150 Hoggs, Lambs & Cull Ewes
For arrangements regarding the Cull Collection please contact the Auctioneers

* * * *

FORTHCOMING SALES
Thursday 31st August
Ashburton Annual Sheep Sale
incorporating 50th Show & Sale of Registered Whiteface Dartmoor Ewes & Rams

Anticipated entry of 1000 head to include Suffolk Mule 2Ts, Whiteface Dartmoor x Border Leicester 2Ts, Mule 2Ts, Mule Ewes Flock Ages, Pedigree & Pure Bred Rams from noted flock masters including 4 Pedigree Suffolk Shearlings from R & M Hallett, Suffolk, Poll Dorset and Texel Shearlings from T & J Tall, Suffolk Ram Lambs from A.W. Wrayford and 4 Suffolk Shearlings from B Harris.

Sale Times
Breeding Ewes at 10.30 a.m.
Rams at 12 noon and Lambs at 12.30 p.m.

* * * *

WHITEFACE DARTMOOR SHEEP BREEDERS AND FLOCK BOOK ASSOCIATION

CATALOGUE OF RAMS

50th ANNUAL SHOW & SALE
of REGISTERED WHITEFACE DARTMOOR RAMS

on THURSDAY 31st AUGUST 2000

at ASHBURTON

President: *Miss. S.C. Needham*

Chairman: *G. Goddard Esq.*

Hon. Secretary: *J.E. Harris Esq. ARICS*
Sawdye & Harris
West Street
Ashburton
Devon

Tel: (01364) 652304

Hon. Treasurer: *Miss. S.C. Needham*
Dipleigh Farm
Widecombe-in-the-Moor
Devon

Tel: (01364) 621227

List of Vendors & Exhibitors

		Lot Nos
Abel, P.	Higher Godsworthy, Peter Tavy	1 + 2
Bond, H.	Pullabrook, Bovey Tracey	13 - 16
Caunter, C.E. & Son	Lower Weekaborough Fm, Ipplepen	22 + 23
Coaker, P.R.	Runnage, Postbridge	8
Coaker, P. & W.	Bittleford, Poundsgate	9 - 12
Cole, A.H.	Greenwell, Clearbrook	3 + 4
Haley, Mr. & Mrs.	Mayfields, Buckfastleigh	17 + 18
Mann, A.W. & O.S.	Great Dunstone, Widecombe	5 - 7
Monro, Miss. A.	Corndon Farm, Poundsgate	24
Pearse, C.	Barramoor, North Bovey	20 + 21
Perkins, R.W.	Town Barton, Manaton	25
Vincent, P.	Bramble Torre, Dittisham	19

Judges:

Rams: *R. Mann Esq.*
Great Dunstone, Widecombe-in-the-Moor

Ewes: *R. Kerswell Esq.*
Bearscombe Farm, Kingsbridge

Ear Mark Steward: *T.A. Phipps Esq.*

The JOHN SAVERY PERPETUAL CHALLENGE CUP kindly presented by J. Savery Jnr. is awarded for the Champion Ram at the Annual Show. The 1999 winner was R. Mann Esq., Great Dunstone, Widecombe-in-the-Moor.

The *'CECIL CAUNTER MEMORIAL CUP'* is awarded to the Member gaining most points at the Annual Show.

Note: The Association wish to point out to all purchasers of Registered Whiteface Dartmoor Rams who are not Members of the Association, that if a Registered Ram is put to unregistered Ewes the characteristics or otherwise of the progeny are in no way guaranteed.

WHITEFACE DARTMOOR SHEEP BREEDERS ASSOCIATION

Competition Classes - Prize List and Previous Class Winners

Class 1: Ram Hogg

1st Prize: The Association's Perpetual Challenge Cup, also £5 presented by Messrs. Sawdye & Harris

1st Prize: £10 2nd Prize: £5 3rd Prize: £3

Previous Winners:

1990	P.R. Coaker, Runnage, Postbridge
1991	P.W. Coaker, Bittleford, Poundsgate
1992	A.H. Cole, Greenwell, Clearbrook
1993	F.A. Mortimore, Grattons, Widecombe
1994	R.H. Bond, Pullabrook, Bovey Tracey
1995	J.W. Mead, Bullhornstone, South Brent
1996	A.W. & O.S. Mann, Great Dunstone, Widecombe
1997	J. Savery, Wheeldon Farm, Halwell
1998	P. Abel, Higher Godsworthy, Tavistock
1999	R. Mann, Great Dunstone, Widecombe

Class 2: Old Ram

1st Prize: Challenge Cup kindly presented by Adams & Howell (having won the previous cup outright) to be won three times in succession or any four times. Also £5 presented by Messrs. Sawdye & Harris.

1st Prize: £10 2nd Prize: £5 3rd Prize: £3

Previous Winners:

1990	Q. Rae, Lower Langdon, North Bovey
1991	F.A. Mortimore, Lizwell, Widecombe
1992	C.W. Abel, Higher Godsworthy, Tavistock
1993	P.W. Coaker, Bittleford, Poundsgate
1994	A.H. Cole, Greenwell, Clearbrook
1995	P.R. Coaker, Runnage, Postbridge
1996	Mrs. P. Haley, Mayfield, Buckfastleigh
1997	P. Abel, Higher Godsworthy, Peter Tavy
1998	P.W. Coaker, Bittleford, Poundsgate
1999	P. & W. Coaker, Bittleford, Poundsgate

Class 3: Best Pen of 10 Ewes

1st Prize: The Richard Coaker Perpetual Challenge Cup kindly presented by Mrs. A.M. Coaker and Mr. P. Coaker

Previous Winners:

1990	N.L. Warne & Son, Heathfield Barton, Modbury
1991-1992	A.W. & O.S. Mann, Great Dunstone, Widecombe
1993	P. Hearn, Oakley Farm, Tavistock
1994-1995	P.W. Coaker, Bittleford, Poundsgate
1996	P. Hearn, Oakley Farm, Tavistock
1997	A.W. & O.S. Mann, Great Dunstone, Widecombe

1998	P.W. Coaker, Bittleford, Poundsgate
1999	P. & W. Coaker, Bittleford, Poundsgate

Class 4: Best Coated Ram (any age)

1st Prize: The Association's Perpetual Challenge Cup. The previous cup having been won outright by Messrs. C.E. Caunter & Son.

1st Prize: £10 2nd Prize: £5 3rd Prize: £3

Previous Winners:

1990	C.W. Abel, Higher Godsworthy, Tavistock
1991	F.A. Mortimore, Lizwell, Widecombe
1992	P.R. Coaker, Runnage Farm, Postbridge
1993	T.A. Phipps, New Cott, Poundsgate
1994	R.H. Bond, Pullabrook, Bovey Tracey
1995	J.W. Mead, Bullhornstone, South Brent
1996	C.W. Abel, Higher Godsworthy, Tavistock
1997	J.W. Mead, Bullhornstone, South Brent
1998	A.W. & O.S. Mann, Great Dunstone, Widecombe
1999	Miss. S.C. Needham, Dipleigh, Widecombe

Class 5: Best Pair of Ram Hoggs bred by Exhibitor

1st Prize: Perpetual Challenge Cup kindly presented by Messrs. Mann Bros. The previous cup having been won outright by Mann Bros.

1st Prize: £10 2nd Prize: £5 3rd Prize: £3

Previous Winners:

1990	C.W. Abel, Higher Godsworthy, Tavistock
1991	A.H. Cole, Greenwell, Clearbrook
1992	C.E. Caunter & Son, Weekabrough, Ipplepen
1993	R.H. Bond, Pullabrook, Bovey Tracey
1994	P.W. Coaker, Bittleford, Poundsgate
1995	T.A. Phipps, New Cott, Poundsgate
1996-1997	P.W. Coaker, Bittleford, Poundsgate
1998	A.W. & O.S. Mann, Great Dunstone, Widecombe
1999	R. Mann, Great Dunstone, Widecombe

Class 6: Best Pen of 10 - 2th Ewes

1st Prize: Perpetual Challenge Trophy kindly presented by Mr. & Mrs. T.A. Phipps

Previous Winners:

1990	J. Savery, Zeal, South Brent
1991	Adams & Howell, Higher Lukesland, Ivybridge
1992	T.A. Phipps, New Cott, Poundsgate
1993	N.L. Warne & Son, Heathfield Farm, Modbury
1994	T.A. Phipps, New Cott, Poundsgate
1995	A.W. & O.S. Mann, Great Dunstone, Widecombe
1996	C.W. Abel, Higher Godsworthy, Tavistock
1998	T.A. Phipps, Newcott, Poundsgate
1999	D.S. Gardener, West Stoke Farm, Holne

Lot	Age	Owner	Bred By	Breeder of Sire	Flock No
1	Hogg	P. Abel	Owner	P.W. Coaker	PA9/R2
2	6T	"	J. Savery	J. Savery	JS-/R1
3	Hogg	A.H. Cole	Owner	J. Savery	AC9/R-
4	Hogg	"	"	"	AC9/R-
5	Hogg	A.W. & O.S. Mann	Owner	P. & W. Coaker	MB9/R1
6	Hogg	"	"	"	MB9/R2
7	Hogg	"	"	"	MB9/R3
8	Hogg	P.R. Coaker	Owner	A.W. & O.S. Mann	RC9/R1
9	Hogg	P. & W. Coaker	Owner	R. Woodley	PC9/R1
10	Hogg	"	"	"	PC9/R2
11	6T	"	Q. Rae	Mann Bros	
12	6T	"	Owner	W.J. Doidge	
13	Hogg	H. Bond	Owner	Q. Rae	BP9/R1
14	Hogg	"	"	"	BP9/R2
15	Hogg	"	"	"	BP9/R3
16	Old	"	"	P.W. Coaker	-
17	6T	Mr. & Mrs. N. Haley	Owner	A.W. & O.S. Mann	NH8/R1
18	FM	"	J. Savery	J. Savery	
19	4T	P. Vincent	Owner	Q. Rae	
20	FM	C. Pearse	P.W. Coaker	A.H. Cole	
21	FM	"	J. Savery		
22	Hogg	C.E. Caunter & Son		C. Abel	
23	Hogg	"		Mann Bros	
24	4T	Miss. A. Monro	Owner	Q. Rae	

Whiteface Dartmoor Sheep Breeders' Association

LIST OF MEMBERS 2001/2

			Prefix
CHAIRMAN Abel, P.	Higher Godsworthy, Peter Tavy	01822 810211	P.A.
Abel, C.A.	Dunkeld, Collaton, Tavistock	01822 614125	C.A.
Brown, A.H.	Tower Hill Farm, Place Lane, Ashburton		B.S.
Bond, H.	Pullabrook, Bovey Tracey, Newton Abbot	01647 277348	B.P.
Coaker, Patrick W.	Bittleford, Poundsgate, Newton Abbot	01364 631247	P.C.
Coaker, Philip R.	Runnage, Postbridge, Yelverton	01822 880222	R.C.
Caunter, C.E. & Son	Lower Weekaborough, Ipplepen	01803 812210	E.C.
Cole, A.H.	Greenwell, Clearbrook, Yelverton	01822 853563	A.C.
Doidge, W.J.	Fullamoor, Whitchurch, Tavistock	01822 852267	W.D.
Goddard, G.	Waytown Farm, Sampford Spiney, Yelverton	01822 854133	G.J.
Gardener, D.	West Stoke, Holne, Newton Abbot	01364 631286	D.G.
Geen, Miss A.	Sherberton Farm, Princetown	01364 631276	G.K.
TREASURER Haley, Mr & Mrs N.	Mayfields, Oaklands Road, Buckfastleigh	01364 643063	N.H.
Howell, Miss J.	Higher Lukeslands, Ivybridge (Ass. Member)	01752 892603	A.H.
Hutchings, R.	Staddicombe Farm, Holne	01364 631119	R.H.
Mann & Partners, A.W. & O.S.	Great Dunstone, Widecombe-in-the-Moor	01364 621233	M.B.
Mortimore, F.A.	Grattons, Widecombe-in-the-Moor	01364 631245	F.A.
Mead, J.W.	Bulhornstone Farm, South Brent	01364 73139	J.M.
Monro, Miss A.	Corndon Farm, Poundsgate	01364 631493	A.M.
Murray, C.	Pennywell Farm, Buckfastleigh	01364 642043	C.M.
PRESIDENT Needham, Miss S.C.	Dipleigh, Widecombe-in-the-Moor	01364 621227	S.N.
Pearse, C.	Barramoor Farm, North Bovey, Newton Abbot	01647 221303	H.P.
Peek, R.G.	Wallover Barton, Bratton Fleming, Barnstaple	01598 710245	R.P.
Phipps, T.A.	Newcott, Poundsgate, Newton Abbot	01364 631421	T.P.
Rae, Mr & Mrs Q.	Lower Langdon Farm, North Bovey	01647 221288	R.L.
Savery, R.S.	Lincombe Farm, Diptford, Totnes	01364 73245	R.S.
Steer, W.E.N.	Crossways, Norland Park, South Brent	01364 73294	W.S.
Stock, Mrs A.E.	Tunhill Farm, Widecombe-in-the-Moor	01364 621265	A.S.

Tregear, Mrs J.	Furze Fields, Furze Hill Cross, Cornworthy	01803 712578 (day 01803 732935)	J.T.
Vincent, P.	Bramble Torre, Dittisham, Dartmouth	01803 722227	P.V.
Warne, N.L.	Heathfield Farm, Modbury, Ivybridge	01548 821269	N.W.
Widdicombe, T.	Woodlands, Haytor Vale, Newton Abbot	01364 661470	T.W.
Wolton, Mrs P.	Locks Park Farm, Hatherleigh, Okehampton	01837 810416	P.W.

Dartmoor's History *and the* Whitefaced Sheep

'Between the North and South Hams (for that is the ancient name) there lieth a chain of hills consisting of a blackish earth, both rockie and heathy, called by a borrowed name of its barrenness Dartmoor; richer in its bowels than in the face thereof, yielding tin and turf, which to save for fuel you wonder to see how busy the by-dwellers be at some seasons of the year; whose topps and torrs are in winter covered with a white cap, but in summer the bordering neighbours bring great herds and flocks of sheep to pasture there. The 'Forest of Dartmoor' as it is called is a wild tableland occupying the centre of Devonshire and with thousands of acres of commonland of much the same nature.'

The Moors – timeless scene.

Whilst researching the Whiteface Dartmoor Sheep it is not difficult to become inquisitive and try to speculate as to when all of this might have begun in light of the words of L.W. Page that were written in 1895, when he records great flocks pasturing the Moor from very early times. They almost certainly transversed these parts when Dartmoor was spelt Dertemore or Dertemora and Widecombe was spelt Wethycombe and Tavistock Tavesto and Bovey Tracey pronounced Beuitraly; all spread along this 'granite-way'.

England before the Norman Conquest was covered with Forest and much of it was the same condition in the reign of Elizabeth. Yet vast tracts were in later times in a state of commonage upon which the inhabitants of neighbouring towns had right of pasturage for cattle and sheep. The report of the 'Bureau of Animal Industry' in 1890 said the native sheep of these ancient forests and commons presented distinctive characters and formed well defined breeds. It says that several of these 'Forest breeds' yet remain and until late into the 1700s were quite numerous, for example in Windsor Forest, Sherburne Forest, Mendip and Dartmoor Forest.

The report also singles out the 'Dartmoor' and 'Exmoor'; 'as of the 'Forest breeds' that remain, these two preserve more decidedly their identity.'

It says they exist in the elevated country between the Bristol and British Channels (now the English Channel) the one inhabiting the healthy tract of granite forming the Forest of Dartmoor, the other the district of 'Greywacke' of the Forest of Exmoor at the sources of the River Exe, on the confines of Somerset and Devon. They were, it seems significant small hardy breeds of sheep. From these modest beginnings their importance grew. The sheep is recorded by the Bureau of Animal Industry, 'as the mainstay of English Agriculture, the foundation of English prosperity and a potent factor in British commercial supremacy.' A Roman writer records the fact that, 'the wool of great Britain is often spun so fine that it is in a manner comparable to the spiders' thread.'

English history is woven with wars entered into to protect her woollen trade or to strike down those who came in competition with her, and her statute books are full of enactments restricting both importation and exportation of wool.

So from scanty, isolated and primitive prehistoric beginnings sheep became England's Golden Hoof and Golden Fleece, nutured by farmer, shepherd, cottager and industry. Rather more of a revelation than perhaps a truth, comes from a letter written to the Farmers' Weekly on the 25th April 1947, by coincidence, a farmer in Tavistock by the name of Widecombe, who wrote that he thought the Whitefaced sheep must be a strain of Abraham's as they resemble the sheep painted on his Church and Cathedral windows, (which at the time was the crest of the Devon Farmers Union and also the local Grammar School). Certainly the stained glass windows were used to depict ancient breeds of sheep as a time-worn definition of their importance in biblical times, and here in Devon at a time of Church building that gave thanks for prosperity in sheep and wool; local sheep of especially ancient origin would have seemed appropriate images to copy and display. Quite likely using the 'Dartmoor' as a popular sheep during this time in its history some 600 years ago. Pictures on stained glass windows before universal reading and writing was a form of teaching and a way of recording history.

In an unbroken line from Neolithic or even Palaeolithic times, Dartmoor's oldest inhabitants are certainly the sheep. For thousands of years the hills have been dotted with their small grey shapes. The blood of many a sheep must have been spilled upon the heather in sacrifice to the 'grim gods' of the great stone circles.

Celtic peoples, drawn from the Marne, Seine and Breton districts of France, invaded by sea from 200–100 BC. They pressed up the rivers at least as far as the foothills of Dartmoor, living as the Bronze Age people lived, in settlements of round huts and confining cultivation to small walled fields, still occasionally in evidence on Dartmoor's high moorland.

It is thought the 'Moorland-type' sheep like the horned Dartmoor and Exmoor are both likely to have the Celtic genes. Once regarded as an island veiled in mystery, recent thinking says that ancient Britain had its origins of farming with its own native peoples, and was not influenced radically by Celts or Romans, and its farming singularly gained control of food production through a relatively fixed society of British peoples and was largely separated from European influence. This ancient culture domesticated dogs descended from wolves, that herded primitive sheep and preyed on other animals. On Dartmoor the evidence of its life, customs and religion is supplied by the Moor's silent stones.

It now seems probable that some time around 4000 BC the pattern of land use in Britain changed radically. The New Stone Age (Neolithic) C4000–2000 BC saw the establishment of the first farming communities in Britain. Improved flint and stone tools enabled these first farmers to start extensive forest clearings. Neolithic flint implements have been found on Dartmoor. Its cairns and barrows have given forth to many remains of the Stone Age and some few of the Bronze, and a tumulus on Hameldon had disclosed implements which point to a Scandinavian occupation (Norse men).

The use of Bronze around 2000 BC became established and stone structures became easy to shape with hard bronze metal tools. The clearance of trees and shrub from Dartmoor was very extensive, and much open grassland with some bracken and heather developed.

The population who occupied Grimspound or used it as their place of refuge belonged to a very primitive age; they were clad in the skins which they cleaned with flint scrapers, and they were a pastoral race having flocks of sheep and possibly cattle. The huts (24) at Grimspound relate to a vastly remote period and the condition of existence of the occupants of their huts was rude in the extreme. That the inhabitants of the huts employed weapons and tools of bone, is probable. The innovative idea of 'cooking stones' i.e. river pebbles which have been 'fired' and used for cooking purposes, also called pot-boilers' may have been used in this very hut circle.

Probably in an early pre-metallic age, certain people (Neolithic) without pot or pan (pottery or metal) used skins and 'cooking stones' to boil their meat.

When meat was killed a hole is dug in the ground about the size of a common pot, and a piece of the raw hide of the animal pressed into the ground the size of a small pot and filled with water. The meat is then placed in this water; in a fire nearby several large stones are heated to a red heat and successively dipped and held in the water until the meat is 'boiled' – stone boiling! Some holes may have been covered with turf and clay and the meat left to cook.

Hut circle at Grimspound.

From the crest of Hookney Down and from Hookney Tor (North Bovey Common) one can look down upon the Bronze Age enclosure lying on the slopes of Hameldon. The Pound is overlooked by both Hameldon and Hookney Tor. The rings of hut circles (many seeming robbed of their stone) within its walls mark the abode of wild shepherd, wilder hunter or of warriors long since passed away. The remains of ancient dwellings encircled by ruined walls are impressive. A great sweep of wild Moor rolls away into the western distance – strange weird mysterious and solitary, and Page continued to write; 'if you want sternness and loneliness pass into Dartmoor, its wastes and wilds, and crags of granite!' The wild Moor also stretches away towards the sister heights of Cornwall.

Now the large sprawl of stone fallen away from Grimspound's original enclosure is very considerable and suggests stone was used to form a wall several feet high (8–9 feet) and with a double wall allowing a gap between it, was impressively wide too. Interestingly many stones seem shaped and cut from 'Tor rock' as is in evidence on Hookney Tor, where stone seems to have been chiselled or cut away; but perhaps for other use, at another time! Other folds or pounds can be seen on the Erme, Avon, Yealm and Dunnabridge; not so imposing but good enough to keep animals. Also 'Creber Pound', says Crossing, was a drift pound for several centuries. It is mentioned he goes on to say, in a document of Charles the First's reign where it is set forth that at the time of the drifts 'Cattle are driven to a pound called Dunnabridge Pound if they are found in the east, west and south quarter of the forest, and if found in the north quarter of the forest to a pound called Creber Pound. 'Strolls' used by the moormen are found here too, and all over the moor.

On the edge of the Forest with haunts of wolves and wild beasts the inhabitants of Grimspound would have grazed their animals on the slopes of Hameldon and Hookney Tors on either side, guarded by herdsmen by day. At night they would have been driven into the pounds, perhaps herds of small, short horned ox, flocks of goats, and horned sheep and hogs which furnished their staple diet. The Forest might have provided nuts, fish, venison and wild boar.

The pound covers about four acres and the outer wall measuring around 500 meters in circumference. Just two or three main entrances, the largest on the south facing side, probably once closed with great baulks of timber!

Grimspound seen from Hookney Tor. (Photo: Colin Pearse).

Robert Burnard too goes far to show that Grimspound's construction reaches back into a remote past, and that its antiquity is greater than any former investigator dared to assign to it. The great numbers of prehistoric people who lived on the Moor is also very remarkable. Shadows of a past world are reflected in its wastes, witnessing prehistoric man; to the tinners who peopled the Moor through the middle ages to the dawn of Christian teaching in the country and to the Normans with their forest rights and laws, all no doubt encompassing sheep that roamed. A wild hill country of tors and stones and the mother of all its rivers tumbling from Moorland marshes.

There is debate that Grimspound's large walls were not just for protection of flocks and herds, and so many dwellings for just a few herdsmen. Author of 'Grimspound and its

Associated Relics', thinks these pounds were erected for storing tin for greater security and must, because of its size, have been built by strangers (Norsemen). These people may just have taken over this aboriginal town and fortified it in a more massive way than originally was the case! It seems there is no doubt that Grim refers to the Devil (Grims Dyke 934 and Grimesdich 1289 ADii) and that the name is one of those instances where a large prehistoric work was associated by the Saxons with diabolic forces!

Shortt, however, expounds the sheepfold (livestock) theory as a village of the Belgic Celts or Dumnonii tribe. It cannot be overestimated what wolves in particular could do to flocks and herds if protection wasn't given in an inhospitable forest area. So Dartmoor still documents life from the early Bronze Age. Ancient rights are so preserved that Hill farmers continue to graze cattle, sheep and ponies as also practised in the 12th and 13th Centuries. On Dartmoor evidence of Bronze Age occupation survives in the form of many hut circles, pounds, enclosures and field systems. Many of the latter are laid out in accord with an extensive system of boundaries known as reaves, constructed about 1600–1500 BC. By the late Bronze Age a deterioration in climate saw a shift of settlement away from Dartmoor. Centuries of intensive pastoral and animal husbandry had largely eliminated the original Forest cover and remaining woodland was confined to lower slopes, depleting somewhat the wild Forest to 'morish land'. Yet our knowledge of prehistoric agriculture will always be handicapped by the acid nature of moorland soil which destroys bone, and can badly damage pottery and metal.

The animals shepherded during the Bronze Age continued to be cattle, sheep and pigs and goats, all smaller than today. The sheep were hairer and looked much more like goats. Similarities on our sheep today with those domesticated around 2000 BC that co-existed with other animals and man is not difficult to realise. These animals could have played a big part in feeding and clothing early settlers.

The horned characteristics is still very dominant in the male Whitefaced Dartmoor sheep. (Photo: Colin Pearse).

Whiteface Dartmoors of today still retain the horn in the male sheep and in the past the females would very likely have been horned, as vestiges remain today. The bearded wiry tuft of hair on the sheep's breast, especially the ram, bears semblance to its heritage, and their hardiness and protective nature suggests a common past. Nothing is known, however, for certain regarding the origin of domesticated sheep. Yet goats are related to sheep and with certain intermediate species are generally regarded as forming one group of the cavicornia or hollow-horned ruminants. So was it a case of 'sorting the sheep from the goats'! The true sheep comprise a considerable number of wild species which fall into distinct natural groups. The one includes the Mouflon of Corsica and Sardinia and the Urial of Persia, Northern India and Tibet. Soays are known to survive from prehistoric sheep and are related to the Corsican Mouflon. The view most widely held is that the Asiatic Mouflon supplied most of the foundation stock, but the Urial and even the Argali of Western Siberia have sometimes been regarded as the ancestors of some domesticated sheep.

The older view, to the effect that the wild ancestor must have been quite different from any surviving species is not now accepted.

The ancestors of some of today's sheep possibly brought here by races from Central Asia who swept across the Continent of Europe to our Western Isles during BC 80–60 to AD 80. The iron age farming settlements and the Celtic kingdom of Danmonii, a division of the ancient Britons continued almost unaffected by the arrival of the Romans in AD 43–50. The garrison at Exeter traded in wool and tin (ref Claude Pike).

No conflicts with the Romans seemed to have occurred west of Exeter, and indeed no Latin name is borne by 'tor' or 'river', and Saxon nomenclature is comparatively rare. Celtic and Cornu-Celtic are the titles of both as they were 2000 years ago.

Scandinavian names then are borne by Hameldon, the hill of the viking 'Hamill' (Ymyl-don the boundary hill the Great Central Trackway passes over it), by Thornworthy Tor which perpetuates the name Thorni; by Grimspound, Grimslake, and Grimsgrove respectively the enclosure, stream and grave of Grim!

Whether the sea robbers of the North have left their imprint upon Dartmoor in this unmistakable fashion, Frederick Widgery and others were not so sure, and may equally be traced to the Anglo-Saxon period.

Sheep dipping supceded sheep washing at 'Sherrell', Ivybridge.

Place names could have their origins with sheep on Dartmoor, like Sheepstor, and Sheepwash, North of Hatherleigh, which in old English is spelt 'Shepwafhe'. The Saxons were known to be washing sheep as early as the ninth century. Carefully sharpened hand shears could easily be made blunt by sharp grit and soil held in fleeces. Although fleece quality was important, washing was later found to extract the essential grease and natural oil of fleeces and reduced the sheared weight of the fleece. Yet early fleece removal was just a case of plucking!

The Old English spelling for sheep is 'Sceap', and a 'sheep clearing' in old English was written 'Sceap leah'. This leads me into one of the most dated names given on Dartmoor in relation to the sheep's presence and husbandry, it is that of 'Shapley' (North Bovey and Chagford parishes). A local pronuniciation even today for the place name on Dartmoor of Shapley is simply 'Sheepley' (or Sheep Lay). In 1086 named as Escapeleia, as 'Scapelie' in 1912; a sort of 'sheep lie' which gives its use away, where sheep were actively shepherded, and in 1230 'Sheppelegha' which means 'Sheep Clearing', and this probably records this piece of land purposely cleared in the Forest to pasture sheep, as one of the first *named* on Dartmoor, as opposed to a place or area of the Forest first *used* to accommodate sheep. Today's enclosed lanes would doubtless have been the ancient tracks leading to and away from the 'clearings' that are still seen at the two Shapley farms, that also gave access to the higher Moor.

Other named features like Sheepfold, Sheepwalk and Sheep-run, Sheepstell, Sheeps Leap, Sheep Shears, Sheep dip, Sheep creep, Sheep measure and Grey Wethers and plants like Sheep fescue, Sheep sorrel, and the Sheep tick that attaches itself in Spring and Summer to livestock on the Moor, are here today. Aptly named 'Lambs-Down'; is at Newcombe, Buckfastleigh.

All this suggests a livelihood with sheep from very early times, and their importance in the social organisation of the Moor, often originating from names given and commonly used by 'Moormen' and farmers.

The Sheepfold in the Little Sheepfold's Newtake under Stannon Tor. The mist blots out the Forest part of the Moor beyond big Stannon Newtake Wall. (Photo: Colin Pearse).

Within the restored Fold old stone posts are built into the outer wall and an even older wall inside the Fold suggests history not now recorded.

The development of agriculture, industrial revolution and the place of pastoral farming all incorporated name changes and new names in changing practices.

Dartmoor was isolated from Roman influence as their roads were built north and south of the Moor. So it is possible that some pastoral-agricultural life continued on the Moor untouched by the changes that slowly persuaded the rest of Devon out of the Celtic way of life to the Romano-British. Vian Smith in Portrait of Dartmoor says further, that hut circles were thought to have been lived in up to the middle of the 4th Century.

Dartmoor was not exploited at this time for tin, because Spain supplied tin for the Romans, and Dartmoor changed little by nearly 400 years of Roman occupation.

The Moor's isolation at this time might have aided the survival of our native sheep. Some farmed, some scattered over the Moor's heathland, and in isolated pockets of wild or semi-wild breeding flocks, grazing the newly cleared woodland areas, 'at home in their own Country.' However, the Romans made a contribution to our country's sheep and subsequent wool production through the Cotswold sheep descended from the 'Roman Longwool' which was imported from the Mediterranean to augment the native flocks, to provide extra clothing for Roman troops, not used to our cold damp winters. 'Cotswold' is derived from the two Saxon words 'Cote' or sheep-fold and 'wold' or barehill. Their hills too once maintained an industry on which much of England's early prosperity was founded.

When the Romans left Britain in the early part of the 5th Century the country settled into economic darkness. The old order collapsed through deterioration, plague and migration, thinning out the native celtic population in AD 540.

This was truly the 'Dark Ages' and little of the written historical record remains of AD 450–600.

By the 7th Century a fragmented society could offer no effective resistance to the determined Saxons. They invaded and settled the land, and began farming. They pushed beyond the Cotswolds into the South West and Devon and finally reached the foothills of Dartmoor. The Saxons did not settle on open moorland above the 1000 feet (320 metre) contour. The land between 500–1000 feet attracted them most. Their open field system of farming, imported from the flat lands of Saxony, can still be seen on the hillsides here, and was the beginnings of the 'strip field' system. Its success grew with sheep farming.

'Worthy' commonly attracted to the name of many farm holdings means farmstead, and has its roots in Saxon folklore! (Teignworthy, Fernworthy, Batworthy and Thornworthy). W.C. Hoskins in his contribution to Dartmoor – National Park (1957) wrote: 'it is certain that the Saxons . . . made use of the vast acres of common pasture' and used the wild wastes for the grazing of stock.

In terms of trying to link our sheeps history with the surrounding districts and counties, it is recorded that during the Saxon Heptarchy, Devonshire belonged to the Weft (West) Saxons, and at that time comprised within its limits the County of Cornwall, providing a big area of land for our sheep to overlap and no doubt bears witness to the Cornish Heath sheep, and its ancestry. The informal confederation of the Anglo-Saxon Kingdoms (seven county units) from the fifth to the ninth centuries included Devonshire under the 'Wessex Kingdom'. The land was recorded as hilly and woody and the soil fertile and by many called the 'garden of England'.

The produce is said to be crops, minerals, timber, fish etc., and wool receives a distinction in that it says; 'its woollen trade as considerable as any in the Kingdom'.

A Saxon perambulation preserved among the archives of Exeter Cathedral and dated it is thought about the ninth century is the first known document relating to Dartmoor. By the ninth century the Saxon Kings (of Wessex) made the Dartmoor heartland a Royal Hunting ground and it once formed a fastness (ditches or banks) for wolves and other wild animals (deer and boar), and it is said that wolves were hunted upon the Moor as late as the reign of Elizabeth 1st.

No little speculation says pastured animals might have been given protection in pounds and folds abounding on the Moor at this time, so as to accomodate their survival within the Royal 'gamesmanship' and against a balance of wild beasts and thieving too.

The Anglo-Saxons were great sheep-lovers and flockmasters and we probably owe a great deal to their shepherding skills and knowledge of sheep.

Anglo-Saxon wills it seems regularly discussed the disposition of sheep by the hundred and excavations reveal sheep bones, sheep shears, wool spindles and weaving batons relative to cloth production (The First Millenium Book).

Two hundred years before 1000 AD there is evidence of English woollen cloth being exported to Europe. Around 1200 AD England was clearly established as the principal supplier of high quality wool to Northern Europe. During the following centuries raw wool became an international trade of huge proportions, whilst also remaining an essentially cottage industry. As the trade developed a road system grew to facilitate the movement of wool and wool traders, and eventually a 'packhorse' trade from the North Devon Coast to Brixham. A prosperous woollen trade over many centuries since this time has been pivotal to our sheeps survival up to this millennium. By 1630 the Devon Kersey Cloth became famous and was made exclusively from Devon wool. Green tells us 'the broadcloths of the West claimed the palm among the woollen stuffs of England.'

Fine 'wool Churches' all across England are like no others, the wealth that built, improved and endowed them came in no small measure from the profits of wool. Buckfast Abbey was founded in the reign of Henry II on the site of a Benedictine Abbey of Saxon days. The Saxon name given in Bishop Aelfwold's charter in AD 1016 was 'Buckfasten' i.e. Deerfastness. It would seem to say the Abbey was surrounded by thick woods, remote and inaccessible! The evolution of the Whiteface Dartmoor as a Forest breed does conjure up feelings of special remoteness and a 'foggy' sort of 'monastic' world of their own too, on this once volcanic born tract of land. This so far back in history that only the imagination can now bring it to life! (In the 12th century in England, it is said there were 10 million sheep!)

The second colony of monks here were 'Cistercians' and the monastery became very prosperous and the richest house of that order in the country. The Cistercians were great wool-traders and did much for both trade and agriculture in the districts near them on the foothills of Dartmoor. The farmer monks had enormous holdings of land and kept huge flocks of sheep. Deals with merchants were made that sold their wool many years ahead in the 13th Century. It has been supposed that the sunken track called the 'Abbots Way' was used in carrying the wool from the moorland farms, belonging to the monastery, towards Plymouth and Tavistock. The Abbots Way leading over the Moor is marked by crosses. It ran from Buckfast and divided at Broad Park near Plym Head in the middle of the Moor, leading to Tavistock Abbey and Buckland Abbey. Some of the guiding crosses were standing long before the monasteries were built, and inscribed with the 6th Century.

In earlier times too sheep were regarded almost as dairy animals and the milk used for cheese making. R. Trow-Smith in 'British Livestock Husbandry' quotes a tenth century document showing the rights of a 'manorial Shepherd' to fold the manorial flock on his own piece of land for 12 nights in midwinter (for the value of their dung) to also keep one lamb and one fleece every year for himself; to have the flock for seven nights in spring, and a bowlful of whey or buttermilk per day throughout the summer.

At Domesday the sheep were valued primarily as a milch (milk) animal, next for its wool and its manure, and last and least for its carcass. In the 14th Century the Tavistock Abbey ewes were yielding about 10 gallons per lactation, which is similar to modern hill-ewes. The practice on Dartmoor may have lasted beyond the 16th and 17th Centuries as Freda Wilkinson records in excellent detail.

In 1066 the Norman invasion occurred, William overthrowing Harold, and he set about recording and documenting his new realm. As documented the Normans created Dartmoor as a Royal Forest (a hunting Chase) where the beasts of the forest; deer, hare, boar and wolf were strictly preserved with harsh penalties for transgressing the law.

However the presence of a great number of sheep on Dartmoor at an early date shows how little it was used as a hunting ground, for sheep were strictly excluded from most forests, the smell being much disliked by the deer! Towards the end of the 18th Century the red deer were exterminated by the Duke of Bedford's stag hounds.

Sadly the Normans arriving in 1066 set about removing evidence of the native culture that existed in England at that time. Every Anglo-Saxon Cathedral was almost totally rebuilt. Recovering early evidence of our sheep is blighted by the destruction of early records. However, the Anglo-Saxon Chronicles record that in 1085 King William I sent men all over England to each Shire, to record how much each landlord held in land and livestock, and its value (every serf and slave, every Lord and freeman, for in those times men were as much property as animals and buildings) and collated into a volume known as the 'Domesday Book', a final register of rightful possession; an analogy from 'The Day of Judgement.' It was written in Latin on the skins of about 190 sheep by a single scribe.

Many areas of England with many breeds of sheep from the South Downs to the slopes of the Yorkshire Pennines were all prosperous sheep areas and through the evidence of the Domesday Survey of 1086 Devon farms were not without their sheep, recorded in number only, so we speculate as to their breed. Early identification no doubt used the names of the shires, where different sheep breeds had their origins.

Its isolation was such that Dartmoor is not mentioned by name in the Domesday Book of 1086. There is no record of it until 1181 when it was called 'Dertemora'. The survey refers to pastoral and other land in the various manors.

The pattern of farmsteads thinly scattered over the whole area varied only slightly over the next two centuries; most had already been founded.

Taking Holne Parish and its Domesday entry, as an example, it was a larger than average manor and included all hamlets and farms in the Parish, except the Stokes farms, which formed a separate manor. The population in the whole country was just 2 million and the majority of these people were living in rural areas.

Surprisingly few sheep and livestock are recorded. It just makes one think, some animals may have been lost amid the rocks and gullies on Dartmoor itself! Domesday said, 'William (Failaise) has a manor called Holle (Holne) which Alvin Abbot of Buckfastleigh held and it rendered 'geld' for one hide and a half (tax rating) and this can be ploughed by twelve horses; (so says Crispin Gill). There were 13 villeins and seven borders (small holders) and eight serfs (slaves) and one packhorse, 6 head of cattle and six swine (pigs) and fifty two sheep (no goats) worth 60 shillings.

Mary Tavy boasted 120 sheep, 16 cattle, 4 swine. Perhaps pockets of wild sheep protected in favourable combes on the Moor were unaccounted in Domesday because these parish numbers do seem few compared to figures today. Perhaps the English didn't entirely approve of the survey by an invading race!

The increased afforestation of land by the Kings of England after the Norman conquest resulted in the whole of Devon being designated a Forest (for their recreation and pleasure). The increase in population from the twelfth century onwards encouraged encroachment upon the untilled land of the Forest. In 1184/85 a South Devon man was fined one mark for 'waste of forest', i.e. enclosing closed woodland for his own use.

Yet Dartmoor has existed as a 'Forest' from time immemorial and the date when Forest laws were imposed on it lost in antiquity and some of the rights imposed upon it are very old. The first perambulation of the Forest boundaries took place around 1224. In 1239 Dartmoor Forest was granted to Richard Earl of Cornwall, and ceased to be a Forest and became a Chase, which meant the common law applied. In 1337 Edward III made a grant of the Forest to his son, Edward the Black Prince, who became Prince of the Manor of Lydford and the 'Chase of Dartmoor'; but it is still known as the 'Forest of Dartmoor.' Since that time the Forest – the parish of Lydford – has remained part of the Duchy of Cornwall. The limits were settled by a perambulation survey in 1240 by Royal command in the reign of Henry III and lays down the boundaries that still define the Forest part of the Duchy of Cornwall today. Commons surrounding the Forest are usually included in any general reference to Dartmoor. Special rights on the Moor relates to owners and occupiers of tenements within the Forest and Venville tenants or owners of land, in particular, vills or towns, adjoining the Forest. Claims and counter claims as to their exact rights and liabilities have been pressed in successive centuries but various documents set forth these tenants rights to take 'all things that might be good except green oak (vert) and venison.'

The rights were subject to a small fee being the 'fin-ville'. These rights were of pasturage (pasturing all commonable beasts) on the Moor, 'turbary' (digging or cutting turf (peat) for fuel) stone and sand (repairing houses and land) and taking heath for thatching.

No one was allowed in a Royal Forest after nightfall; all beasts put there to pasturage had to go in 'by sonne and goo home by sonne'. When they could remain by day and night, the holders of rights of pasturage paid 4d yearly for night rest.

As special tenants of the King the owners or occupiers of Venville land were called upon to perform special duties, like attending the Prince's Courts and drifting bullocks and ponies and assisting the Moormen in driving animals to selected points, especially in the Spring/Summer drifts to Dartmoor and Autumn identification of animals for pony 'colt' sales, and return of animals home from Summer grazing to their rightful owners. It was said, 'no man may pasture more cattle upon the Forest than he could winter on his farm.' It he did, he must then pay 'as a strange man'! (William Crossing).

The relaxation of the Forest laws by Henry III resulted in the recolonisation of Dartmoor, including the establishment of the Ancient Tenements such as Runnage, Riddon, Babeny and Pizwell. It was from this time onwards (13th to 17th Centuries) that the piecemeal field enclosures of land of the Commons of Devon, which surrounded the Forest took place.

In AD 1260 there were only two Churches in the Sextor of the Moor Lydford and Widecombe. So at this time Bishop Bronscombe granted permission to the inhabitants of the villages of 'Balbeny and Pushyll' (the ancient tenements of Babeny and Pizwell) on the Wallabrook, to attend Widecombe Church instead of going to their Parish Church at Lydford (the other side of the Moor).

They were expected to attend three times a year taking their 'tythes' (taxes) with them and these paid in the form of 'Lambs'; a really important record of the sheeps place in the general order of things at this time. (Sheep were obviously needed).

The wool trade had its peaks and slumps, but in its best years it rivalled the tin trade in importance and in towns like Tavistock, Ashburton and Chagford retained its importance after the stannaries had declined.

During the 11th and 12th Centuries the population increased right across Europe, and this increased the viability of the English wool trade, and provided the foundation of the whole English economy.

As early as the 12th Century, Italian merchants were making regular visits to this country, buying up whole clips of wool for several years ahead and paying in advance in cash. The wealthier Italians were demanding high quality cloth and their buyers soon rivalled the Flemish in their demand for English wool. Monastic flocks were favoured as large amounts could be ordered in one place and the quality was usually higher as the monks could afford 'professional' Shepherds. Sometimes it is said, this method of selling wool had disastrous results as an outbreak of sheep scab could decimate a flock, and the monks could find themselves bankrupt, and unable to fulfill orders and repay money previously advanced. The raising of revenue from the export of wool began when the whole clips from several monasteries were taken to pay the ransom for Richard I after his capture in 1191 and soon regular custom levies were made on all wool exports and successive monarchs exploited this commodity to such an extent that a decline in the late 15th Century was largely as a result of over taxation.

In 1299 Edward I had relieved wool of taxes and by 1306 it was forbidden to export wool out of the country and Edward III (1327–1377) offered Flemish fullers and weavers his protection in 1335 to encourage them to settle in England and practice their craft. He introduced the Woolsack into the House of Lords at this time, a symbol borne centuries before in Saxon times. Its presence was intended as a lasting reminder of wool's importance to the kingdom. Nearly abolished in 2003! The prestige of the wool sack as a seat of the Lord Chancellor is alone sufficient to indicate the estimation in which wool was held on England in the middle ages. 'The source of England's wealth the backbone of its economy and culture.'

Market towns sprang up very quickly all over England during the 14th Century. It was a requirement that there should be seven miles between each market!

Walter Stapledon (1261–1326) 15th Bishop of Exeter, in 1310 chartered a three-day market and fair in Ashburton, which would have had a marked effect on the town's economy. However, during the fourteenth century a succession of disasters destroyed a great deal of the peasant farming of Medieval England. A deteriorating climate with its attendant crop failures and a series of epidemics of Bubonic Plague (The Black Death) arrived from Europe with the 'black rats' coming off the ships in 1348 and 1349 and it decimated the population of England and its people in the countryside. Out of an estimated population of four million at the time in England, at least half died. Devon being an agriculturally based county with a high level population in the countryside suffered more than any other county. Change was inevitable and land was taken in hand by Lord of the Manors, and the feudal system slowly dissolved.

Only slowly after such a disaster did the prosperity of England re-establish itself. But rigorous taxes and market tolls were levied relieved by Henry IV in 1399. Market tolls are still deducted today, from sellers commodities and animals, as recorded in this history.

Exeter became a staple town from 1354. Staples or merchants exercised a monopoly and the King taxed their profits. Wool was taken to the staple towns where it had to be offered for sale for forty days. It was only after that time that it could be sold for export. The idea was to prevent direct trade between wool producers and foreign merchants. A Chief Shepherd (in 1444) could earn 20 shillings a year with 5 shillings for meat and drink and his clothing. The working day began at 5 am and ended at 8 pm, with two hours allowed to sleep in the midday! Work in winter was from 'dawn to dusk'.

The influential wool merchants wanted a single staple town abroad where they could enjoy a monopoly of trade. The staple for English wool was fixed at Calais, still part of the English territory in 1399, and most of the English wool had to pass through Calais before sale. In July 1470 38 ships sailed from London with 1,160½ sacks of wool and 268,227 fells (hides). Regular sailings from other ports made up an enormous total export figure taking into account an English population of something around 2½ million!

Wool too is woven deeply into Devon's historic economy; Exeter, Credition, Tiverton, Ashburton, Chudleigh, Tavistock, Okehampton, Chagford, Rattery, Buckfastleigh to mention but a few, where their livlihood depended on wool.

The development of the tucking (or fulled or felted) mills in the 13th and 14th Century brought cloth making out of the towns and into those areas where wool was produced and where there was water power to work the mills, and streams were led by leats to work the fulling mills. These mills involved Dartmoor in the wool trade, and they are of particular interest for they partially mechanised weaving skills developed in cottage crafts and utilised the wool of Dartmoor sheep. Even Widecombe and Dean Prior had Tucking Mills in the seventeenth century and a thriving cloth industry into the eighteenth century. Wealth derived from sheep farming and tin streaming must have helped lay the foundations of longhouses on the Moor. Occupational surnames have also sprung from 'woollen' origin; names like Tucker, Fuller, Weaver, Carder, Shearman, and Comber, Woolman, Dyer and Walker!

Medieval Dartmoor wool was though coarse, short and spikey. It was said that taken by the Tavistock Mills off the western quarter of the Moor was of such 'grossness and stubbornness' it had to be worked up with 'lambs wool and flock' to make it more saleable under the name of Tavistocks, a light coarse serge. Soil type, nutrition, breed, and severity of climate all play a part in determining wool quality.

In 1463 the inhabitants of Roborough, Lifton and Tavistock Hundreds (parishes) were allowed by act of parliament to continue to use flockwool in the manufacture of 'Tavistocks' (mixing lambs wool with native wool). So a series of events occurred in making wool cloth. The farmer brought the wool to the town market, where it would be sold. Then carded and washed and then the spinsters would spin it. It was returned to the market as 'yarn' to be bought by the weaver. Once woven into cloth it could be fulled (tucking). Tucking was a local phrase, i.e. worked, pounded with heavy wooden hammers, and shrunk, much like the process of felting, after which it was dried, i.e. it could be stretched on racks, or 'tenters' to be partly dried. The surface could be then raised by 'teazle heads' and cropped and sheared to make a nap. Then it might be sold on again for dyeing (woad, madder and umber). Lichen collected from the rocks on Dartmoor produced a dye, as explained by Annie Randall King in 'Dyed in the Wool'.

She goes on to say that there were two main types of wool cloth. 'Woollen', made from the short fibres of wool and 'Worsted', made from the long fibres of the fleece and left unfulled. Many of the trades became centred around rural craftsmen and guilds were formed, e.g. Weavers, 'Sheremen' and Tuckers.

Everything to do with the wool trade was regulated. In the early medieval period weavers were forbidden to work at night. This later changed and weaving was done in tiny upstairs rooms. Long windows can still be seen in Ashburton, giving evidence to this activity.

In the mid 1400s wool sacks were used to ballast Wadebridge in Cornwall. Wool doesn't rot in water. Large quantities would have been needed. Drill bits used to test the foundation of the bridge have come up with wool on them. It might not be unrelated that the terrible Black Death in the mid thirteen hundreds and a population that was stagnant in its growth, might have left stock piles of wool and other commodities over into the next century, that somehow found a use. Here as a natural binding for the bridges platform and piers.

During the first half of the fifteen hundreds the Dissolution of the Monasteries gave Henry VIII vast new holdings in land and money. Some of the land he sold back to local gentry and wealthy London speculators took on these country estates.

Henry saw Devon to be one of the richest counties. 'Trafficking' in wool and woollen goods was the most important trade, and though passing its zenith in the 17th Century, it continued to do well until the latter half of the 18th Century. At the end of 1540 only £5,000 per annum in raw wool was being exported.

The 'serge manufacture of Devonshire' was a trade it is said by Defoe, 'too great to be described in miniature'. At the weekly markets commonly £50–60,000 worth of woollen goods were sold in a week and sometimes eighty to a hundred thousand pounds value in 'serges' was sometimes sold. So in 1540, £100,000 worth of serge left the staple of Exeter each week, it is said!

During the Civil War of 1549 when war broke out Exeter's defences were put in order, and arms collected, and amongst other expenses was recorded £300 for 17 packs of wool used for the barricades!

In 1552 an act of parliament enacted that wool could not be bought unless it was for the buyer's own use. This brought great hardship it seems to wool producers and strangled trade. It had to be weaved within the household or sold through the staple. They could not afford a horse and the poor people were forced to carry their wool to market on their backs, as far as five to ten miles! If fleeces were not sold within a year, they had to be sold to the local clothier at the current market price at the local market.

It is clear throughout history and through many centuries that wool and wool products prospered and declined and the fluctuations showed both great profits with Merchants Adventures, and many lean years for farmers as wool was stored for many years, risking deterioration on Devon's farms.

During the reign of Henry VIII special statutes were enacted affecting cloths called 'White Straits' of Devon and Devonshire Kersey called 'Dozens'. (F. Widgery).

In Elizabeth I's reign (1558–1603) trade prospered here as elsewhere. However, later the importation of Irish Worsted to weave into cloth was met by violent opposition from the wool-combers. As late as 1749 troops were despatched to Tiverton. On John Waldron's Almshouses on one wall there used to be a pack of wool bearing his staple mark and a ship and the words 'remember the poor'. So the 'see-saw' of fortunes is again in evidence, for Crediton had for a long time a very important trade in woollen goods made here as early as the thirteenth Century. So writes Lady Rosalind Northcote (*Devon, Moorland, Steams and Coast*).

'Kirton' (Crediton) spinning was very fine and it was said that 140 threads of woollen yarn spun in that town were drawn through the eye of a tailors needle – which needle and threads, were for many years together, to be seen in Walling Street in London!

Sir Walter Raleigh managed to obtain licences to export unfinished White Cloth, something not allowed at the time. He became wealthy, and Ashburton's prosperity might have come from Raleigh's success as a visitor to the town.

The sixteen hundreds seems to have acted as a springboard for our modern Whiteface sheep, coinciding with the prosperity generated by the wool trade, but not forgetting that their ancestral roots were embedded in the Bronze Age, and so constitution was not a problem, having no doubt existed too, as a scavenging Forest breed of olde England, gaining the title of 'one of England's most ancient sheep breeds'.

The present day 'Soays' are exactly similar to the remains of sheep discovered and pieced together from Neolithic settlements. They have it seems survived from Prehistoric sheep. With their horns and agility they are like mountain goats, and it seems there is a relationship between them and the Corsican Mouflon. The majority of Soay are chocolate covered with buff markings, but in the Hebrides a fair proportion range from fawn to black, some having white spots. Working with the latter the Institute of Physiology has bred an almost pure white strain, which suggests a link between the Soay and today's commercial breeds, and the traits of our Whitefaces today.

It is reported in the early records of the 15th and 16th Centuries that the Western Peninsular was inhabited by a small agile sheep; W. Youatt (1837) referred to the Cornish Heath Sheep of 1602 as sheep with little bodies and coarse fleeces. These sheep, it's thought descendants of the Bronze Age Soay-type, were isolated from Danish and Norman influence. Whitlock (1980) suggested there were two main types of sheep by the end of the 17th Century. 'The West Country Mountain Type' a shortwool sheep, and 'the Devonshire Nott' a large long woolled type.

Therefore it seems the 'modern Whiteface' has its origins in the 'native heath sheep' (1600) and the 'West Country Mountain type' (1700) producing the recognisable 'Dartmoor Moorland type' and today's 'Whiteface Widecombe Dartmoor' and the 'Improved Greyface Dartmoor'. They were both known as 'Dartmoor'. The locals knew of the two breeds' existence. Nowadays the Dartmoor sheep breed refers to the Greyface that developed as the 'improved Dartmoor' in the 19th Century. It was influenced by several breeds. Unlike the Whiteface it was not as isolated, and inhabited the fringes of the Moor, but sometimes the 'old Dartmoors' were seen on the high Moor around Princetown. They spent much time in the valleys and lowlands off the Moor. They were crossed with the Leicester, Lincoln and Devon Longwool for increased size and wool. Lovely curled coated, 'top knotted' and with speckled face and legs.

The Whiteface Dartmoor was isolated by geography and husbandry methods and as a result was less affected by other breeds. Whitlock (1980) says 'the Whiteface represents one of the oldest types of Moorland Sheep with less influence of introduced breeds than other breeds.' M. McCaughan 1951 says 'the 'Dartmoor' has been native to these wastes since time immemorial', and is a very old breed once covering a large area of West Somerset and Devon. However with the coming of the enclosures (1760) they were driven back to Dartmoor and are now a localised breed.

Descended from these native 'Heath Sheep', the 'Devon Inventories' then revealed an important piece of history of the 16th and 17th centuries, edited by Margaret Cash and the Devon and Cornwall Record Society (no. 11.1966) (and with thanks to Peter Dracup at Broadaford), with Sheepe included and the prices they made recorded in 1628. It says 'all this time ago (7th April 1628) Broadaford was spelt Bradaford', and Devon Inventories recorded the rest of Edward Gould's (the occupiers) belongings. Bradaford is situated in the parish of Widecombe-in-the-Moor in the County of Devon, and possibly recording a 'Widecombes' birthright, and the wonderful references all over, include sheepe, hoggettes, (fat and store), ewes and lambs (Fowrescore and Threescore) and surely part of a 'Widecombe's tale', some four hundred years ago:- One hundred fortye and three sheepe £47.13.4d. Forty Ews and Lambes £16. Sixeeene Hoggettes £18. Sixeteene Hoggettes £18. Sixeteene fat sheepe £8. Other inventories at the time record Fowrescore Ews and lambews £32. Thirty six sheepe (store), at £11 and for Eighteene sheepe £6.

Here also at this time farmers were referred to as 'Yeomen'. As examples of *the way of life* at this time from different inventories, there written:- Oxon, Packsaddles, Wheeles and a Cart butt, one Sellocke and a Lanthorne, one pecke and three seaves, a sive, Evells (prangs), a ricke of woode, a reape hook. Corne in a barn unthreshed. Wooll and yarne in the cockloft (£3). A foote of leather and a pigges skinne (15s). Brandirons to mark animals going to the Moor. Bushells of barley, oats etc. The poune house (Pounde), Saltinge tubs. One Nagge £2.10s, sixeteene Oxon £60, nyne poundes of wooll and a wooll sacke 15s etc. Candlestick, 5 Hogsheades of Syder (Cyder) £5. Warminge Pann. Dunge 10s. Crockes. Rackes 20s. Trusse Ropes. Eighteene Kyne (cattle) £54, one Bull 46.8d. Two Colts £8, all at Bradaford. Goose pannes or drippinge panns and iron plates 13s 4d. Three pairer of 'Fullers Shears', 20s. Possibly these were not for shearing the sheep but for preparing wool for the weavers! One steare (steer) 33.4d. Four acres of barley and half acre of beanes £8.

Packsaddles were used to carry ferns, peat and wool, held by crooks and truss ropes attached to the saddle. Oxon were formerly employed on the Moor on the roads and they were 'shod' ('Q' shoes). Bygones then were referred to as 'goodes or things forgotten'! Brasen crockes, one yron Gridiron 'Brandiron', pothangers and fryeing panne (£2) one windinge sheet, with sackes and seeves 3s 6d. Pot crokes (over the hearth fires) and tonges 3s.

Ken Soper was insistent I read a reference dated 1849 in the 'Rural Cyclopaedia' edited by the Rev. John M. Wilson. The article says, 'Dartmoor sheep are hardy and well adapted to the district from which they take their name. They are small wild and restless; their face and legs are white.' These sheep it goes on to say, are little known outside their district. Also in a book that Cyril Abel holds called 'Breeds of Sheep' dated 1912 the emphasis on Whitefaces is confirmed, when it says Dartmoor sheep are Whitefaced as a rule.

Similarly a handbook called 'Sheep Breeds and Management' written in 1913 by John Wrightson and held by Matthew Cole, it writes of the 'Wild Dartmoor Sheep' of which Youatt speaks; 'the White-faced races of sheep with such an amount of the old nature as suffices to enure him to the severe winters of his native home'. Its place as a 'Forest Breed' too is one of the most significant records of its place in history on the Moor, as told by Quentin Rae. The varieties of British sheep today are numerous, but can be divided by the length of their wool, the presence or absence of horns (termed the scientific or physical classifications). A third classification, as with our breed, may be adopted having a reference to the 'place or district' in which such breeds are supposed to abound, to have originated or gained 'their greatest perfection', termed geographical system.

Ashburton deriving its name from its place as a settlement on the banks of the River Ashburn, long before the Norman Conquest, was an ancient Market and Old Stannary town. It sprang up where tracks left Dartmoor and on which there were 'sheep runs' or walks (pasture areas for sheep). It has parliamentary privileges dating back to 1198 and a successful market in the twelfth Century. Local markets were essential to support farming on the Moor and Ashburton was ideally placed to receive animals driven from Dartmoor settlements, and received its first charter for its St Lawrence fair in 1310. The seal of the 'Port-reeve' (Saxon for magistrate) bears a Church between a 'teasel' and a Saltaire (a x shaped cross) with the sun and moon above, the 'Fullers Emblem'. The teasel was used to raise the 'nap' in making cloth and was a symbol of that industry;' as the sun and moon were symbols of mining. Bishop Walter Stapledon saw the possibilities of the nearby sheep runs on the Moor and a market.

'Fullers Emblem', Ashburton's coat of arms and St Andrew's Cross.

Parliament in 1571 decreed that everyone over the age of six had to wear a hat on Sunday and on Holy days. These had to be made of English woollen cloth. By 1630 the Devon Kersey cloth became famous and was made exclusively from Devon wool. The cloth industry reached new levels of production increasing the demand for Dartmoor wool and enhancing the value of Dartmoor flocks.

The Civil Wars of 1642–1652 damaged trade; it is said the recession of 1650 was so bad that to boost the trade shrouds were made of wool. In a time of misfortune and plague this was a huge number of wool clad corpses. 'The Burial in Woollen Enactment' made it compulsory to wrap every corpse in woollen before burial (1667–68).

The restoration of Charles II in 1660 increased trade and small towns flourished and prospered, and between 1689 and 1702 (William and Mary's time), Irish wool by law was imported through Exeter, Bideford and Barnstaple. In 1672 a yarn market was established on Tuesdays in Ashburton and continued until late into the 19th Century. To this sheep owners from Dartmoor and southwards brought their wool; it was bought by combers and spinsters, mainly poor cottagers, many from the Widecombe district, who combed it and spun it into 'yarn' which was bought by cloth weavers in the following market. Merchants tucked it and dyed it for export. A great deal of wool for the Ashburton industry came from Cornwall and even Ireland it seems. From 1688 through the ports of North Devon, wool was bought by Packhorse along the 'Mariners Way' through Chagford and past 'Beetor Cross', and Natsworthy down the Webburn Valley and on to Ashburton. The terminus was the old Barnstaple Inn in North Street, probably by the site of the present 'Barnstaple' Cottages. After manufacture the woollen goods were taken on again by Packhorse to Brixham and French Imports exchanged.

All tracks (or so-called roads) for that's what they really were until the end of the eighteenth Century or later, were often distinctly perilous. They might be impeded by fallen timber, boulders, deep pits and mud. Turnings were obscured by thick hedgerows and trees, and could sometimes be hiding robbers, and highwaymen! (Devon D. St. Leger-Gordon).

Westcote wrote in 1630; 'passing from Chagford we are travelling to the Moor, if we take not great heed we may soon wander and stray, and thereby make longer our stay in this coarse place than we willing would'! So wrote Ledger St John (Devon). Even so the Dartmoor tracks were often used in preference for 'pack-horse traffic' trading between North and South coasts. Yet it could be a real hazard meeting a string of laden packhorses in full flight. No doubt some horses would also lead another fully laden with wool and other produce, and the train could be quite long and dangerous; advancing with little warning! To help this situation Packhorses were then obliged to have bells fitted to the harness to signal a warning of their approach. Special packsaddles were fitted to carry their heavy loads, this recorded in 1628.

Yet by the end of the 17th Century Dartmoor and Devon's sheep had been improved to produce a dense medium length fleece giving an acceptable middle-grade wool and with an admixture of Irish wool, providing much of the wool for coarse serge-making around Dartmoor. [Wool – middle English – Wolle Wull – old English – Wull]

However, War affected trade again, and in 1713 the Treaty of Utrecht seriously affected the wool trade in Devon and with the Continent.

In 1769 came the first 'spinning Jenny' and in 1817 approximately, a worsted spinning frame was installed at Ashburton. Yet in 1831 hand weaving ended in Devon.

Yet figures reveal that in 1791, it was said out of a sheep population of 700,000 in Devon, 80,000 were summered on 'Dartmoor proper'. Vancouver also reported the native Dartmoor sheep as horned, white face and legs, moderate long staple wool; wethers are fit to kill at 30 months. Average weight per quarter 16lbs and average weight of fleece 8lbs, and average value of fleece 6/8d.

Widecombe Church and Whiteface sheep nearby. (Photo: Colin Pearse).

Vancouver also explained, 'the Commons belonging to the Parish of Widecombe (1808), the October previous there were estimated to be no less than 14,000 sheep, besides the usual proportion of horned cattle. Many of these sheep would surely have been Whitefaces!

A fair is reported to have been held at Widecombe-in-the-Moor in 1850, and with all these sheep recorded here, it is likely much sheep 'bartering' took place long before this date. A large show of cattle and a quantity of 'Moorland sheep' were offered for sale (736 sheep were penned) at the fair. Miss Needham attended the fair in 1922, when she was just eight years old.

As time went on Tavistock and the area to the North and North East became a centre of coarse cloth manufacture using a large percentage of Dartmoor wool, while the middle Dartside towns of Ashburton and Buckfastleigh which served as catchment areas for the fleeces from the Moor's southern slopes and valleys became mainly spinning centres. This pattern was well preserved into the 19th Century. In 1838 100 looms weaved cloth at Tavistock. Along the Taw between Okehampton and Sticklepath there were 500 looms in the early 1800s (near Old Cleave or Willmott's Mill Belstone).

In Ashburton, Buckfastleigh and Buckfast a third of the population worked on 1300 looms. Merchants from Ashburton (which has a teazle in its Fullers Emblem) went to Rattery and Brent to buy carded spunwool from the Cottagers.

Coarse cheap cloth for the British Army in 1914 kept the district and Buckfastleigh busy using Darmoor wool for its blanket and serge combing mills.

In 1800 700 weavers finished 700 serges a week at John Berry's Chagford. The ready availability of cotton goods and the loss of the East Indian Company market, and a better organized Yorkshire woollen market killed the industry by the 1860s.

By the end of the 19th Century Moreton, Okehampton and Widecombe had forgotten about wool! And Tavistock's history ceased with the closing of its combing mill in 1960.

Like the tin trade, cloth making on and around Dartmoor was an industry springing from the area's natural resources; its sheep, and their wool, its water and even lichen to dye the wool, explains Crispin Gill in detail!

Yet pride never deserted the farmers in appreciation of their animals and the competitive

Royal Agricultural Society of England.

FIFTY-FIRST COUNTRY MEETING

PRACTICE WITH SCIENCE

AT PLYMOUTH, JUNE 21 TO 27, 1890.

CATALOGUE

OF THE

HORSES, CATTLE,

SHEEP, PIGS, POULTRY,

FARM & DAIRY PRODUCE,

COMPETING FOR THE PRIZES OFFERED AT THE

FIFTY-FIRST ANNUAL EXHIBITION

AT

PLYMOUTH,

JUNE 23RD TO 27TH, 1890.

edge, and showing was part of their shop window at the Devon County, Bath and West, and Royal Shows. The Royals first show was in 1839 at Oxford (Phillip Sheppy R.A.S.E.).

Classes for 'Dartmoor' sheep began in 1890 at the 51st Annual Exhibition held at Plymouth.

In 1952 the Royal Show moved to Newton Abbot but livestock classes were cancelled due to an outbreak of Foot and Mouth.

Entries had been made by Leonard Ball, Cecil Caunter, John Coaker, French Bros' (Corringdon), Mann Bros', Miss Sylvia Needham, John Savery and William A.F. Webber. Whitefaces were expected to be shown in their own right, but it was not to be.

In 1958 another opportunity arose with the Royal Show still as a travelling show arriving at Bristol.

The judge here was Richard Coaker from 'Runnage' and success greeted Cecil Caunter with first and second for shearling ram and third place went to W.J. Doidge, Whitchurch, Devon (Fullamoor) and for two yearling ewes, C.E. Caunter was first and third and Mann Bros were second and W.J. Doidge achieved fourth place. The latter were shown in their wool.

However, something else positive for Dartmoor and the country was nearly a hundred years of the Railway. Railroads pushed out of towns to the foothills of Dartmoor. The first was the Newton Abbot to Moretonhampstead line completed in 1866. It dealt a blow to the road toll; but was greeted with pleasure when the gates were removed and burned.

The Old Toll House at Moreton's Southgate from Bovey Tracey

TABLE OF TOLLS
'THE TOLL HOUSE KINGS BRIDGE MORETON'

1. Horse or beast drawing any cart – coach – waggon – 'landau' (a 'Landau' – a four-wheeled closed carriage, seats facing front and back, and a roof made in two sections for lowering or detaching), also early type of car.

Every Horse or Beast laden or unladen	1½d
A score of Oxon or Cattle	10d
A score of Calves – Sheep – Lambs or Swine	5d

1. Head of Cattle – one farthing

Church and funeral traffic exempt.

Signed:- Clerk to the trustees of the said turnpike, or toll-gate.

A road whose upkeep was paid for by tolls levied on its users.

Middle English 'turnepike', a revolving barrier furnished with spikes used to block a road: turnen, to TURN + PIKE. (Courtesy Eve Bygrave).

Turnpikes were introduced around 1770, at the time of the first road across Dartmoor.

'To a deserted Turnpike Gate-House!'

I look at you, and memories sad
Come floating through my brain,
How oft on bitter winter nights,
I've lingered in the rain;
In murky darkness waiting for
That wretched Turnpike man,
Who crawls down grumbling from his bed
As slowly as he can!
Then opening wide his swinging gate,
He claims his wretched toll;
Could that house speak of anecdotes,
'Twould tell a lengthy roll!

Anecdotes of the West Country by J. W. Ley

The railway must have come as a great boost to Moretonhampstead's new cattle market for, as recorded in the News in Moreton, 'Exeter Flying Post'of October 1827 reported that in addition to existing Fairs, a new Cattle Market to be held annually on the 1st Saturday in October took place for the first time this month. '. . . filled beyond the most sanguine expectations the 1000 or so sheep and 200 bullocks driven into it met a ready sale, the former at about 5d (2p) a lb, the latter at 8s.6d to 9s (40–50p) per score.

The 'Wool Fair' was an important addition to other business of the day and the show of grain was very large; the large quantity of butter and poultry was soon brought up. Apparently the bells rang merrily and the Town Band paraded, and the whole appearance of things promise of this being the precursor to the formation of a large and permanent market in this hitherto neglected district'! (Gina Adams researched).

Later cattle were driven from Chagford Market by road to be trucked away from Moretonhampstead railway station, resulting from sales on its market days.

The 'Newton Abbot – Moreton' line was twelve miles long. It enabled farmers to easily reach the cattle and panier markets of Newton Abbot (to sell eggs, cream, chicken, honey and veg etc). Cows and calves for example were walked to Moreton Station, put into 'lairage' there for the night and put on the train to Newton the following day to be offered for sale there.

The Plymouth – Tavistock line opened in 1859 and later extended northward and to the West. Ashburton was by-passed by the Exeter – Plymouth railway in 1846 (says Vivian Smith). However, the south-eastern villages of Dartmoor had their rail link in 1872, when the Totnes – Ashburton branch was opened. This enabled farmers in the neighbourhood to truck their cattle. In its early years its main trade was seemingly the woollen industry of Buckfastleigh. Sadly the line closed in 1962. Richard Coaker journeyed from 'Runnage' to Ashburton to catch the train to Totnes Grammar School.

It is reported in the first issue of the 'Field' journal in 1853 that the railways offered enormous facilities, (and 'coasting steamers') and there was competition afforded by the 'West of England' in respect of cattle and sheep.

Princetown had a line in 1883, but that closed in 1956, victim to cars and so called progress!! The aptly named 'Silent Whistle' pub near to the Ashburton market pens recognises the loss of Ashburton's 1872 branch railway line, which played a large part in previously reviving a market town in difficulties, after the passing of tin and cloth industries.

Silent Whistle.
The sign shows the smoking train on the viaduct.
Previously called the Railway Inn.

Sheep were sometimes packed so tight on their journey away to their new homes, that at their destination they were hardly recognisable explained Richard Mann. Yet the railways were much used and avoided many extra journeys on foot as animals used to arrive in the streets of Ashburton in great numbers. Long horns used to protrude from the sides of trucks witnessing tightly packed cattle, travelling away on a new journey from the markets auctions.

The Farmers Weekly April 1947.
The yearly movement of sheep from the coast to the hills (Wales) 4,000 at a time.

The livestock market in Ashburton moved from the streets to St Lawrence Lane around 1910 and 1911. A market had been in existence from C 1555. Today's market is under the twin control of Sawdye and Harris and Rendells.

Ashburton market.

'Rendell and Sawdye' (Arthur Rendell and Ted Sawdye) can still be seen written on the front of the old market auctioneers selling box. They had amalgamated between 1918 and the late 1920s, but by 1938 were operating separately again.

Mrs Pauline Adamson of Ashburton spoke of the importance of St Lawrence Fairs and St Lawrence Lane.

Also she referred to the market place for sheep around 1940. Also the field higher up Whistley Hill was called the 'second meadow' or 'The Meda'; this was sited across the old A38 opposite Ashburtons Old Market place. It seems some sheep were penned the day before a sale. So market outgrew itself, and sheep fairs spilled over. There was in the past a 'Fair Day' for St Lawrence, in St Lawrence Lane. Cattle were held in North Street in the Bull Ring; given its name as a result of large rings put in granite blocks to hold some of the cattle.

She also spoke passionately of the railway link at Ashburton that opened in 1872 (closing to passenger traffic in 1958 and eventually to freight in 1962), stationed at Chuley Road.

Ponies were sold as a long tradition at Ashburton, but were usually lorried away. However, Pauline said cattle were trucked (by train) heavily, travelling down to Totnes via Staverton for long journeys to up-country buyers premises. Goods trains unloaded to horse and carts.

Tradition has it that the first Portreeve of the borough of Ashburton was appointed in the year 820AD, the time of the first Saxon King of England, Egbert. The name Portreeve is derived from the Saxon words for market town 'Port' and 'Gerefar' which means official. The chief duty of the person appointed by the Crown to oversee a market town was to be 'a witness and recorder for the sale of livestock and property'. Also he oversaw coinage, taxes, fines and kept a register of suspicious characters etc! 'So he originally supervised the trade of the market', and became the main representative of the town as their duties increased.

The Portreeve and Bailiff were and still are elected at an annual Court and Open Day. (Courts Leet (Jury) and Baron). 1086 – Ashburton became a flourishing part of the vast estates of the Bishops of Exeter and the town began to prosper from 'Cloth and the tin trade.' 1305 – Stannary tin weighed, stamped and taxed. Bishop Walter Stapledon had a home in 'Aschpertone'.

Reading the history of Ashburton, it's not surprising that the Whiteface Dartmoor using the nearby sheep runs were sold in street and market for so long, nurtured in great numbers on the land around and the Moor's pastures. Yet modern history will probably not be so kind in its accountability of our sheep in a wonderful sheltered coombe on the lower south eastern slopes of Dartmoor.

Sometimes the weather, disease, loss of export etc can quickly shift the balance of the fortune of a particular breed of livestock and numbers can be quickly depleted as preferences change too. The Whiteface Dartmoor has been on that 'Wheel of Fortune' since prehistoric times through the invasion of different peoples who farmed and shepherded these sheep for skins, wool and meat, and had tribal disputes that changed boundaries and displaced animals.

The evil of the 'Black Death' and bubonic plagues meant whole villages lost their people and unseated manorial systems, and affected livestock populations.

Snow winters that were more prevalent in the 1600–1700s and again in the mid–late 1800s and the 1900s meant blizzards buried thousands of sheep and their losses were high.

Beatrice Chase writes in 'The Dartmoor Window Again' of the 'Great Cold' in the early Spring of 1916 and again in the November of that year that lasted until the April of 1917, and its effect on *wool* too.

A few of the drifts shaped by the high winds were designed like a gigantic shell as large as a small cottage. Across to Cold East Cross, Dartmoor was one vast sheet of snow, measuring thousands of acres. It was so deep that the tops of the walls and the tops of Hawthorn trees were entirely buried, and it was weeks before the road was open, with gangs of men working continually. Pony-back or Shank's mare were the only means of locomotion.

The furze (gorse) died wholesale. It was a surprise that anything could kill gorse says Beatrice Chase. The great bushes of it were withered to powder by the perpetual wind.

A lot of swaling took place in the spring of 1917, hoping to save the roots for another year

All eyes focussed, digging for sheep, during the severe blizzard winter of 1947 (Photo: *Farmers Weekly*. Courtesy of Reading University Rural Archive).

Farmer and dog, horse and wagon, looking for sheep.

by getting rid of the dead boughs, which were killing the roots. It seems had the dead furze been left there would have been next to no wool. The gorse's prickles had been withered down to dry powder, and this filled the sheep's fleeces and one's dresses, and everything that touched the bushes and was absolutely impossible to remove, even with a brush. It seems men burn't and burn't, and saved the wool.

In 1947 in England and Wales alone including the loss in the years lamb crop, sheep losses came to 4,000,000 (3,000,000 in the hills); some 50,000 cattle also perished, 200,000 acres of winter corn was frosted damaged, and penetrated potatoes in clamps; the loss in potatoes

Windswept, lucky survivors.

estimated at 40,000 tons. At their height the floods that followed the blizzards saw 600,000 acres of land swallowed up and more livestock lost. Surviving sheep and cattle were in poor condition. The blizzards and snowstorms which blanketed the whole country, cutting communications, isolating farmsteads and burying sheep and cattle in the drifts dealt a severe blow to the farming community. Despite all efforts to salvage, losses were high. Helicopter food drops (RAF) were later made (hay). In some counties the loss of sheep alone was as much as half the total population. (Farmer and Stockbreeder, April 1947).

The 1946 summer was disastrous and crops were not even salvaged up to October because of a wet summer and autumn. Some areas in the South West, and the Farmer and Stock Breeder mention Exmoor, had only one fine week in which to make hay in 1946, it reported. The National Farmers Union set up a disaster fund and Government promised to match it pound for pound. The NFU had estimated that losses from frosts, shows and floods directly and indirectly amounted to £20,000,000.

The story of the storms and floods of 1946–1947 and of the devastation on the land which followed was compiled by E.J. Smith and called 'Black Winter' and published by The Farmers Weekly in aid of the Agricultural Disaster Fund. Some of the extracts make chilling reading in more ways than one!

Sheep seemed to be on the mind of many livestock farmers, and the depleted rations for man and beast. 'A bad winter that followed a poor summer'!

The severity of winters like 1947 and 1962 should not be underestimated, and bring heavy losses, and much hardship on farms and can undermine decades of breeding, and cause insecurity in businesses, and demoralise those whose whole lives are spent caring and nurturing livestock and crops, and working hard-earned machinery.

'A few days before the snows came, we read the signs,' said a Devonshire moorland farmer. 'The sheep ran together – in a heap, as we say. The wind stood between north and north-east and then began to rise, blowing strongly off and on, with a whirring sound. There was a very thick haze in the sky,' These signs were seen with fear all over the hills of Britain. The blizzards they foretold were to hold a large part of the country in an icy grip for nearly three months and were to melt afterwards into the worst floods in living memory, wrote E.J. Smith. As the storms went on, from a Dartmoor hamlet in mid February came a message – 'No bread since January 27'. From the North came stories of farm carts being broken up and used for fuel; of half starved stock being slaughtered in the 'byres'. Some farms didn't have a forkful of hay or straw left. The hill sheep, trapped in drifts, were dying in tens of thousands. In some places, near dead sheep which escaped the drifts were raided by hungry foxes, and starving birds pecked animals eyes.

'Winter it is said is Summer's heir' and the hay crop on the fells of the North, the mountain slopes of Wales and on the Moors of the South had been almost a total failure in the harvest of 1946.

Farmers and shepherds looked for tell-tale yellow stains in the snow and holes and probed drifts with long poles to find buried sheep – drifts exceeded twenty to thirty feet.

One farmer wrote, 'the sheep we are digging out are a pitiful sight. We are finding some of them with their skins split open by the frost and the weight of frozen snow, as if they had been butchered'. We shall be fortunate to recover a third, the Yorkshire farmer explained and they won't be much good. The intense cold (26 or 27 degrees), a thick cover of snow, ice and a high wind of gale force have a devastating effect. Mountain sheep were not very strong going into the winter, and after three weeks of starvation, sheep died from exhaustion and suffocation. 'No man could stand out long in the hills'! Farms were 'all one piece, it was possible to walk over all the fences (hedges) and gates, for they couldn't be seen', came a message from Devon. The cold wind hadn't stopped blowing for ten days.

One farmer's wife, whose husband was ill, had no fuel for heat, (also no fodder for the cow, the sheep were starving and the roads blocked) but the only fuel she found was frozen rabbits with which she kept a fire burning! Horses in tandem pulled a 'sled' loaded with bales of hay from the next farm, but the horses became stuck in the snow and bales had somehow to be carried over the drifts. Struggling through snow 'feets deep' as I and others know is a killing experience, and with a bale to carry too!

At the height of the blizzard one shepherd recorded that it took him five and a quarter hours to fetch a bale of hay three quarters of a mile. Some of the most serious losses on the Welsh mountains were not necessarily in snow drifts, but sheep starved and froze to death on top of the snow. The freezing snow gripped the long wool of the sheep, and bound them to it; then, as they became weaker and could do nothing to free themselves, the shepherd had to go round where he could lifting them, one by one, each morning after the hard night's frost. Stories of this nature are told of 1962/3 as well as 1947 in this book.

On March 15th, the blizzards wound up again, with a gale of driven snow, followed by frozen rain. Sheep hanging on by a thread also died. Ewes that survived were too weak to suckle their lambs. The hardships of shepherds and their wives it was said were unbelievable. Brecon and Radnor reported 100,000 sheep dead on the hillsides. Thousands of sheep died of snow fever, and corpses were piled up in barns.

The Government authorised the issue of 'emergency' rations to hill flocks wherever they might be needed and the NFU co-ordinated voluntary schemes for the collection of hay and straw. But aid to the hill farms, through no lack of endeavour, often came too little, or worse it was written, too late. In other winters previous, the farmhouses had warmed to the constant glow of the peat fire. Some farmers on Dartmoor used pieces of galvanise to eventually ferry food stores behind their horses back to the farmsteads. 'Yet anxiety was about sheep, and the years it would take to restore flocks'. The faces and fleeces of the sheep are frozen masses of ice, but where found alive, later freezed to the ground. It was said by one farmer's wife that walking after the sheep one hears the curious jingle-jingle of the lumps of ice on their fleeces, because the ice is frozen so hard.

The Government offered acreage payments, and the hill sheep subsidy was to be adapted to help hill farmers in rebuilding their flocks. Yet most hill farmers had lost at least half their capital and many were faced with a total loss of income.

It was not until May, long after the snows had melted into the torrents which burst dykes and waterways and added further tragedy in flood, that any serious attempt could be made to measure the extent of the livestock losses. Altogether, it was found, more than a quarter of all sheep in Great Britain had perished. More than two-thirds of the entire clip of hill wool had been lost.

The severe depressions of the 1920s and 1930s brought hardship, misery and economic chaos; and stock piling of products like wool on farms awaiting better prices, might be over many years! Farming became the forgotten industry, E.J. Smith wrote. Land was neglected for want of capital and young people were forced to leave the countryside. Yet the arrival of the 2nd World War realised how important the dependence on farming had to be. Farming was ironically regenerated and rewarded in this time of great need, to help produce the nation's food, when previously its strength of continuity had been let down.

The worst weather in living memory in 1946 and 1947 with floods, blizzards and floods again, saw how the nation's precious food supply could be affected for a totally different reason, and its vulnerability very much highlighted.

Nature it seems in one of her cruellest moods blasted Britain's farms, people, animals, crops and communications, and produced an unparalleled tragedy suffered by farmers – a major disaster! There were many casualties, but the industry eventually made a fresh start, and improved conservation methods, ensiling and baling grass in silage has safeguarded food supplies for farm livestock, unless there are severe droughts.

Another issue involving the conservation of energy has taken on a fresh urgency in this millennium as fossil fuels are consumed at alarming rates. Solar energy (sustainable) with homes heated by the sun (70%) are designed to be low maintenance and economical to run and also insulated with 'sheep's wool' and with other materials used from recycled materials or from natural renewable resources.

Something quite different, but right up to date with our Millennium is the 'cloning of sheep'. With some herds and flocks kept in a wild or semi-wild situation a form of cloning takes place, and where small in number, a natural selection and male dominance takes place that helps to hold the breeding together.

Cloning by scientists could have far reaching implications for farm animal breeding programmes. They have produced genetically identical sheep, identical to the animal from which their cells were taken.

Genes can be added for desirable characteristics in another generation of clones. Perhaps traits relating to the Whiteface that are in decline can be sustained or rejuvenated!

"I've always had my doubts about Shep!"

The Farmers Guardian goes on to say that flocks of genetically identical animals given the same environment and management conditions would enable large numbers of a standard product to be produced. But we risk by cloning reducing the 'selection base', and lose genetic variety by concentrating only on those breeding lines deemed to be the best or most useful. 'A Rare Embryo Survival Bank or Trust', might soon be needed. It is suggested that Breed Societies might need to think soon seriously about registering their breeders rights in animals they have bred, before someone else does it and takes the history away!

Wet Wet!

We've seen all the flood signs,
As the rain moves in vertical lines,
Like the sails on a Clipper's mast;
Then horizontal, driven by a wind in a gale past;
Towards anywhere,
And this misery together we share,
Transparent through the downpour,
The moor seems to say, we've seen it all before;
Weathered by a history of the same,
Moods all of its own, but nothing to shame.
Sheep in erratic rows,
Line up under fence, bank and wall; poor souls!
When will it all end? But not even a moan,
For under their coat, by nature sewn,
Rarely is it *all* wet,
As the wool hugs their skin, as if set.
Anyway, it's just Dartmoor in winter,
'And nowhere else have us bin'!
So there will be plenty to drink at Christmas,
But not *all* in a glass, alas!

Colin Pearse

The Stories - A Preface

The mere mention of Whiteface Dartmoor Sheep to these people seems to trigger passions and a depth of history that has laid dormant and awaiting its release; in combination with sheep and wool, heather and moor, wall and pound, gate and grid, horse and dog, dip and fold, clapper-bridge and ford; fairs and markets, trains and lorries, woollen mills and water, grass and 'turnips'. Inextricably linked together and fused with all facets of farming industry and life that distributed these sheep throughout the greater part of Dartmoor and its surrounding parts of Devon, especially the 'South Hams'.

Once recognised as with all breeds of sheep as 'golden hoof' for their part in adding fertility to the land where 'roots' were folded as part of a 'Norfolk Four Course Rotation', and where corn and seeds (grass) followed, but a year of fallow (to 'lie fallow') where a field has been ploughed but left unseeded during a growing season. The story of these wonderful Dartmoor sheep with the white faces and the important part they played in moorland life has probably evaded the historians simply because of their sheer continuing presence over hundreds of years. It is difficult to imagine another animal, other than the Dartmoor pony, that is so much at the heart of the moor.

'A marriage twixt man and beast' where death us do part, is probably a silent vow! Once a magnet for these native sheep, little of the land of the parishes, commons or forest of Dartmoor has been left untouched by grazing Whiteface sheep; in summer the ewes with their lambs and with wethers through the bleak moorland winters. Wethers were kept for their wool and the sweet tasting mutton. Wether has been proclaimed 'angel's meat'. All this moulded into the moors history, and became an intrinsic part of the social fabric of the moor as generation succeeded generation. Cottage woollen industry grew up around precious sheep-walks (sheep pastures) on the moor, and incubated the massive production and processing of wool that followed in and around the moor's edge, and of meat too. During one hundred and fifty years, and even longer in some families, the same family names on the same farms held the same breed of sheep; the Whiteface Dartmoor Sheep, and Dartmoor is their home.

My passion for sheep, and in particular this historic breed is driven no doubt by a shepherding survival instinct passed down from some relative long since passed away, a blooded genetic link, that's part of a long ancestral line.

The Whiteface Dartmoor Sheep is affectionately and quite universally known as 'The Widecombe' or 'Widecombes', due to their great popularity in the parish of Widecombe-in-the-Moor. Perhaps this might hold the key to the origins of the breed and where things began for sheep and shepherd.

Written one hundred and fifty years ago, it was said, 'Widdicombe Fair' still exists; a sheep fair held on the second Tuesday in September, and then Widecombe is a stirring place indeed, 'and you may see some "proper ship" (sheep) (or prapper shape) there', as one old farmer said at that time. They are mostly 'ruddled', that is coloured red (dialect) 'reddle' (redding) was used to mark sheep to tell one flock from another. It was in use as early as the 13th century; no doubt some of that colour was from the red Devon soil on which they were kept away in winter and spring, (but their skin is quite pink too). It is said, they filled up the green all around the church pens where they stand and bleat until they are sold and driven off the moor.

It was also said that in the Old Inn there was a grand lunch of cold meats to be had, and you may hear the finest Devonshire talked all round you and if you belong to the county your tongue could slip into the dialect quite naturally, and you will most certainly meet 'Bill Brewer, Jan Stewer, Peter Gurney, Peter Davy, Dan'l Whiddon, Harry Hawk, old Uncle Tom Cobleigh and all; ay and recognise them too with the old grey mare 'erself'. Names still to be found on Dartmoor.

A 'moorgate' closed the roads from Widecombe, but they were found all over the moor, replaced now by cattle grids. Many of the lovely redundant granite posts still remain, hangings intact, that once held the moorgates where they were placed many years before; now just a reminder of the way things used to be a century or two ago.

All this to help prevent cattle and sheep straying off the moor or deserting their moorland lear (lair). An old term for the moorgate, was 'leapyeat' (enclosure gate). So the sheep I have grown to love as the 'Mother of all Dartmoors' for their quiet acceptance of their harsh surroundings on these farms – 'the moorlings', form a link that goes back unbroken to its 'wild and restless' ancestors, spanning many centuries, roaming 'moor to tor' in a once wild corner of England. All of this before we knew of boundaries and newtake walls.

A sheep fashioned in its anatomy, its teeth and its feet, with a 'yark' temperament and so equipped to withstand most that nature could throw at it, that is little wonder that they are still farmed today.

Sometimes referred to as the 'definitive' or authorative sheep, because of its alertness and vitality; this once small Dartmoor sheep was documented in the moors history as 'indistinguishable from the granite clatter amongst which it searched for its living' and as if born to be wild! Many of these ancestral sheep grazed the high moor of the 'forest' in far greater numbers than they do today. Now depleted, only a few survive to exercise the privilege of grazing the moor in summer; displaced by the competing interests for the use of the moor, and in no small measure by the introduction of the Scottish Blackface many years ago as a hardy competitor able to survive by grazing the heather all the year round; but not as inherently hardy as the Whiteface.

The change of emphasis from wool to mutton heralded the cross breeding of pure breeds and brought about a 'sea-change' in sheep farming across the country and preceded by the collapse of the woollen trade that had been the lynch pin of England's greatness throughout the middle ages. The popularity of longwools and our Whiteface sheep in the past had been sustained by a thirst for wool at home and especially abroad 'for in Europe the best wool was English'. The packhorse routes were well established at this earlier time.

'Reliving the Past'.
Whitefaced sheep's wool 'on the balance', over the stable door,

Our ancient long-woolled breeds were now challenged for their very survival, and declined through the lack of unrelated bloodlines; however, despite this they said, 'everyone had Whiteface Dartmoor Sheep' in days gone by, at Widecombe and many parishes across the moor.

The difficulties of the farmers and shepherds lives and the monotonous repetitiveness of the work is not to be taken lightly. Driving sheep on foot, horseback and also later, push bike many miles from 'Darthead to Dartmouth' and from the breeding heartlands on the moor, shepherding through gale or blizzard, wind or rain was a daunting task indeed!

Through ancestry, many sets of brothers from farming families seem to have been destined to care for these endearing animals. They had to fulfil all that a shepherds year involves; feeding, lambing, tail docking, shearing, dipping, worming, foot trimming, repairing fences and organising movement on and off the farm to market. Then there were fairs and shows to show off your best animals, and moving the flock spring and winter off the moor to 'keep' on the lowlands. A dedicated years hard work.

These brothers links with their sheep was almost a maternal one and frequently whilst looking after their Whiteface sheep, South Devon cattle would be found on the same farms; a fact of farming life on the moor going back the centuries. So a sort of partnership between two native breeds of animal commanded mutual respect and harmony; to and fro, in by-land, in-country, and upon the moor. It was a hard won self-sufficiency on these mixed stock and crop farms.

Sadly though it seems that this could be a record of sheep husbandry that can never be repeated.

Never again will so many Whiteface Dartmoor sheep graze the long summer days peacefully on the sheep walks of the high moor, or grace the lush green fields of the South Hams or fold their its 'swede-turnips', through the cruel months of winter.

No more will they be walked from Goose or St John's Fairs deep into Cornwall by drovers (drivers on foot) for their farmer buyers. Neither will they swell the numbers of sheep once sold in their thousands by the musical banter of the auctioneers at Ashburton Sheep fairs or at the Associations' Sale these past fifty years. An association that from humble beginnings, and the tireless efforts of the founder members has tried to ensure that only the finest characteristics of the breed are encouraged, through constant inspection, tattooing and rewarding the very best of breed every year.

If the 'Dartmoors with the Whitefaces' were to become extinct it would leave a vacuum in farming life that has been nutured over many centuries, creating something so unique and so protected that it would be an irreplaceable loss to a nations history and shepherding on Dartmoor would be all the poorer.

So, where the imposition of laws by Kings and Queens and governments has been stricter now all the while, it didn't necessarily change the 'old ways' of tending to the land, and encouraging its succession with man, and his livestock, which is as perennial as the grass.

Stories of the Members of the Whitefaced Dartmoor Sheep Breeder's Association (W.F.D.S.B.A.) Past and Present – 1951–2001

The Abel Family – Cyril and Eileen Abel

FORMERLY HIGHER GODSWORTHY NOW AT DUNKELD, COLLATON, TAVISTOCK

Widecombe Fair 1980. Cyril judging, Edward Caunter, Archie Mortimore, Geoffrey French and J. W. Northmores daughter and son-in-law to record some in the line-up.

Cyril remembers Leonard Ball and his family farming Whiteface sheep for generations. He recalls Leonard's sheep being driven out in the summer to Fur Tor and Cut Hill along lanes and roads when Cyril was only a boy, to graze the Moor in the Forest of Dartmoor.

'Dartmoor Sheep', taking into consideration Cyril's mother's family the Reddicliffe's at Higher Godsworthy and the Abel's at Lower Godsworthy, have been kept for around 200

Eileen Abel and Bridget Cole. The perks of sheep judging day!

Eileen and Cyril judging on a wet day (Miss Needham's flock). Cyril has his pipe upside down to keep his tobacco dry!

years in the family. As I stepped over the threshold at Dunkeld, on the carpet by the door it said, 'Good of you to come-bye,' which epitomises the families humour, and hospitality.

Wethers were kept solely for their wool during earlier times and might reach 4–5 years old. Very much a Moor practice of walking sheep to keep as from Godsworthy to Bere Alston, is remembered by Cyril. Candidly Cyril said, 'Sheep live to die' perhaps witnessed here!

He then said his father brought back Whiteface rams from Princetown Fair (held in the past) and tied two up together beside a hedge, about 16" apart, using a plough chain (part of a horse's harness). One of the sheep jumped up into the hedge and in so doing wound the chain around a tree and hung the ram on the ground. In farming folklore sheep especially seem to have a habit of letting one down, and blunting one's expectations. Whiteface Dartmoor rams were bought to cross with the Greyfaced Dartmoor ewes on some farms.

Tricia Gerrish writing on Dartmoor Fairs for the Dartmoor Magazine (no. 62) said,

Princetown Fair in the early 20th century (courtesy of Devon Library Services).

Princetown's Fair flourished chiefly in the 20th Century. By 1900 an early September Fair was established. If haymaking and turf stacking had finished on the Moor, the fair was well attended. In the photograph the 'Plume Feathers' Inn is boldly signed across from the parked carts. Previously called the 'Princes Arms' and built in 1795.

The unmistakable Whiteface Rams are tied to the wheels and shafts of the extraordinary 'market carts' that brought the rams to the fair. Some of the carts are fixed with lamps, no doubt to guide 'boss' early in the morning along bumpy tracks, and for affording some dim light travelling home after celebrating the fair! However, they were 'candle-lit' and more often then not would go out!

The rams portray a ruggedness, and look dishevelled in appearance that equates with the environment afforded by high Dartmoor at Princetown. However, their clean legs and tight coat serve to shed the heavy rains of winter and contribute to their survival in one of England's meagre 'alpine landscapes'.

At the fair as many as seventy rams were exchanged between farmers. Cattle in the village sold between £11 and £17 each in 1900. Just a few shillings would have been enough to exchange rams. The last Princetown Fair and Pony Sale was held in 1956.

At the Prison Farm 5,000 lbs of the first class wool, 3 cart horses, ponies (famous for) sheep and pigs found buyers.

It's again reported in the Dartmoor Magazine that a Mr Berry of Buckfastleigh purchased the entire wool crop at 3¾d per pound, fourpence (4d) *less* than the 1895's peak year price.

The disparity in the above prices brings to mind a folksong in Devon (north) dialect called 'The Mortal Unlucky Old Chap' and just *one* of the many verses, the one relevant to wool prices is quoted here, and the chorus verse: (the prices are surprisingly similar to the 1900s!)

I zold all my wool t'other day
Vor vour pence dree vardin's a poun';
But the very next day
I yer'd the vokes zay
It went up to vive pence all roun' . . .

Chorus: Vor,
I'm a mortal, a unlucky old chap,
You niver yerd tell zich a caze,
Vrim mornin' tu night
Nort niver go'th right
'Tis enough tu draive any man maze.

'The Devonshire Dialect' by Clement Marten.

It's not uncommon for the heavens to open on Princetown Fair Day and cause chaos, and on September 3rd 1946 it poured all day.

Bill White, living at Shapley Farm Chagford and working for his brother-in-law at Thornworthy, was sent by Harold Wonnacott to sell at Princtown Fair a four year old colt that had been 'broken in' to ride. This involved a journey via Postbridge and Two Bridges. When Bill arrived at Princetown the weather was so bad the Fair had been cancelled. By the time he arrived back at Postbridge the river (East Dart) was out over the old Packhorse bridge and the weather quite intimidating, and still a journey over the Moor to come to reach Thornworthy, cutting in at Statts Bridge towards Fernworthy. All this with a 'colt horse' he hadn't been able to even offer to sell at Princetown Fair.

Cyril Said, Ian Mercer, formerly the Chief Officer of the Dartmoor National Park, played a large part in championing the subsidy status placed on the Whiteface Dartmoor sheep when it was finally recognised as a hill breed by the Ministry, despite its origins on the Moor going back hundreds of years!

At Yealmpton Show, the John Harris Trophy for the best Whiteface Dartmoor sheep in the Show was won by Cyril Abel (C.W. Abel) in 1991, 1993, 1994 and 1995. Then in 1997 and 1999 by Phil Abel (P.G. Abel) so the practice of farming and showing Whitefaces is shown here, and all through the Whiteface story, as very much a family tradition of succession and dedication.

Cyril produced a very interesting book written in 1912 on Breeds of Sheep.

It says Dartmoor gives its name to a breed of sheep little known outside its own district, but although confined to a restricted area, it is none the less an interesting breed, well adapted to the high district in which it is kept. 'Dartmoor Forest' is a large tract of forest and moorland in Devonshire and its total area has been said to be between two and three hundred thousand acres of wild, varied and uncultivated land. Cyril remarked that when it rains and only after a short while, some of the 'bog and mire' areas, even if seeming dry before, suddenly become very wet and dangerous on the moor and in the adjoining 'newtakes', especially where the old turf-ties were cut in the past.

No fence separates the Moor from the forest, though the actual boundary line is known. (The Forest itself is 130,000 acres). Thousands of acres of the forest land have been cleaned and exhausted, and abandoned shafts of tin mines are to be found at various places. The moorland is covered in many places with immense rugged rocks and masses of granite, while to the north-east are large tracts of swampy land; such is the home of the 'Dartmoor sheep.' Dartmoor ewes are exceptionally good mothers and crossed with a Southdown ram, 'bring some very fine fat lambs'. The climate of Devonshire allows the ewes to lamb in the open. Even up until 1970 it was still common practice to lamb outdoors and this is the case with many hill flocks at this time. The small and sheltered fields in the valleys help this during early March. The lambs are hardy and born with plenty of energy, as lambing extends into April. In many cases the ewes and lambs are turned out on the Moors in summer where they are left to fend for themselves until Michaelmas, when some of the lambs are sold to farmers who feed them through the winter on turnips and other roots. The wethers are kept for several years and many winter on the Moor. This matured mutton is of fine quality. Dartmoor rams are often used on Leicester or Devon Longwool (and South Devon) ewes to produce tegs (hoggs). For breeding purposes these rams were making in 1912–1913 from 5 to 15 gns. Draft ewes are commonly sold at Tavistock Goose Fair at prices ranging from 35s to 40s.

Farmers on richer soils of Cornwall and the South Hams would buy these and get a final crop of lambs from them by a Leicester or Devon Longwool 'tup' (ram), fattening off both ewe and lamb as soon as possible. Dartmoor sheep have sometimes been spoken of as 'scavengers'; but perhaps as the Whitefaces were smaller, and restless, they gained this reputation. But it was said they are without doubt an exceptionally hardy breed with an excellent constitution. They can survive on very scanty fare. The herbage of the Moor on which they have to subsist consists chiefly of lichen moss, cotton grass, small fescues, and other minor and varied plants.

The crossing of some 'Dartmoors' occurred with the English Leicester; the latter was improved by Bakewell's careful selection and breeding and was the foundation breed of many Longwools.

The old-type of sheep was not fit for the butcher before it was five years old, and even then was of comparatively small weight; now as written in 1912 they mature much earlier at weights varying from 60–80lbs in carcass.

But a concluding statement here is quite revealing for it says 'Dartmoor sheep are Whitefaced as a rule'; but grey or speckled faces are not uncommon.

Where the heath and mountain type sheep are recorded as far back as the 1500–1600s the

White faced Dartmoors seem to have their origins firmly rooted in this distant past, the modern greyface sheep seeming to be bred off the 'mountain type' of Dartmoors at a much later date, and then considerably 'improved'.

Referring to the very cold snow winter of 1947 Eileen Abel said 'that Cyril's father's Greyface Dartmoors were wiped out because they died frozen to the ground as a result of their heavy fleeces!' Cyril remarked that his father went with sticks to prod the snow drifts for buried sheep, but the snow was too deep to find them, yet to dig them out! Also in 1978 in February Cyril said for a couple of weeks a blizzard seemed as bad as 1962/3. Several sheep pulled out of drifts died, and on the moor under Mis Tor some of the sheep died in groups, but seemed OK from a distance, but it was very cold. In the winter of '62/3 when the snow began to thaw, eight Bluegrey cows were washed away down the Walkham river as a result of severe flooding, and could not be recovered. L.W. Page wrote an amusing story of local history. Apparently Peter Tavy (Petertavy) shares with the adjacent village of Mary Tavy (Marytavy) the honour of having created a joke at the expense of one of our judges. His lordship was presiding at a trial in which the title to certain land in these parishes was in question, and not unnaturally perhaps thought the names belonged to two witnesses, and he astonished both bar and audience by ordering Peter and Mary Tavy to be summoned into Court, of which of course there was only the said Parish names!

1994 Devon County Show Championship to Phil's champion female.

The Godsworthy Flock, Peter Tavy (Phil and Alison Abel)

Our Flock started in 1967 with the purchase of 9 ewes at £7 each from Mr L. Ball. They were a wedding present for Eileen and Cyril from Cyril's father. Cyril and his sister-in-law then left Eileen at home with new arrival Colin and went to Ashburton and bought a £13 ram from Mr S. Mann. They arrived home later rather the worse for wear, explained Phil.

The biggest influence on our breeding policy was Mr John Savery with the purchase of numerous rams over the years, some going on to unprecedented showing success including 2 old rams that went unbeaten all year.

The best ram used was a ram purchased from Mr E. Caunter which matched well with our ewes producing good ewes. The flock now stands at about 46 ewes tupped per year.

Female champions at Cornwood Show 1990 and reserve breed champions. Female champions and breed champions at Moretonhampstead in 1991 and Okehampton in 1992.

We started showing in 1986 with several High Commendeds until 1988, since when we have had a remarkable decade at shows, winning 36 breed championships, the most notable being Devon County Show Champion 6 times in the 90s. Phil achieved 5 breed championships in the year 2000 and with the 2000 shows taken into account the breed championships have risen to 41. We have won the Under 50 Flock Competition 7 times (the Ewe Lamb Competition 5 times) thereby winning the Perpetual Challenge Trophy presented by H.G. Woodley for the best Flock Under 50 Ewes.

We have been fortunate enough to have bred 2 outstanding ram hoggs in the last 5 years, both breaking the price record. The current record holder, a ram hogg bred by a Mann's ram out of the Devon County Champion of 1993, was sold in 1998 for £388.50 going to Mr J. Caunter. This ram hogg was unbeaten in showing all summer. This broke the old record set in 1997 by a ram hogg bred by a Brown's ram sold for £367.50 that went to Yorkshire to a Mr Ryder Howard to promote the breed outside of the area who now has a flock of 70 ewes. Both rams were sold at the Show and Sale at Ashburton. The 'wool on the hoof' was won for the first time in 1997, at the Devon County Show. The ram hogg was first in its class and judged Male Champion and Reserve Breed Champion by Terry Phipps.

Alison and Phil with their champion ram; Widecombe Fair 2000. (Photo: Colin Pearse).

Left: Totnes Show champion 1988. Judge: A. Mortimore. Best hogg ever bred Phil said out of a 1993 Devon County Champion ewe.
Right: Okehampton and Cornwood Champion 1996.

The flock was increased in 1998 with the purchase of John Savery's flock. John was a founder member and president of the Society, and his untimely death was a sad loss for the breed. This was a chance to strengthen our own blood lines and hopefully keep the breed going into the next Millennium.

We have used rams from the flocks of Mr S. Mann, Patrick Coaker, Philip Coaker, John Savery, Mr E. Caunter, Mr A. Brown and we are now using a John Mead ram purchased in 1999 alongside a Mann's ram.

Phil, in the year 2000, is now the Association's Vice Chairman and will take over as the 2001 Chairman in the year of the W.F.D.S.B.A.'s 50th anniversary. Cyril is also a past Chairman.

Male champion 1997 at Devon County Show. Left to right: Terry Phipps (judge), Nick Abel, Colin Abel.

THE GODSWORTHY FLOCK CHAMPIONSHIPS

DEVON COUNTY	YEALMPTON	CORNWOOD
1990	1991	1989
1991	1993	1991
1993	1994	1992
1994	1995	1993
1996	1997	1995
1999	1999	1996
2000*		1997
1999		

TOTNES	OKEHAMPTON
1992	1994
1995	1995
1996	1997
1997	1999
1998	2000
2000	
2002	

MORETONHAMPSTEAD	WIDECOMBE	AUTUMN SHOW AND SALE IN ASHBURTON CATTLE MARKET
1991	1993	
1992	1996	1992
1993	2000	
1994		
No longer a Show		

FLOCK UNDER 50	EWE LAMBS
1977 C.W. Abel	1975
1987 "	1979
1989 "	1987
1991 "	1989
1993 "	1991
1996 "	
1998 P.G. Abel	

THE ASHBURTON ASSOCIATION SALE YEAR 2000
1st – Old Ram
2nd – Ram Hogg
Champion Sheep – Old Ram and 1st with wool

*DEVON COUNTY 2000: A silver plate tray awarded this first Millennium year for farmers gaining most points for either cattle or sheep awarded to under 35 year olds plus a special keepsake.

Detailed in the Tavistock Times Gazette the local success at the Devon County Show (May 1999) including a win for Peter Tavy farmer Phil Abel and champion Whiteface Dartmoor ram.

Phil and daughter Bethany with ram and champion and rosettes from Devon County 1999.

Roger Malone reported the last show of the Century at Westpoint. He explained it worked magic for Peter Tavy farmer Phil Abel who walked away from the judging arena with not only male champion in the Whitefaced Dartmoor class, but also breed champion. In 1998 he achieved male champion, but this time went one better.

Phil was quoted as saying that his pre-millennium show was made that extra bit special. He remarked that his sheep seem to have peaked at just the right time. His entries pleased the judge with their general quality, the wool and the conformation.

Since the Devon County Show moved from its old location at Whipton to Westpoint in 1990, things have been looking up for Phil. Since coming to Westpoint Phil has won the Champion five times. He was obviously elated to have won the Champion in the last show of the Century.

Phil said the secret to success has a lot to do with feeding. Also you move them around to make sure the sheep don't get bored. So Phil rotates his flock and wryly recalls a piece of old farming wisdom which recommends moving sheep from field to field so they don't hear the same church bells twice in any one week!

Roger Malone reported that apparently some sheep are cleverer than we give them credit for and some can, it seems, even read:

One sign by a sheep enclosure bleated 'A NOTICE TO EWE; this is a designated judging ring, not a baa baa shop! Please do not use the area for grooming, exercising or grazing; right, got the message!'

Considering the disability Phil has, the above is a huge achievement and success story, combining determination and passion in no small measure for his sheep, with which he excels!

The Ball Family

AXNA, MARY TAVY – ONCE KNOWN AS 'TAVY ST MARY'

As one turns off at the Mary Tavy Inn and start to head towards Horndon, and the Elephant's Nest Inn too, the moor faces you again. This time it's the harsh west and north-west terrain. Just half a mile from the Mary Tavy Inn, the farmstead of Axna can be found. The lives of stockman and shepherds here at Mary Tavy and Peter Tavy are dictated by sheep, cattle, harvest and weather and the adversities of the moor; only subtle changes divide spring from autumn.

Leonard Balls' sheep were leared in summer on the moor, but never went much beyond Cut Hill (1981 ft asl). (Fur Tor and Tavy Head are not far away). The story of Whitefaced Dartmoor sheep in the vicinity of Fur Tor (1877' asl) hardly gets any better then this, and if the sheep only knew it many other impressive tors of the moor are in view and even Kit Hill, in Cornwall, for the moor here is peppered with tors on its hills at one of its highest points; affording meagre grazing on their steep slopes for these native sheep to scavenge and search in summer. A variation of Fur Tor is "Vurtorre" 1346, Forterfote 1528. 'Furre' also suggests 'further'. It is in a remote situation!

Rights on Mary Tavy Common also belong with Axna and from the top of Gibbet Hill probably twenty tors are in view and nearly all of Black Down which is mostly in Mary Tavy. Some of the grandest tors of the moor can be seen – Great Mis Tor, White Tor, Fur Tor, Staple Tor, etc.

The bounds of the North Quarter of the moor are from the confluence of the Wester Red Lake and the Tavy to the head of Spriddle Combe and thence to the bottom known as 'Horse Hole' on the West Dart. Horse Hole is about a quarter of a mile NW of Row Tor and is the junction of the north, west and east QUARTERS of the forest, four miles from Two Bridges and further north again is West Dart Head (two miles from the ford above Wistmans Wood).

This is an extraordinary area to be caught if the fog comes down and Peter Hilborn, Leonard Balls' son-in-law, spoke of just that happening on one occasion whilst riding on the moor to gather sheep. Without any warning it was 'fog down' in 'Horse Hole' and although he knew his way out, Peter couldn't find it and they were kept there all day, but the lad that was with him was so scared, he never went back to Dartmoor again! ('Black mist', is one of the most dreaded of Dartmoor terrors!) As Sir L. Morris wrote, 'a mist creeps over all the sky, and fields and pools and blots them'; and the moor too it seems!

Grandfather farmed Axna and kept Whiteface Dartmoor sheep. Leonard's mother was a servant maid at nearby Kingsett Farm at the age of eleven years.

The only part of the original Axna remaining is the granary and the horse stabling below, and the substantial granite steps rising beside the barn's outer wall.

Peter explained horses were kept underneath the granary and sheep were shorn in the 'cartshed' replaced long ago, and as many as eight shearers would come to shear in the old shed; neighbours like Sid Friend and the Lillicrap family, etc.

Leonard Ball was a founder member of the Association and, on the alphabetical list of prefixes with owners and identification letters, is the first member named of twenty-seven who first joined the Whiteface Dartmoor Breeders' Association in 1951.

Leonard is also seen in photographs at the Old Ashburton stock market (now a cattle market showing his Whiteface Dartmoor sheep alongside the likes of Cecil Caunter and

Leonard Ball (on left of picture) and members of the inspection committee, in the lane with Leonard's Whitefaces, beside Axna Farm (11th May 1957).

Horace Nosworthy. In 1951 and 1955 he won the W.F.D.S.B.A. Challenge Cup presented by Sawdye and Harris for the best pen of ten ewes. The Association leaflet produced at a later date after the formation of the W.F.D.S.B.A. also recognizses Leonard Ball as President at one point and Cecil Caunter as Chairman. Photographs show sheep being tattooed in a lane at Axna during the earliest days of the Whitefaces being registered. Leonard was at this time the chief tattooer!

All hands on tattooing.

The inspection committee, some pictured here, that came to Axna were Hermon, J. French, Geoffrey H. French jnr, Cecil Caunter, Sylvester Mann, Cecil Harris and Reg Hill.

At around this time the team went on to Cudlipptown, Peter Tavy, and joined up with Harry Rowse, the farmer there, and sheep were inspected in his higher yard, and Leonard Ball is seen with his sheep in the line up.

Leonard's daughter, Jennifer Hilborn, remembers Mr Norman Friend of Dingle Farm, Mary Tavy, taking her father to Ashburton and to the Golden Lion Hotel in 1951 for the Association's first meeting and to the Association's first sale, there were not many cars back then she said. Norman Friend's farm is just a stone's throw from Axna. Norman Friend said John Coaker was its first Chairman and Cecil Caunter its first President. Norman said he drove his Morris 10 and acted as taxi driver. Father and Grandfather Friend kept Whitefaces but never joined the Association. Norman said 'the more the wool bred on a Whiteface, the less milk it gave'!

Mrs Margaret Ball stayed with Gladys Mann at Widecombe when the men went to meetings.

Other Whiteface flocks were also kept around Leonard Ball in the Mary Tavy area seeming to thrive on the fringes of the moor here too, yet being kept the other side of the moor to Widecombe's indigenous Whiteface.

Edward Maunder at Higher Kingsett bred the Whiteface ram on the Greyfaces. Harry Rowse, an original member in 1951, and Bryan kept Whitefaces at Cudlipptown, Peter Tavy, during the early days of the Association where inspections also took place.

In the ram judges' book between 1954 and 1960, we see considerable mention of Leonard Ball both showing and buying and later judging Whiteface rams. At the fifth Annual Show and Sale on Thursday, 1st September 1955, Leonard purchased a third prize ram hogg belonging to Richard Coaker of Runnage for 19 guineas.

During 1958 in the Old Ram class at the eighth Annual Show and Sale of Whiteface Dartmoors, Leonard achieved second behind Mann Brothers. At the ninth Annual Show and Sale in 1959, first prize was awarded by the judges, Peter Hannaford and Reg Hill, to Leonard Ball for an Old Ram. Mann Brothers and French Brothers, Corringdon, Brent, were second and third in the same year. During 1960 Leonard turned to judging all the sheep classes at Ashburton Show and Sale, in this year too he was President of the W.F.D.S.B.A.

Sheep grass keep for the winter was taken at a Mr Barber's Dippertown, Lewdown, where the area was better for sheep to thrive. Often Jennifer (Leonard's daughter) lambed them away. Then in spring, Jennifer Hilborn remembers helping to walk them back to Axna via Chillaton and Brent Tor. She also recalls that her father took winter keep (grass and roots) at a Mr Wakeham's Hazard Farm, near Totnes. Her father she said 'would go away and stay and lamb his sheep at Totnes in March'.

In summer, Leonard's sheep leared mainly around Fur Tor. Sometimes they would come around and across the NW side of Fur Tor and mix with Richard Coaker's sheep.

Crossing says 'Fur Tor is a wilderness of stone, and none that covers so large an area or whose surroundings are of the desolate character as those upon which this lonely tor looks down!' and yet the Whiteface Sheep found a summer-home here!

Peter Hilborn (Jennifer's husband) explained that Leonard Ball lived for his Whitefaces and was a good stockman. Even today, their 'yark' character and thriftiness is still needed and can be seen on the high moorland farms that is their home, and there is a true bond between these sheep and farmer and dog and the moor around.

Peter remarked that many breeders would try and obtain his father-in-law's breeding.

Marvellous first cross sheep too were bred off the Greyfaces in the area, using Whiteface rams.

Peter remembers Leonard's sheep being unloaded at Ashburton Sheep Sale flying down the

Jennifer and her tame Whiteface lambs

tailboard and Leonard and other breeders seeming to accept, even before they were judged, that Leonard's sheep were going to win! ('I got 'em this year' Leonard would say), i.e. the winning sheep and cup.

Peter remarked how good a hand shearer Leonard was. He said 'Leonard had hands as wide as a clipper' (big strong hands to shear and grip with) and he taught Peter to hand shear. Peter recalled that Leonard used to shear 'big scats' of wool by hand off the sheep leaving big grooves of wool marked and lined on the sheep caused by keeping the heel of the hand shears down tight onto the sheep's skin.

Jennifer and Peter Hilborn's son, Kevin, won the Open Young Farmers sheep shearing Trophy at the Devon County Show in 1999. During 1999, Kevin also spent some time in Australia perfecting his shearing skills and gaining experience with large numbers of sheep. With his family pedigree it's not surprising Kevin is a good shearer. Kevin's record number of sheep shearing in a day is 420!

FROM WATERN OKE, LOOKING E. (Crossing)

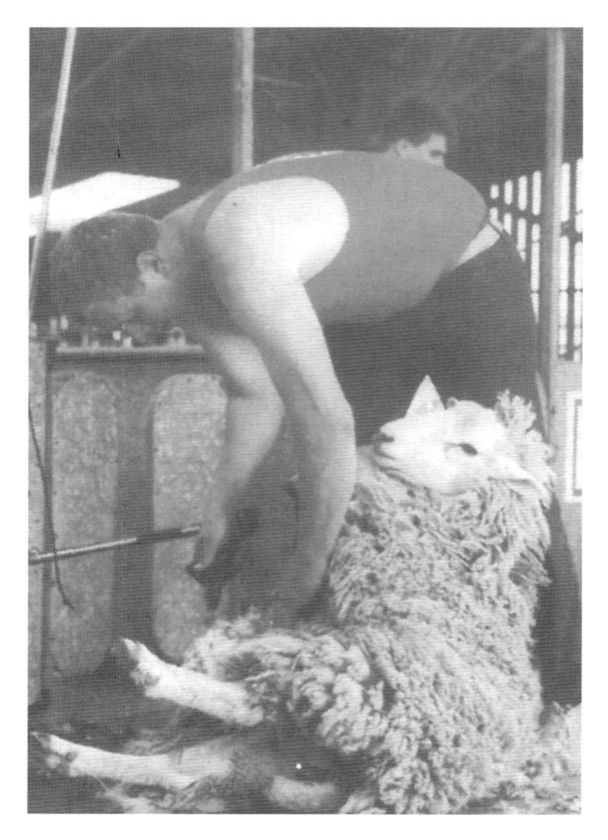

Kevin Hillborn winning the Open Young Farmers' sheep shearing trophy at the Devon County Show 1999.

I find it fascinating that his interest in sheep has still come through the family and the 'genetic link' continues from Great Grandfather to Kevin's generation, and is repeated with many livestock farming families all over keeping the Whiteface Dartmoor sheep and other sheep, and with other animals farmed with continuity in the farming arena.

It seems the 'black spots' frequently seen on Whitefaces even today (especially on the ear) were a very old breed trait. Peter Hilborn remarked that when Whitefaces were being registered there was much controversy about these 'Guinea Spots' said to be worth a guinea, adding value to the sheep. Some breeders liked to see these spots and regarded them as a purity sign, but others would want to reject sheep from the register where these spots were found! But they still occur in sheep today. Norman Friend previously mentioned taking Leonard to the Association's first meeting and also highlighted a story concerning Venville Rights, the right to use the 'forest of Dartmoor'. Only a shilling a year had to be paid in order to turn up sheep and lambs onto the 'Forest' in summer but, if this small amount was somehow overlooked and not paid, these Venville Rights could be lost and his family experienced this error and lost their Venville Rights on the Forest. Mary Tavy didn't seem to be registered with Venville!

The right for Mr Friend existed around Walkham Head and Stannon Down and Lynch Tor (Lydford side). Mr Friend said Hernspitt Pearse's had some good sheep and would probably have used Burrator Common in the past.

Norman's father and grandfather crossed their greyfaces with Widecombes every two or three years to keep them harder, on a flock of some fifty sheep. He said when the Greyface was bred for more wool, it lost its constitution. Also he remarked that he felt the Whiteface would have originated from Goats (other sheep too seem to have asiatic connections), hence the 'goatee' beards sometimes seen in rams even today, on their chin and chest.

Recalling Tavistock Market, Mr friend said 'John's Fair (St John's Fair) used to be full of Dartmoor sheep'. A buyer called Tamblyn bought many Whitefaces to go to Cornwall where they were crossed with the Suffolk breed; many bloodlines were lost. The railways, no doubt, came into play as transport at Tavistock, South Brent, Ashburton, Totnes, Princetown, Moretonhammpstead, Okehampton, Lydford, etc. Tavistock will celebrate in 2005 nine hundred years as a market town; a market charter was put into place in 1105.

There was a lot of friendly rivalry it seems at Widecombe Fair and with breeders such as Manns with whom Leonard got on well and at Devon County Show with all the clan!

On one occasion Richard Coaker and Roger Whale were tattooing Leonard's lambs; afterwards they ended up in the Elephant's Nest Inn (Mary Tavy) and it seems Leonard was worse for wear.

At home in Leonard's kitchen, his wife had prepared a meal. Roger remembers looking in around the kitchen door and seeing this huge saucepan of cabbage packed three high, he wondered how many people Mrs Ball was preparing to have for dinner! Mrs Margaret Ball (Leonard's wife) told me she often cooked 'Flatpoll cabbage,' which of course was also fed to sheep and cattle in the past and the centre of these cabbages the animals relished and once exposed revealed wonderful 'white fleshed' leaves. The 'Tuckers seeds catalogue' of 1986 still promotes Flatpoll cabbages. Plants were hand dug into place in a field and large crops were grown and recorded.

Jennifer emphasised that sheep used to even come up from Bere Alston in the past for the summer on the moor. This followed the same pattern of agistment and pasturage as seen on other parts of the Southern and Eastern Moor as already recorded.

Peter also remembered 'that he and Leonard must have travelled most of Kingsbridge for 'away keep' for their sheep over many years (to over winter) for this was on the whole a kinder and safer environment, food and weatherwise'!

Eric Wonnacott explained how strong a man Leonard Ball was; he said Leonard on one occasion had a puncture in one of his tractor tyres and so the tractor had to be 'jacked up'. However it fell off its jack and Leonard it seems just came along with the repaired wheel and lifted the tractor up by the axle to put the wheel back on again!

The Barons Family

CHARFORD AND BENEKNOWLE, DIPTFORD, AVONWICK

William Barons moved to Charford in the year of the bad snow winter of 1962/3 from Shearlangstone, Modbury. His sheep were in the field below 'Charford Hill's and lambing would have been the end of February (1963). Sheep survived under the snow eating bare the hedges and scavenging for anything they could find to eat. They were recovered a week before lambing. Bill Barons (William) had Greyfaces and Devon Longwools at this time.

William Barons watching his flock being judged.

In 1967/8 Whiteface Dartmoor rams were bought and crossed on these sheep. Les Barons (son) ran his own flock of Whiteface Dartmoor Sheep from the mid-seventies and recorded and showed his own sheep. He used to also buy Suffolk x WFD ewe lambs from Les Hopkins who, himself bought Whiteface Dartmoor ewes from the Association Sale (a couple of pens a year). Les Barons showed at Yealmpton, Widecombe, Cornwood, Totnes, 'Brent and Devon County'; all over. There is a notable photo of Les showing sheep at the old Brent Show with Ned Northmore judging.

The mid-late seventies were busy years with the Whitefaces and in fact his father (Bill) started taking an interest in Whitefaces later on again.

In 1976 and in 1978, W. Barons, won the W.F.D.S.B.A. Brian and Julie Harris Memorial

Cyril Abel judging William Barons sheep.

Challenge Cup for the best flock of ewe lambs judged on the farm. Judging and showing became a regular habit with the family.

Along with Norman Stephens, Les Baron's father wanted to try and cross the Whiteface at one point with the Llywn breed of similar Whiteface, clean sheep. However, the idea was not accepted by the Association.

Les Barons keeps a diary every day of his working life. This proved very useful because he was able to explain in exact detail his management of his Whiteface Sheep. 6th September 1975, he put 40 two and four tooths to an Abel ram and 40 ewes to a Mann's ram to lamb in February.

On the 4th September 1976 (the drought summer) he bought 150 ewes from Ashburton Sheep Sale and the 13th September he put 38 sheep to a Mann's ram. 61 to Abel's ram, 52 to Suffolk being 151 W.F.D. ewes in all.

Les has always had a bit of a passion for the Suffolk x Widecombe ewe, which certainly is an excellent mother, and crosses well with continental or Down sires, as practised over many years by cross-breeding shepherds.

On 30th August 1979, Les bought two Whiteface Rams and 20 full mouth ewes.

On the Ashburton Sheep Sale day in August 1978, he sold a Whiteface Dartmoor Ram for 40 gns.

On 30th August 1979 he bought a Whiteface Dartmoor ram for 115 gns from Norman Warne at the Association Sale.

At Widecombe Fair in 1979, Les achieved two thirds and two fourths for showing Whitefaces. Previously in 1977 at Widecombe he had a first for ewe lambs (11 entered) third for two-tooths (14 entered) and fifth for a ram (11 entered).

On 30th August 1984 the diary of Les Baron recorded thirty-two Widecombes purchased and this included 12 two-tooths at £33.50 and 10 at £44 and a further 10 at £46. Good prices paid in relation to today.

His uncle, Bob Kerswell, and his son Harry, the latter a cousin to Les have attended Ashburton Sheep Sale for many years as buyers and as judges. They have used different females to cross with the Whiteface rams and Les also explained they found the Teeswater ram on the Widecombe or on the South Devon x Widecombe to be an interesting hardy milky and prolific cross.

One of Les Baron's final outings to buy Whiteface ewes was in 1983. He paid

£42 for 10 two-tooths
£43.50 for 10 two-tooths
£44.50 for 7 two-tooths

This recorded an average of £43 a piece. However, in 1980 he lorried 84 sheep to Ashburton Sheep Sale with a Bedford lorry. It was Norman Stephens of Barleycombe who asked Les to take the sheep and they made £10 each.

Les Baron's moorland rights now extend to Gribblesdown, Brent Moor, Ugborough, Aishridge and behind Bulhornstone.

The Bond Family

PULLABROOK, BOVEY TRACEY

Whitefaces have been kept at Pullabrook since the 1920s. Also Mrs Bond's (Heather) Grandfather, Father and Uncle respectively; Jack (John) Mortimore at Jurston, John Osborne at South Hookner and Will Mortimore at Beetor Farm had Whiteface sheep in the parishes of Chagford and North Bovey.

Pullabrook where Henry and Heather Bond farm has ancient Saxon origins. The river Bovey itself is supposed to get its name from a Saxon Theign called Bofa or Boui and gave name to several hamlets: North Bovey and South Bovey (later Bovey Tracey), Little Bovey and Bovey Coombe among them. Heather recalls walking sheep to Chagford from Jurston and Hookner to where the market used to be held behind the Globe Inn and Steven's Garage. Sheep used to be sold penned in the street in the old days in Chagford, and around the 'Market House' in the village square (using hurdles). This building replaced a market building called 'The Shambles' in 1862. The ancient village of Chagford (derived from 'gorse at the ford'!) is an old Stannary Town where the tin miners too weighed and stamped the tin.

Ashburton Fair 1993 – Heather holding ram. Second from left of centre.

The first Whiteface ram to be sold for over 300 gns at Ashburton Show and Sale was bred by W.R. Bond (1981 – 315 gns). The two bidders were Mr W. Barons (Bill) and Mr John Hearn. The former bought the ram. Henry continues to sell ewes and rams at the Ashburton Sale at the end of August every year.

The flock records of 1987 says there were 120 ewes in the flock. During this year too (1987) the Bond family were winners of the breed champion for the Whitefaced Dartmoors at the Devon County Show. In 1990 and 1992 the Bond family won the Yealmpton Show Cup (John Harris Trophy) for the best Whiteface Dartmoor Sheep in the Show. The Whiteface Dartmoor Challenge Cup at Totnes Show was won in 1993 and 1997.

Heather Bond also recalled a Whiteface Annual Sheep Sale being held at Haytor, in fact at

Haytor Vale, the auctioneer was Ted Sawdye up until the Second World War. Jack Mortimore, Heather's Grandfather, never sold a Whiteface wether until it was full mouth and the 'boys' used to adjust the rails across a gateway to see how high the sheep could jump!

'Swaling' on North Bovey Common below 'Kings Tor' and near to 'Kings Barrow' by Heathers brother Malcolm Osborne farming 'South Hooker' that joins the Common.

Interesting too, Heather explained that originally all ewes were horned as well as the rams, somewhere in their history and vestiges of horn still appear on a few ewes today!

The importance of wethers as already hinted at by Heather Bond is revealed in 'Dartmoor A New Study' edited by Crispin Gill; 'From the number of sheep annually summered on Dartmoor Forest, the ewes and lambs of which are always brought down "in-country" on the approach of winter, it will be readily supposed that a large proportion of sheep stock is always found to occupy the surrounding districts in the winter season. The greater part of these flocks, however, being wethers, and chiefly preserved for their wool, are left on the Dartmoor Forest during winter', so wrote Charles Vancouver in 1808. On the commons belonging to the Parish of Widecombe (spelt Widdicombe) wethers were greased to protect against the winter rains and 'scab' in the past. Although producing good long wool the Dartmoor Whitefaces were known throughout England in the past for their excellent mutton, no doubt some of it coming from such wethers already mentioned.

A serge-weaving industry was flourishing in Bovey Tracey in the past in the parish for there is a record of a small 'fulling mill' for the dressing of the cloth, and survived until the 19th Century.

The name wethers even seems engrained in the history of Dartmoor in another way: a couple of miles from Scorhill Circle, on the slopes of Siddaford Tor (Sittaford) are two Bronze-Age stone circles. These are known as the 'Grey Wethers'. William Crossing wrote, they are popularly supposed to have been derived from a fancied resemblance of the group of stones to a flock of sheep (no doubt mistaken for grazing sheep). These stones were once the object of a practical joke, having been sold by a man named Debben to a farmer who was a stranger to this part of the Moor, as so many 'Grey Wethers'. The bargain was struck in the Warren House Inn and the farmer was directed to the Newtake near Siddaford Tor, where he would be able to see his purchase. This he did but, unlike Bo Peep, found not only that the sheep would not come home, but also that they had got no tails to bring behind them! They

Shearing instructors using Whitefaces.

are the largest stone circles on the Moor, and form an impressive sight. No doubt the name 'Grey Wethers' is derived too from the grey looking granite stones that from a distance look like grey-shaped sheep, but again highlight the history of wethers and sheep on the Moor.

Henry and Heather's daughters (Rosemary and Hilary) show a keen interest in their Whiteface Sheep at home and at showing time, and with shearing instruction during Young Farmers Club on farm classes (seen centre back of photo).

John Hearn (judge) inspecting a sheep's teeth; Heather Bonds ewe, Widecombe Fair.

A mix of sires bred by breeders across the board were used to help continue the Bond family's sheep; Mann Bros, Adams and Howell, W. Doidge, Brown Bros, A. Mortimore, R. Norrish, C. Abel, S. Northmore, W. Stone, J. Hearn, T. Phipps and J. Stephens.

Accidents on farms to farmers and farm workers working in a hazardous industry have over the years been sadly remembered. Malcolm Osborne, Heather Bond's brother farming at South Hookner, North Bovey, conveyed one such very sad story.

A great uncle of Heather's and Malcolm (Osborne) called Harvey, was riding his horse back from Lizwell Widecombe-in-the-Moor to Holwell, where he had only been farming for six weeks, after getting married. Mr Harvey had been shearing Whiteface Dartmoors at Lizwell and had also taken a couple of wood hooks out with him for his uncle to sharpen on the grindstone.

It is thought he carried the two hooks and sharp pointed sheep shears in a hessian bag that was tied and thrown over the saddle. Hand sheep shears would have been well sharpened for a day's shearing. The story goes that a stallion on the open Moor attacked the mare he was riding and threw him off onto the hessian bag and no doubt on top a rock, and the sharp tools badly injured him, and he bled to death before anyone found him. This wasn't before the horse had gone home to Holwell with just its saddle on, and it was realised something was seriously wrong. The dogs faithfully stayed with their master until he was found.

Due east a quarter of a mile from West Coombe is the hamlet of Hookner. It was once named as Hokenteon hamlet in 1307 prior to disafforestation. Hookner venville rent was once recorded as: hamlet of Hokyn – 4d.

An ancient lane says Eric Hemery (High Dartmoor) threads the Hookner enclosures to reach the common near the Dartmoor Gate. Above here is Hookner Down, it spreads out above Coombe Head, leading to King Tor (≅ 1600 feet asl). By August a whole swathe of heather is seen along Hamel Down towards Natsworthy Gate and the Widecombe Valley. Not far is Grimspound to the west (some of the old 'inclosed' wall was once twelve feet high!).

The site lies on the side of Hamel Down above 'Widdicombe'. The beacon barrows and trackways upon the Down suggest that it was a point of trading importance and settlement (Phoenicians and Britons).

Some of the tors recorded by N.T. Carrington in 1826 as High Tor, Three Barrow Tor, South Brent Tor, Hamil Tor and Cawson downs (old names), were frequently beacons or 'fire towers' (Celtic implication). The latter two high points would have been Hamildon Beacon and Cawsand Beacon (Cosdon, also 'Cosson'). Anciently there were 'watchings and wardings' of the beacons, as recorded in 1626 at other places on the moor (N.T. Carrington, Dartmoor, 'A descriptive poem').

The Brown Bros

FORMERLY OF STADDICOMBE FARM, HOLNE
NOW TOWER HILL, PLACE LANE, ASHBURTON

Arthur Brown and sons Henry and Michael founded their flock in 1952 from 'moorman' Harry Norrish, (who it was said made his money in the saddle). Harry was living at Dockwell, South Brent at the time.

It seems Harry Norrish was fed up with fetching his sheep at Huntingdon Warren and had become too old, so he wanted Arthur's boy's to have them. They leared near to the source of the Avon Dam. He told the Brown's he was offering the sheep in Brent Sheep Sale. They were, of course, reserved at £6. Arthur bid just 2/6d and bought the sheep for £6 2s. 6d.!, so Henry explained.

Then they later added to the flock with some more of Harry Norrish's sheep, which were being kept by a Mr Prendergast at Hayford Hall, Buckfastleigh. The price was £4 per ewe on condition the Brown's helped Harry with shearing at Dockwell.

On taking them back to the Brown's rights on Holne Moor, these sheep (some 130) would head in a straight line from Coombestone to their lear back at Dockwell and Huntingdon Warren and some would be found at Moorgate, Holne; an instinct hard to reverse.

Harry Norrish (left) initiates Henry Brown at the 1951 Holne 'Beating of the Bounds'. A tradition of the Parishes. Henry is tilted on the stone (Photo: Courtesy of Michael French).

The Leamons (related to Arthur's mother's side of the family) had as many as 300 Widecombes at and around Dury and Bellever Bridge before the flock book formed.

The East Dart river flows under the sturdy Bellever Bridge. Bellever a corruption of Bellaford. The ancient homestead called Bellever Farm, is according to Rowe one of the oldest moor farms in the forest.

In 1953 the Brown's bought a pen of ten ewe lambs at Horace Nosworthy's sale (tragically killed in a tractor accident) for £11 2s. 6d.

The flock at Staddicombe was inspected for the flock book entry by Cecil Harris and

The Ram on the far right shows clearly a 'bearded tuft' of hair on its chest!

members in 1954. Henry recalls buying a ram from Wilf (affectionately known as Wif) and Jack Irish at Grendon, Widecombe, which was bearded like a goat (an old fashioned trait). Also Walter Irish, Cator, Widecombe, supplied the Browns with a ram. Henry explained that it came from a wonderful flock of sheep. In 1983 Arthur paid 375 gns for a ram bred by Norman Stephens. This ram fathered the flock competition first prize lambs and ewe hogs, that made £72 each at Ashburton in the mid eighties and were judged first prize by Abel & Cole. £60 was also made of two-tooths in 1998.

In 1988 the Brown Bros won the W.d.s.B.A. Brian and Julie Harris Memorial Challenge Cup for the best flock of ewe lambs. From 1979 sires used to breed the flock came from P.W. Caunter, Adams and Howell, J. Hearn, M.B. Ogle, N. Stephens, W. Bond and F.A. Mortimore. There were 120 ewes recorded in the flock in 1987.

In mentioning other members at the time who kept Whitefaces, Henry said the French's at Michelcombe had 800–1000 Whiteface sheep, enough to breed a replacement for every day of the year. Caunters, he said, had sheep the other side of Holne Head and Sid trant was a flock book member. Arthur Wrayford of Higher Wotton Farm Woodland spoke of his families connection with Whitefaces and he said 'that Whitefaces were strong to buy at Ashburton', and many breeders in the area sold sheep at Ashburton.

Forty-three sheep of the Brown's summered at Woodhuish Brixham sheared an average 8lbs of wool per ewe. The Brown's sheep kept at 'Cumpston' developed immunity from ticks; their wool was 'moor-tainted' (peaty), but the sheep were fit in body and feet. 'Whitefaces on the moor have been known to drive Scotties away', Henry remarked.

Winter sheep keep taken at Slapton, Michael said, would involve at least two day's travelling; sometimes stopping at Diptford. Often it would be dark leaving their fields at Buckfast of a morning and too dark to count them in when they arrived at their destination at Slapton.

Henry explains the story of buying a one-eyed ram from Ned Northmore. Patrick Coaker remarked, 'Why on earth did you buy that one; he won't be any good like that'. Henry replied, 'He'll be alright 'cus I didn't buy him to look around!' Also the story told of bringing sheep back from Huntingdon Warren and Arthur met the then Archbishop of Canterbury (Michael Ramsey) walking the moors from where he stayed at Holne. The sheep were going home in July for dipping. The Archbishop remarked, 'You must have a job with all of them at lambing time' and Arthur replied, 'Not so much trouble as you might have with your flock!'

Roger Hutchings - Staddicombe Farm, Holne

Some of the Brown's sheep now form the Staddicombe flock owned by the new tenant, Roger Hutchings, when he took on the farm in 1998. Already in the year 2000 Roger has won the Under Fifties Flock Competition held on the farms by the W.FD.S.B.A. Roger explained the difficulties he has encountered since coming to Staddicombe. The immediate hard work needed to lear fresh sheep for their first time on the moor. Using just a small flock of ewes to start with, placed on Holne moor he used to try and 'beat their movement', that is to stop their right to roam!

He even calculated their regular movements. Roger found the sheep moved predominantly at 10 a.m. and 4 p.m., so if he came to 'dog' the sheep to their place on the moor at 9–9.30 a.m. and again at 3.30 p.m. they were usually still there!

Learing near to Venford Reservoir on Holne Moor, Michael French explained the reservoirs ancient ford and clapper bridge and the small-holding of Venford Cot (Venford Bottom), were flooded between 1901 and 1907 when the dam was completed to form the reservoir.

Some say the above were seen again in the very severe drought of 1976. Rogers sheep, if they decided to travel, could end up near to the Forest Inn, Cumpston and Horn's Cross The Abbots' Way crosses between Horn's Cross and Holne Moorgate.

The very alarming consequences of Foot and Mouth disease and animal movement restriction meant Roger couldn't renew his Whiteface ram, so rather than end up with no lambs at all he used his Beaulah ram, and not without good results; a pretty hardy combination. Roger hopes to 'top grass' again with a Scotch Blackface to increase his flock.

As the E.S.A. scheme extends to Dartmoor, Roger explained how he is 'fern crushing'; a permitted exercise under E.S.A. to control ferns. A harbour for ticks, and bracken poisoning can occur in dry summers, as animals are forced to graze anything to offset a lack of grass!

Whitefaced sheep at Staddicombe 2003.

Buckfast Abbey Monks, Buckfastleigh

ERIC JOHN HANNAFORD, SHEPHERD AT FURZELEIGH

Furzeleigh Farmhouse was in 1836 a Coaching House between Plymouth and Exeter, so Pam (nee Hannaford) Burningham told me. During the early part of this century, in a book called 'Yesterday Villages' published by Dartington Rural Archives, a picture is shown of George Hunt (Mary Casely's Father) sheep-shearing at Furzeleigh. The sheep definitely resembles a Whiteface Dartmoor and so Whitefaces would have been grazed at that time at Furzeleigh.

Hand shearing at Furzeleigh (George Hunt).

Around 1940 the Buckfast Abbey Monks took back in hand 'Furzeleigh Farm' from the Hunt family, who had been renting Furzeleigh from the monks. The early Cistercian Monks of Buckfast, as the story tells, could well have pastured 'Dartmoor' sheep in very early times on the moor around.

During the mid-sixties (1966–7) when John Hannaford and his family were living at Furzeleigh, John was offered the job of shepherd on the Monks' farm under Father Gregory, the Farm Manager.

Eric John Hannaford was born near Kingswear and his first connection with sheep came when a Mr Thomas of 'Colton Fishacre', who it seems had big sheep, ('South Devon') was taken ill and John, who was only fourteen at the time, had to lamb the sheep.

When he was first married he lived with his in-laws (the Dowells) at Nurston (pronounced

'Shepherd of the sheep!' Whitefaces very much in evidence at Furzeleigh with Tom Elliott, John Hannaford and Father Gregory.

Nur'son) Farm, Dear Prior around 1945. The farm was rented off Lord Churston as part of his estate. They kept about 80 Whitefaces at Nurston. The farm extended to about 220 acres. Recalling the farms around Nurston with Whitefaces, John mentioned Dockwell and Skerraton and also a Mr Codd who kept a lot of Scotch sheep but he remembers Whitefaces with him too (and Addislade).

John thought Whiteface sheep at Skerraton were kept by a person by the name of Thomas, who bought the farm from the Churston Estate. The Ogles (under M.B. Ogle) also kept Whitefaces at Skerraton when they farmed it and in the Flock Book Record of 1979, 83 ewes, 36 lambs and one ram Hogg, sire bred by Norman Stephens were recorded. By 1980 and 1981 the ewes in the flock had grown to 80.

The Ogles both died at Christmas 1999 in a very tragic accident crossing the A38 carriageway on their way to a church service at Dean Prior.

John Hannaford remembers the Norrish family at Addislade and the Norrish Brothers including Frank he thought and Henry (Harry) when they farmed Dockwell, Brent. Harry Norrish's workman, a certain Mr Tucker, left a note with John that explained that Harry was unwell so could John help lamb some of the Norrish's Whitefaces. John took in about 35 Whitefaces. He put them in the 'breaks' at Nurston for a while and then in fields near to the farm. Within 3 weeks they all lambed and John didn't have to touch one!

Harry was very much a moorman and John recalls Harry saying to him one day in winter, 'make sure you get some "grub" (animal fodder) in about now soon'. The explanation was that Harry felt there was a lot of snow on the way because his blacks (moorland Galloway cows) had moved in from Redlake nearer to the farm sensing bad weather. (It seems they and Harry were right because it did snow.)

John also said that Harry Norrish always wore a big mack and a Southwester hat (sou'wester) and when John asked him why he didn't sometimes wear something different, Harry replied, 'If I changed my clothes my bullocks wouldn't know me'!

John Hannaford also remembers a nice lot of Whitefaces at Wallaford Farm, Buckfastleigh owned by Charles and Albert Abbot.

John said that the first sheep the Monks had at Furzeleigh were the Devon closewool; having asked Eddy Tucker (working with Sawdye & Harris) to look for some sheep to start a flock at Furzeleigh, but the sheep did not prove a success. They were very prone to getting on their backs and John recalls that as many as eight times on any one day motorists passing the sheep in the fields beside the road came in to say there were sheep on their back! The closewool was getting too fat at Furzeleigh.

Both John and Father Gregory, however, liked the Whiteface Dartmoor and so some were purchased as a starter flock in the mid-sixties from the French Bros. at Corringdon, South Brent. John said that it was difficult at that time to find enough Whitefaces to buy.

A John Savery ram was bought to work on the flock. John said, that once this ram had been used for several years, he asked John Savery for a replacement. However, when John came with another ram he asked John Hannaford if he could take home the old ram (no doubt not wanting to miss out on any important breeding!)

About 80 ewes were established and then Buckfast Abbey joined the Association for several years (15). Then in 1980 records show that the flock had dropped to 50 ewes and 30 ewe lambs by a J. Savery ram and the flock was sold.

John Hannaford became interested in crossing the Whitefaces and used a Finn-Dorset ram on some of his ewes. This increased the lambing percentage and he kept some of the first cross ewe lambs and crossed them with a Suffolk again. The lambing percentage achieved was 188%.

Then following this experiment he crossed the Whiteface Dartmoor cross Finn Dorset back to a Whiteface ram. John said when Ken Soper came over on a flock inspection and looked at the lambs he thought they were all Whitefaces.

Penned near the new buildings, Whitefaces predominate.

However, market returns were dropping and the Abbey decided to try indoor sheep. Whitefaces indoors with their full coats and not shorn was going to bring problems.

However, on one occasion near to Christmas and it was snowing outside, the Monks had Peter and Will Hutchings, Terry French (and Roger Winsor on other occasions) to shear the ewes indoors. This took place on the 13th December 1981. It was only snowing a bit at Furzeleigh when Peter's wife Ben Hutchings rang the Abbey to say 'it was snowing heavy and beginning to drift at Dury Farm Postbridge', and it would be wise if Peter, Will and Terry left for home. Terry arrived home but Peter and Will got stuck along 'CATOR STRIPS' on their way home to Dury.

Pam Burningham spoke of her father as an excellent shepherd and said he was looking after around a thousand sheep in total (with the Whitefaces) in the 1970's, probably lambing around 600 ewes for the Abbey Monks. He achieved top A grades through the sales to Maunders on dead weight grading of the Abbey's lambs.

Before shearing came into fashion with indoor sheep it was a case of trial and error in determining the control of the temperature indoors. At one point John used an electronic thermometer to check the sheep's temperature under their fleece. John said the Whiteface was used to 'harden up' the South Devon sheep through crossing.

The first caesarean operation on a sheep was apparently performed at Furzeleigh by local Totnes vet Michael Webster (of the Hair and Beaumont practise).

As in the photo shown at Furzeleigh, black sheep did appear in the Widecombe flock. John remarked 'that you haven't lambed a sheep if you haven't had a black lamb'!

The issue of wool was obviously raised, so close to the hub of things in the past at Buckfast and Buckfastleigh. John explained that the Buckfast Spinning Company wanted to invest in their own Drysdale sheep (a longwool sheep from New Zealand) with special wool qualities, but the wool board wouldn't allow it. The texture of the wool was wonderful, John said, and would have crossed well with the Whiteface and produced ideal spinning wool.

Wool prices of late have been poor and a frustrating part of the Whiteface Dartmoors falling income. However, having said that, Pam Burningham, who works at the Buckfast Spinning Co., said that a square metre of Axminster carpet would cost £32, so compared with 50–60 pence a kilo for Devon Wool depending on the grade, things seem a bit uneven.

Wadebridge, Cornwall. Described by Puvsner as one of the best medieval bridges in England. The old bridge built on bales of wool. (Photo circa 1890s. Supplied by Andrew Langdon).

Something more positive, and a very interesting story, was told by John Hannaford with regard to Wadebridge in Cornwall (one of the bridges of Wadebridge). John's son is a civil engineer and investigation work, involving drilling into the foundations of the bridge, came up with wool on the drill cores. Apparently, the bridge was reputedly built on bales of wool in 1468. (the nearby pub is called 'bridge on wool'). The money to fund it derived mostly from taxes on the profits of the wool tade. The bridges foundations rest on bales (sacks) of wool put there to firm up the quicksand on the river bottom to avoid differential settlement of the bridge. Wool does solidify when wet and compressed and once the river sediment has covered it, the oxygen is kept out and then it doesn't rot in water. The presence of the 'bridge on wool' is a reminder that the local source of wealth at that time was the sheep-rearing country around the Camel especially on Bodmin Moor. (Churches, cathedrals bridges sprang up through the wealth of wool all over).

So according to the findings of John's son actual wool was used to ballast the bridge, as well as funding for the bridge coming from the profits of wool. Natural products, including wool were used to bind the whole foundation of the bridge together, building up a wooden floating, boat-shaped platform (Sterling). Designed to force strong currents away and stop erosion of the piers placed as such in the river bed.

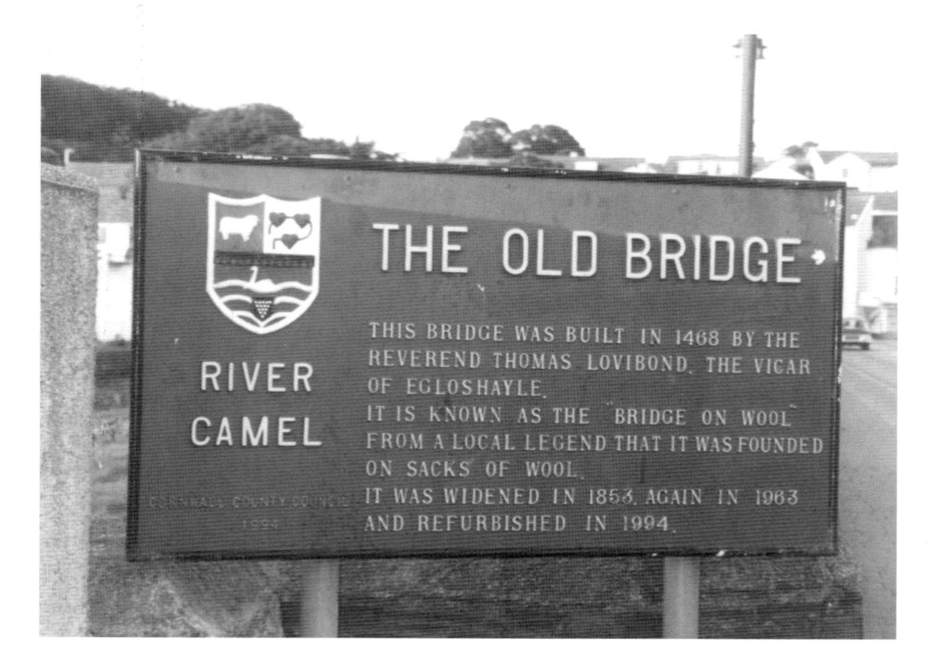

The Old Bridge over the River Camel. (Photograph supplied by Mrs Joan Rabey).

The development of the tucking mills in the 13th and early 14th Century brought cloth making out of the towns and into those areas where wool was produced and where there was water power to work the mills.

After wool had been carded and spun it had to be scoured to cleanse it of superfluous oil or grease. On Dartmoor this was often done by dipping it in baskets into streams and at Ashburton the grease and scum washed out was collected into pits as a highly prized fertiliser.

By the end of the 14th Century, England developed a thriving and expanding home cloth trade and to help it Edward III prohibited the export of English wool in a raw state in about 1350. This seemed to lay the foundations of our national superiority in these respects (weavers, dyers and fullers spread nationwide). Significantly for Devon a 'wool staple' was fixed at Exeter in 1354.

Joyce Young, in Devon and Cornwall notes and queries volume 30, part 3, says, Crispin Gill (Dartmoor New Study) refers to the purchase by a Florentine merchant of wool from Buckfast Abbey in about 1340. The price ranged from 7–12 marks a sack of 364lbs, well below the price paid for better quality wool from Ford Abbey which fetched 15 marks or £10 a sack. The merchant was connected with the great banking firm of the Bardi, but as stated, an Act of Edward III forbade export of English wool except by alien merchants.

Dartmoor is good sheep country and it was important when wool was the staple of England's Medieval trade.

Medieval Dartmoor wool, it seems, was coarse, short and spikey. On the cold pastured ground they were likely to grow coarse fleeces with too much hair, after, it is said, the manner of their prehistoric ancestors. In fact, that taken by the Tavistock Mills off the western quarter of the moor was of such grossness and stubbornness that it had to be worked up with lambs wool and flock. Edward IV in 1464, prohibited the mixing of lambs wool or flock with other wools in the same cloth.

In around 1467, the inhabitants of Roborough, Lifton and Tavistock 'Hundreds' were allowed by an Act of Parliament to use flock wool in the manufacture of Tavistocks. This was extended in 1534 to the manufacture of plains, a similar variety of cloth, made in South Devon. No doubt all the commoners of all other Dartmoor villages took advantage of the laws concession in 1467. Much of the wool for cloth made in the Totnes and Dartmouth area came from Dartmoor.

By the end of the 17th Century Dartmoor and Devon sheep had been sufficiently improved to produce a dense, medium-length fleece giving a middle grade wool. This, with a mixture of Irish wool imported through Barnstaple and Bideford, provided much of the wool for coarse serge making around Dartmoor. Then sprung the packhorse trade. Traffic from Barnstaple and Bideford through Chagford to Ashburton and on to Brixham.

In 1791 it was estimated that out of a sheep population in Devon of around 700,000; 80,000 were summered on Dartmoor proper. The weekly market for wool, yarn and woollen stuff estimated at Exeter in 1538 rapidly grew and in 1540 their sales were said to be £10,000 per week.

In 1838 around Tavistock there were over a hundred looms weaving cloth. Along the Taw between Okehampton and Sticklepath 500 looms. In Ashburton, Buckfastleigh and Buckfast something like a third of the population was employed on over 1300 looms.

To Ashburton, which incorporates in its arms a teazle, the fullers emblem, the wool trade had been worth £100,000 a year and its merchants went to Widecombe, Rattery, South Brent and all over to buy carded and spun wool from the Cottagers.

Mixing 'Dartmoor wool' with the long woolled fleeces of the valley sheep, Ashburton turned increasingly to serge manufacture in the last century and in the late 1860's was supplying army serge to India.

By 1914 cheap cloth for British uniforms kept the district, particularly Buckfastleigh, busy. Buckfastleigh used much Dartmoor wool for its blanket and serge combing mills and produced navy serge and blankets until well into the present century.

Blanket and serge manufacture spilled over into Chagford in 1800 when John Berry, finding labour scarce in Ashburton, moved there to employ over 1200 weavers finishing 700 serges a week. Chagford was on the old wool packhorse route between North Devon and Ashburton and spun for itself a modest living from the wool trade. The industry declined here in the 1860's, as it had before this date along the northern fringes of the moor, being killed off by the more ready availability of cheap cotton goods, the loss of the East Indian Company market and the better organised Yorkshire woollen trade.

By the end of the 19th Century Moretonhampstead, Okehampton and Widecombe had forgotten about wool and Tavistock only just recalled it in a combing mill which finally ceased working in 1960. Only around Buckfastleigh and further down the Dart Valley at Harberton, did the industry retain some importance.

Today the trade lingers only at Buckfast, where as detailed, a quantity of Dartmoor wool is taken for yarn spinning and in the tweed and blanket manufacture at Dartington Hall. Like the tin trade, cloth making on and around Dartmoor was an industry springing from the area's natural resources.

The sheep, the water, the wool and even the moss to dye it came off the moor and in the so-called Tavistock serges it produced its own distinctive coarse cloth. If in scale, its relationship to the Devon Wool Trade as a whole was small, it was a highly characteristic one.

The wool trade had peaks and slumps but in its best years in the 14th and 16th Centuries, it rivalled the tin trade in importance. So cloth incorporating Dartmoor wool was milled or 'fulled' in the towns and settlements of the moor's perimeter, but the carding and spinning of the raw wool, and often its weaving, was an industry of the cottage and lonely farmstead. For its beginnings the Dartmoor Wool Trade owed much to the Cistercians. The abbey now supports a community of Benedictine monks.

Buckfastleigh as a woollen centre producing serges, once had four mills, although by 1850 two were empty. Two streams flow to the Dart here and this was good for combers to wash their wool.

Buckfast Abbey was originally an extensive place and home in 1137 to monks of the Cistercian order, but after it was dissolved by Henry VIII the building fell into ruins, which in 1806 had been largely cleared away. The stone was used for building elsewhere and only after the First World War was the Abbey rebuilt.

The farmer Monks of the Cistercian Monastery at Buckfast (1137), introduced flocks on a big scale and/or their predecessors the Grey Monks. Flocks apparently soon appeared all over the country where suitable grazing could be found. Wool was set to become one of Devon's most prolific industries from the 12–18th centuries and was the backbone of its economy and wealth.

The Cistercian Monks of Buckfast Abbey ran their flocks on Holne, Buckfast and Brent moors and their brother Cistercians of Buckland Abbey owned much of the South West moor. The Benedictines of Tavistock owed much of their wealth to wool sales.

Moretonhampstead had a tucking mill before the end of the 13th Century, and Ashburton too about the same time. (where cloth was hammered to felt and shrink it). Now the woollen mill is a private residence at Moretonhampstead.

Tavistock serges were marketed under the towns name and by Tudor times kept fifteen mills busy. There were, in fact, tucking mills all around the moor. Sticklepath, Bridestowe, Belstone and Dean Prior all had tucking mills in the 17th Century and so did Widecombe which had a thriving cloth industry well into the 18th Century and also South Brent, utilising the wool of Dartmoor sheep.

Wool is woven deeply into Devon's historic economy. Though only blankets coming from Buckfastleigh into our own times. The last mill now left at Buckfast still spins wool producing yarn which goes to Axminster for the famous Axminster carpet manufacture.

Those early Cistercian Monks played a bigger part in shaping the country's history than any other influence before or since. They introduced Devon's most profitable industry. It is said the proceeds of wool built Bideford Bridge and probably its rival structure at Barnstaple.

It also founded Blundell's school and various benevolent institutions, while many stately homes and fine estates came into being upon the fortunes provided by the trade.

Buckfast Abbey was founded in the reign of Henry II on the site of a Benedictine abbey of Saxon days. 'Buckfaesten', i.e. Deerfastness the Saxon name given in A.D.1016. Cistercians were great wool-traders and did much for both trade and agriculture in the districts near them. It has been supposed that the 'SUNKEN TRACK' called the 'ABBOT'S WAY' was used in carrying the wool from the MOORLAND FARMS belonging to the MONASTERY towards Plymouth and Tavistock.

Looking after vast flocks was a responsible job, especially when one considers that a single monastery could sell more than 30,000 lbs of wool a year!

The Caunter Family

WEEKABOROUGH FARM, IPPLEPEN

Ram bred by C.E. Caunter and son. Prize winner Devon County Show (1960s). Held by Cecil Caunter with judge Richard Coaker. A winner in 1960, 1961, 1962 and 1963.

Cecil Caunter's father Ned farmed at Tunhill, Widecombe-in-the-Moor in 1898 when he married Florence Hannaford, where interestingly Whiteface Dartmoor sheep are still kept today. Ned Caunter also farmed Ring-O'-Bells Farm, Hexworthy at one point, which was to link their moorland rights to Weekaborough. Cecil's grandfather Albert farmed at Sweaton, Poundsgate.

Later the Caunters moved to Weekaborough, Ipplepen in 1905–6. This happened because Cecil's father went to take swedes at the farm and was offered the tenancy under the Duke of Somerset's estate. Cecil was born in 1907 and married Lucy Darke in 1930. Ned moved back to Hexworthy in 1939. Edward Caunter (Cecil's son) was born in 1941. June Caunter (nee Vallance) who became Edward's wife said that Whitefaces in the family probably go back to the later 1800's to early 1900's and were well in place at Weekaborough where the Caunters have farmed for 95 years, and the Whiteface Dartmoor sheep's attachment to this family is one of the oldest stories of their continuity as a pure breed.

So Cecil was born at Weekaborough and kept South Devon cattle and Whiteface sheep all his life, as do his grandsons, Adrian and John today, and son Edward and daughter-in-law June in the past. There is still a flock of around 170 Whitefaces at Weekaborough in the year 2000.

Wool was an important commodity and always stored every year on the farm to achieve a better price.

Cecil Caunter was a founder member of the Whiteface Dartmoor Sheep Breeders Association and became its first president. Cecil was the first member of the family to show. Rosettes and cups went hand in hand with sheep. Sheep were lorried to Devon County Show with their own lorry which was high sided and had an open top, and Cecil in the fifties, and father and son Edward during the sixties and seventies always came home with prize-winning sheep.

At the Devon County Show in 1978, C.E. Caunter and Son won the Interbreed Wool Competition with a pair of two-tooth hoggs and the Lloyds Bank sachet. Sadly Cecil was not to see this for he passed away on the 17th November 1977. The evening before, by coincidence or not and respectfully, Cecil had attended the Whiteface Breeders dinner!

Cecil had showed regularly at Widecombe and started a Whiteface class at Totnes Show, and in 1981 Messrs C.E. Caunter and Son won the Totnes Show Cup (a Whiteface Dartmoor Challenge Cup for best of breed).

Winning sheep for wool on the hoof.

Their moorland rights are still used from Hexworthy via the moorgate that takes them to Green Hill where the sheep are leared, the crest of which is 1555 feet above sea level. June tells the story of how sheep used to be driven from Weekaborough back to their moorland newtake grazing rights at Hexworthy and Green Hill during the summer months. With a distance of around two miles from the farm to the main road, the leader sheep would reach the road before the last sheep left the farm! Their instinct was so strong, the sheep knew what was happening and they were keen to get back to the moor. Sheep like to be moving up the

Devon County Prize Winner 1971, held by Edward.

Young Caunters in the line-up at Widecombe Fair.

hill, as the weather in the summer becomes warmer. Archie Mortimore, a brother-in-law of Junes also explained that one particular sheep and her lambs at Weekaborough when the time came in May to move up to Dartmoor and Hexworthy, would decide to leave the farm on her own to arrive at The Ring-O'-Bells ready for her moorland stay in the summer. Also she and her lambs would make their way home before the rest of the flock in the autumn! Green Hill is six miles and Weekaborough fifteen miles from Hexworthy.

Rough weather in the summer often drove the sheep back towards Hexworthy for three or so miles from their grazing area at Green Hill. Similarly in the autumn sheep might start moving towards home if gathering was late.

June said Edward's cousin 'Bart' set out with about sixty of their sheep from Weekaborough on one occasion but he became quite disillusioned on arriving at Cumpston Tor near Hexworthy because he found he had around one hundred and sixty sheep, because others had tagged along on the way!

Pitch marking on the sheep's wool was common practice to identify sheep, especially on the moor. It is important that sheep are kept apart after marking for the pitch to dry. June said that on one occasion the sheep got under a trailer and rubbed the pitch all over themselves! In the photographs below the C-C-mark is clearly visible! (Cecil Caunter).

Ewes and lambs went out to Green Hill after shearing at Hexworthy. All the family sheared and Phil Cleave helped at different times.

Edward Caunter, horse and dog, driving his Whitefaced Dartmoors on their summer pasture area around Green Hill.

Caunters Whitefaces make for an historic picture amongst the rolling pasture moor of Green Hill near Hexworthy.

June said Weekaborough wintered the sheep and they were summered at Green Hill near the Avon Dam, renowned as a grassy lear, as history has recorded. Sheep were driven and returned using horses and dogs. Sometimes other sheep came along with the Caunters sheep when gathered in late September to come home for weaning. June recalls having to gather sheep on horseback and finding it very difficult to get the sheep to cross where there was water and a stream. Once this was achieved the sheep knew their way home via Nakers Hill and Fish Lake Mire.

The practice of swaling in March June explained, took place on 'Down Ridge', the Holne side of Hexworthy. Her husband would light a huge 'bonfire' as June called the burning of the moorland vegetation. She spoke of the small areas of swaling that seem to take place today. This could be a problem because sheep could unwantedly drift away from their 'lears' to find another small area to graze. Whereas bigger burnt areas as done in the past would help hold the sheep, grazing the young regrowth. June also mentioned how rough and bumpy Green Hill was to ride her horse over and yet looking at the swathe of pasture shown in the lovely moorland photo's of Green Hill one could easily be fooled. She felt it was due to the pits left from cutting the 'peat vags', (from the peat ties) when taken off from the moors surface!

Having explained all this history it seems Green Hill itself was little burnt and the sheep stayed and seemed content with their 'leir' (a feed and resting place)!

Ned's great-grandsons, Adrian and John, taken at Totnes Show (1970s) with prize-winning ram hoggs. (Edward and June Caunter's sons).

Green Hill may also be reached from Princetown by way of White Works and Fox Tor. There is a natural path to Fish Lake between the fen and the bank of the Erme, on Green Hill, beyond which the way goes over the shoulder of Cater's Beam. It then crosses Nakers Hill (no doubt derived from 'naked hill' devoid of tor compared to other parts of Dartmoor), leaving the mire known as Little Anne to the right, a short distance from which it reaches the Hexworthy track at Anne Head.

In an Agistment Roll attached to an account of John D'Abernon, Constable of Lydford Castle and Custos of Dartmoor in the reign of Edward III, mention is made of the 'Preda de Irm' (Erme), so that we know that one of the recognised pasturage grounds at that time was in the Erme Valley, so Crossing writes in his guide to Dartmoor. This was not improbably Green Hill a little northward of the Erme Pound and within the forest.

The Abbots Way can be followed to Red Lake Ford near to the mire and Brown Heath. It is part of the old monk's road that the moormen generally refer to when they speak of 'Jobbers Path'.

Paths form a continuous way from the in-country at Cornwood to Hexworthy and the settled parts of the forest beyond, and are of great service to those engaged in looking after sheep and cattle pastured in the South-Quarter.

The presence of the Whitefaces here in numbers during the summer is where they thrived on the natural grasses of the moorland pasture that developed their constitution and to which the climate of the high moor is to their liking; a sheep very much in place, 'at lovely revisited places.'

My research on the showing of the Whiteface Dartmoor's at various shows where breeders like Cecil showed their sheep, led me to John W. Davis (who was 13 years as Bath and West secretary) who revealed the classes for Whitefaced Dartmoor sheep at the Royal Bath and West Shows (not however when at Shepton Mallet).

John said it appears that classes for the breed were only provided whenever shows were held in the particular South West area and when the Royal Bath and West was still a travelling show,

1954 – Exeter,

1955 – Launceston

1958 – Plymouth
Classes were scheduled at Cardiff show in 1956 but cancelled due to insufficient entries.
The exhibitors at the above shows were

1954 – L.S. Ball, Mary Tavy, Tavistock, C.E. Caunter, Ipplepen, Newton Abbot; French Brothers, Corringdon, South Brent; W.A.F. Webber, Hawson, Buckfastleigh; Miss S.C. Needham, South Cott, Manaton
1955 – Miss C. Boddington, Cecil Caunter, Miss S.C. Needham, F. Webber
1958 – C.E. Caunter, W.J. Doidge, Whitchurch, Tavistock, J. Savery, South Brent, J.K. Soper, Moreleigh, Totnes

In 1959 on the 8/9th October Cecil Caunter attended Harrogate Show in North Yorkshire with Whiteface sheep, possibly as an invitation to the W.F.D.S.B.A.!
These are some of Cecil and his family's cup and show successes:-

In the first year of the Association at the old Ashburton Market, 1st prize for Old Ram (1951).

1953 – C.E. Caunter – The Whiteface Dartmoor Sheep Breeders Association Challenge Cup presented by Messrs Sawyde & Harris for the best pen of 10 ewes. Also won in 1959 when presented by Richard Coaker.
In 1966, 1967 and 1969 the Whiteface Dartmoor Sheep Breeders Association Challenge Cup presented by Messrs Mann Bros. for the best ram hogg.
In 1972 under C.E. Caunter & Son (Edward), the family won the Whiteface Dartmoor Sheep Breeders Association Challenge Cup presented by Richard Coaker for the best pen of 10 ewes.

Mrs June Caunter with the ram hogg which was judged best in its class and the best coated. With another, it won the best pair of ram hoggs award.

A memorial cup in the form of a Perpetual Cup for the most points gained for sheep (ewes) and rams at the Association Show and Sale at Ashburton was presented by the family in Cecil's memory.

Headlines in the South Devon Journal (Wednesday, September 13, 1967 reads 'Three top prizes for Mr Caunter'. It also says 'Ipplepen Sheep Breeder Mr Cecil Caunter carried off three major prizes at the Whiteface Dartmoor Sheep Breeders Show at Ashburton.

He was awarded trophies for the best ram hogg, the best pair of ram hoggs and the best coated ram. He also won third prize in a competition for the best pen of 10 ewes. The paper also reported that the rest of the major prizes went to a hard-core of breeders; Irish Bros of Widecombe (Grendon), Richard Coaker of Runnage, Princetown; Mann Bros., Widecombe; W.J. French & Sons, Michelcombe and J. Savery, South Brent.

About 4000 sheep were auctioned overall during the day and prices were well up on 1966. Judges were Bob Kerwell, Mr H.G. Woodley (George) and F.H. Fox. Ram prices; Whiteface Dartmoors prize winners; 23 gns to 51 gns. Mann Bros. were 2nd in three classes.

A varied range of Widecombe breeders sold Whiteface Dartmoor ewes at Ashburton and quite large numbers of sheep sold per breeder in 1967.

Richard Coaker, 50 six-tooths realised £10.12s.6d. to £11.7s.6d. (Runnage)
W.J. French & Sons (Michlecombe) 70 four-tooths at £8.5s. – £10.5s.
Irish Bros. (Grendon) 30 six-tooths £9.7s.6d. to £10.1s.
C.E. Caunter 60 six-tooths £8.10s – £9.12s.6d.
R. Norrish (Sherrell) 30 six-tooths £9.1s. – £10.8s.
W. Hext (Pudsham) £9. – £9.15s.
S.E. Northmore (Ned) 40 six-tooths £8.10s. – £9.17s.6d.
J.S. Mortimore (Shallowford) 34 six-tooths and full £8.10s. – £9.10s.
Mann Bros. 34 six-tooths £8.12s.6d – £9.2s.6d.
H.J. Lentern 40 two-tooths at £10.7s.6d. – £10.15s.
Others to £8.17s.

The Whiteface Dartmoor Sheep Breeders Association Challenge Cup presented by Miss Needham for the flock of over 50 ewes was won in 1977 and 1981 by C.E. Caunter and Son and by Edward Caunter alone in 1979. Also the W.F.D.S.B.A. Brian and Julie Harris Memorial Challenge Cup for the best flock of ewe lambs was won by C.E. Caunter Esq. in 1970 and 1971. C.E. Caunter in the years 1960, 1961, 1962, 1963, was winner of the breed champion at the Devon County Show. C.E. Caunter and Son (Edward) also won in 1971 at the above show.

Also annual Flock Competition certificates were awarded for second in 1952, third in 1953, second in 1954 and 1955 for C.E. Caunter and Son.

In 1979 the flockbook records reveal, under Edward Caunter at Weekaborough, 121 ewes, 56 ewe lambs and 4 ram hoggs sired by a John Savery ram.

In 1980 140 ewes were recorded, 70 ewe lambs and 4 ram hoggs by a John Savery ram.

In 1982 the flock number peaked at 180 ewes; during this year an Archie Mortimore (F.A. Mortimore) ram was added to the Savery ram for its second year on the flock, having been purchased in 1981.

During 1986, 1987 and 1988 a P.W. Coaker ram sired the flock.

The photo shows William Caunter (Bill) of Sweaton, the youngest of the older generation of Caunters driving an exceptional flock of Whitefaces (horns and tails are evident) up the hill from 'Dartmeet' back to Sweaton from land farmed at Hexworthy. The road winding down to Dartmeet is visible, as is also the road to Hexworthy near the top of the photo' from whence the sheep came; (Huccaby and Brimpts in view).

On Dartmeet Hill, Dartmoor.
Whitefaced sheep in the early 1900s.

I think Mr Caunter is leading a horse!

Very few Whitefaces ever left their native homeland and not many of their owners either, but something that stirs the imagination was attendance at the Royal Show by a few breeders and their sheep when the show was still a travelling show in 1958 (before settling at Stoneleigh in 1963). Richard Coaker left Runnage, Postbridge, Dartmoor to judge the Whiteface classes at Whitchurch Airport, Bristol on July 1st to 4th. C.E. Caunter was first with a Whiteface shearling Ram and Yearling Ewes (shown in wool). First prize was £12, second £8, Third £6.

The first show held in Oxford in 1839 offered prizes of £30 maximum! In 2000 the prize money on offer was £35 – £25 – £17.

Records would indicate that there were no classes for Dartmoor sheep prior to 1890. (R.A.S.E. Phillip Sheppy).

The Royal Show came to Newton Abbot in 1952, but livestock classes were cancelled due to a Foot and Mouth outbreak. The judge was to have been W.J. Mann Lizwell. Entries were made by Len Ball, Cecil Caunter, John Coaker, French Bros., (Corringdon), Mann Bros., John Coaker (Sherberton), Miss Sylvia Needham, John Savery, and W.A.F. Webber.

Great Sherberton Coakers

HEXWORTHY, PRINCETOWN (ALSO SPELT 'SHERBURTON')

Whitefaces in the backyard at Sherberton, 1933. (left to right): Anne Coaker (now Anne Belam), Mildred, Teresa, Irene Coaker (Anne and John's Mother painting on the 'Coaker' mark with a stick. Ear notches can also be seen) and Penelope Ogle.

The Coaker family history can be traced back to at least c1691 and a marriage in Widecombe, moving from 'Bellever' (Bellaford) to Sherberton in 1845, taking their sheep with them. The Coakers possibly farmed at Hartland before Bellever. They farmed at the latter from the late 1700s. A picture painted of Sherberton near to the West Dart River, running beside the farm, in 1893, in Anton Coaker's Great Grandfather's day, has Whiteface Dartmoor sheep grazing in the foreground. The painter was a John White (R.A.) and the picture hangs on a kitchen wall at Sherberton. Such is the aura diffused by this unique settlement in the Moor, another artist 'Eve' Bygrave, now living in the toll house at Moreton, painted John Coaker, horse, dog and Whiteface Sheep, commissioned for Diana's (Coaker) 70th birthday. Diana married John Coaker. The steep lane winding up to the farmstead (seen at the top of the picture) is clearly visible. The house in 1907 was thatched. Below the house at Sherberton the Swincombe runs down to meet the Dart, where John is on his horse (Hello Dolly).

There is a sale poster of Albert Wilcocks' sale at Huccaby (his daughter was Mildred Wilcocks), which states that Whiteface Dartmoor sheep belonging to the family were for sale in the 1920s (probably 1925). It is recorded by Alison Coaker that the Scotch sheep and Galloways bred at Sherberton originally came with Mildred from Huccaby. She was very much a 'hands on' person, said Alison, and the above photo amongst the sheep clearly shows this. The 'bosses' hand can be seen pointing in the direction of the sheep, and the person is probably saying, 'there's one over there you've missed!'

John Coaker's outstanding passion for livestock and the Moor, and his continued interest in Whiteface Dartmoor sheep at the sales and fairs at Ashburton, Brent and even at Tavistock, resulted in him being appointed the Association's first Chairman in 1951.

Although John Coaker was a founder member of the Whiteface Dartmoor Sheep Breeders

John Coaker on Hello Dolly.
Painting by Eve Bygrave.

Association in 1951, Anton says his father's Scotch sheep and Galloways around the 1920s, began to see the Whiteface's decline at Sherberton.

However, Anne Belam, John's sister, recalls their father renting turnips and grass field runbacks from Uncle Gordon Coaker at Tristford, Totnes. Winter keep sales still take place today, but are only a shadow of their previous self.

John would also stay away from Sherberton sometimes for a whole month with their Whiteface sheep, and even lamb some away at places like Rattery, near South Brent. Diana Coaker's (John's wife) first impression of the 'Dartmoor Whiteface,' as she referred to them, was that, 'they were a bit active!' When turnips with an 'out-run' (grass runback) as Diana called it, was bought at the Kingsbridge Winter Keep Sales, it was not unlikely that the sheep would soon move themselves to a neighbour's field! Diana explained that keep sales (of grass, 'turnips', hay, corn and straw etc) were in the past very big sales and well attended by Dartmoor farmers, always needing to move their animals away from the Moor before winter set in.

John Coaker's Autumn Draft Sale was never later than the 15th September (or therabouts), and not without good reason, for little grass would grow again in that year, enough to feed a cow *and* her calf, until May or June of the following year, John's experience mirrored by the Moor's 'cutting edge' in winter.

Diana thought Ron Hill used his lorry to help take stock away to grass and winter keep. Many of the farmers in the Southhams would even lamb Whiteface ewes if asked by the moorland farmers, no doubt with a certain fee! She said the Dartmoor Whiteface was the

'Sheep in the side'.
Overlooking 'Swincombe Meet'. The River Dart (West) left and centre, and the Swincombe River on the right coming in to Meet the Dart (Swincombe Meet).

predominant breed when she arrived at Sherberton, because there was, at that time, little choice of what sort of sheep to keep.

As I quizzed Diana about the problems of sheep and snow, she remarked that she never had to 'dig a whiteface sheep out' at Sherberton, simply because they were being kept away to keep.

A workman called Reg and John did the shearing. Also Diana confessed to liking to shear herself too, especially the Scotties, because she could hang on to their horns.

Anton, she says, still turns sheep 'down the valley' (Deep Swincombe).

Inevitably the Moor's management and the practice of swaling was discussed by Diana. She distinctly remembers Peter Legassick helping things along by dragging a lit hessian bag behind his 'bay cobbey horse' he was riding ('a lighted piece of sack') to burn the Moor, and he could just drop the rope it was attached to if things became too warm and gallop away. This all happened at the top of Deep Swincombe towards Fox Tor.

Old photos suggest that dipping took place at Sherberton in the past.

An old diary writes, 'the sheep were also run through footbaths containing arsenic and pearlash' (oil-base) in 1908.

Caroline Belam produced the old family Inventory of 1829 (hurdled flocks). Many dates detail activities on the farm. Dates for example for drilling mangolds; June 2nd 1908.

It recorded too that in 1935 during June, 'it was very wet all through; very wet month, not a sheep shorn until 24th June'! There was very little scope back then for housing sheep to dry them off. A lot of shearing, before hay harvest, was expected to be completed early in June! The title of 'King of the Moor' was given to one of John's ancestors, (Great-Great-Grandfather) who it seems was called 'King of the Moor', because he was simply a big person! (1792–1871).

The family's Scotch sheep used the Moor rights near to Fox Tor and Deep Swincombe. The Whitefaces used the newtakes. The Swincombe River rises in Fox Tor Mire and pursuing an easterly course for about 3½ miles and flows into the West Dart at Sherberton Firs, says Crossing in 1888, the confluence of the two rivers.

The Whitefaces were re-established in 1997 through Alison Green (Anton's wife) and Dave Kingwell. The flock won second prize in the under 50's flock competition in 1998 in their first showing year.

According to Crossing: The estate of Sherberton which is one of the oldest Forest tenements, is situated on a tongue of land around which the West Dart makes a bold sweep. The ground rises rather steeply from the river in places. There were it seems formerly three tenements here called Sherborne 'or lying in Sherborne', (Swincombe) Shirburnecroft 1379. This form of the name is found as early as 1360. There is mention of 'Sherborne Wood' in 1358, 'Sherborn Croft' in 1416 (Sherborne Croft 1476). In Queen Elizabeth's time it appears as Shurbora, and 'Sherborne Foot' about 1521.

The names of Sherling, Shirebourne and Sherland are also met with, Gover, Mawer and Stenton: 'The place names of Devon' (English place names Society 1931) says that the name 'Sherborne' must originally have designated a piece of land or 'croft' by the Swincombe River.

Previous to 1301 a Joel Bird held a ferling of land at 'Sherling in Dartmoor'. In 1307 Walter Dernelof held a ferling and four acres at 'Shirebourne in the King's Waste of Dartmoor' and in 1349 Abraham Elyett paid rent, sixpence for two acres of land in 'Dunbridgeford', and one parcel of land upon 'Sherlond'.

It is seen from this that the Coaker family with 'Bellaford' and 'Sherberton' had their roots in the two oldest settlements carved out of Dertemora!

Sherberton has been part of the Duchy since its foundation in 1337, and a tenement of the Moor since 1307.

Anne Belam, sister to John Coaker, has bred ponies for many years and still has descendants of her Grandfather's Dartmoors.

She recalled field names at Sherberton like 'Clay' and 'Wood', and the sloping land running away from the farmstead and down to the 'meet' was known as 'out side' (abbreviated Devonshire); no doubt 'out along the side of the hill'!

Anne was born in the old house at Sherberton, now a stable, in 1925, and has ridden ponies for as long as she can remember. With her brother John Coaker she spent many hours on Dartmoor, and she said one of her earliest recollections was gathering sheep off the high Moor at Fox Tor which taught her how to ride. Whilst John rode the home bred geldings, Anne's job was to ride the mares.

At the Moorland Pony Show at Princetown in 2002 a pony 'Haida Honour Bound' won the Moorland Scheme Class. Its Great-Grandmother was given by Anne's Father to her son Alaric John Belam as a christening present.

'Return Journey', 1940. Driving sheep up the hill to Sherberton Farm. Left to right: Miss May and 'Punch', Mildred Coaker on 'Shannon', Pop-Frank (George Francis Richard) Coaker on 'Dreadie', Riderless native 'Dartmoor ponies' have inevitably joined the Coaker drift!

Expanding on her memories of riding across Dartmoor in all weathers, she remembers taking sheep from Sherberton to Combestone and onto Brent (South Brent) and the Southhams to keep, always moving animals to food-keep. Somehow she said, 'they seem to get there and cross the hazardous Moor'.

Such is the remoteness of this moorland tenement that in the winter of 1947, that started at the end of January, a car became stuck at the bridge approaching Sherberton and remained there in deep snow until March, and it seemed to be 'snow on to snow' so Anne Belam recalls.

As I climbed the steep lane that takes one up to Sherberton to attend John Coaker's annual draft sale every year, and where the high Moor seems to embrace the farmstead and this place apart, I too, began to imagine due to my own experiences in 1962/63 what the consequences of a severe blizzard winter might be at this isolated outpost for the people and the livestock. During the winter of 1962/63 the *Western Morning News* reports the feeding and rescue of 50,000 animals from freezing drifts, formed from seven to ten days continuous snowing. Diana and Peter Coaker said, 'it was an unbelievable time.' Diana recalls snow reaching the top of her outhouse and Peter at the age of nine remembers digging himself out of the back door and the snow being up to the upstairs windows. 'We had provisions because we thought we might not get out and we just accepted it, although we didn't expect it to come like it did' said Diana.

It is one of nature's most sudden and cruellest types of weather, and people and animals are bound to perish in these conditions, however much protection is provided.

Diana recalls men breaking down a wall in order to get out the Land Rover to cross the fields and reach the main road.

The whole sequel continues to grip the imagination and memories come flooding back too.

Whitefaces aside, one cannot sign off from writing of Sherberton without recalling something about Dartmoor ponies and Peter, Anton and Sue's mum Diana's eventual marriage to John Coaker, the WFDSBA's first Chairman.

The final Sherberton Pony Sale on the 17th November 2001 was the end of an era for the Coaker family. For 40 years pedigree Dartmoor ponies have been sold at the Sherberton Annual Fair, which has become a form of local tradition.

The ponies have been here for a hundred years, and one can trace lines right back with her husband's farming too.

John also went in a pony and trap to Ashburton. He was also schooled at Ashburton and stayed during this time with his mother's sister.

However, Diana is retiring from the Duchy owned farm. Anton is taking over the tenancy and all but twenty of the ponies and a handful in the trekking school will be sold.

Diana herself began breeding the ponies after the Second World War. She bought a Dartmoor pony at Exeter Market just for three guineas (some things don't change) and it was branded 1C, which didn't mean a thing to Diana (apparently the 1 represented or replaced a J that was not used in branding). She took it to Exmouth Show and the Coaker family from Dartmoor were there, who Diana had known for some time. Old Frank Coaker (John and Anne's father) came up and said 'that's Two Tails'. The pony had apparently been hand reared, and at one time had worn a skin of a dead foal in the hope that a mare would accept her, hence, said Diana, the name 'Two Tails'.

Skinning dead lambs and calves to 'hoodwink' the mother to take on another foster animal is still practised today to make use of the dam's milk. The skin is tied on the new progeny for two to three days.

'Two Tails' was eventually put on a train at Exmouth and met at Princetown by the Coaker family who put her with a stallion.

Diana explained that she had to go and visit her, and in so doing ended up courting John for seven years until they married and was to live at Sherberton.

She runs mares with a stallion in the 'Newtakes', open moorland enclosed by walls. The ponies run wild, but they will come into sheds to have their tails trimmed and become quiet very quickly. They seem to lear very tightly to their own area, with their recent colt following, and often a yearling close by too, year on year. And Diana explained, 'they never seem to forget where they are from, or where they belong, but I don't think they can actually think about the past, but if you bring them back year on year as with the sheep they can remember and remain on their lear.'

Diana says, 'we will always have ponies here'. Seemingly like the Whiteface sheep it's another lifetime bond, only this time with the pony, and the Dartmoor family.

Sue Martin (nee Coaker), John and Diana's daughter said, 'She was always helping her father drive something to keep somewhere!' She remembers bringing cattle through Buckfastleigh on one occasion, 'her father was on in front, as always, and the dogs bringing up the rear'. Apparently there was quite a disturbance, because someone had left their door onto the street open, and a bullock chose to enter and even went upstairs! As to the rest the imagination boggles!

Anne Belam's daughter Caroline now has her own Whitefaces too, at 'the Stole' Ludgate, Buckfastleigh, thereby continuing a tradition that is truly blooded in her Mother and family. 'A Strole or stroll' (also spelt 'strowl' earlier on) is a space between two enclosures. These are useful as affording shelter to cattle during stormy weather, an area also of service to the 'moormen' for driving cattle or sheep into occasionally for certain stockman's tasks, patiently funnelling them off the Moor into the Stroll. When newtakes have been formed on the banks of a stream, a stroll becomes necessary in order to permit the cattle and/or ponies reaching the water. Crossing also comments 'there are instances of land grabbers having turned strolls into enclosures'; probably because it only required the building of just one more wall to close the space between.

However, few things are sure in this life, and a reply to a letter I sent Alison and Anton during foot and mouth left a lump in my throat.

Anything that happens to farming to remove your neighbour's or your own animals by force more than hurts! A contiguous cull put Sherberton inside the ring.

However, Alison Coaker said, 'The support the Coakers received from the community helped them through some of their darker days'. She went on to say 'It was hard to let MAFF or DEFRA come into the farm,' as it must have been with all farms involved in the cull! It is really disappointing that such a devastating disease with also such far reaching social and economic consequences, and no fault of farmers here, should coincide with this book being written, and blinker the real dedicated world of animal husbandry and 'Shepherding' by farmers all over.

It is harder to understand all of this bearing in mind that Sherberton is such an ancient farmstead settlement born of a primitive nature 'when in existence *before* the bounds of the Forest were set out'!

'A Fair at Two Bridges' was researched by Caroline Belam. Two Bridges is the most important junction of the Moor. The roads from Moretonhampstead, Ashburton, Tavistock and Princetown come to it. But Two Bridges Hotel, originally an Inn and called the 'Saracens Head' was not built until 1822 by Sir Francis Buller, around fifty years after the roads in 1772 were constructed across Dartmoor. The Old Bridge could be early seventeenth century, so Vivian Smith in 'A Portrait of Dartmoor' records.

This Fair, or something like it taking place in the Moor's heart, not far from Princetown, Prince Hall and Wistman's Wood, could only be at its best in late August, as Summer is late to shed itself of retarded Spring, and before once again Autumn colours warn of yet another 'hard-grinding winter to come on the Moor'. Things look at their best around this Fair's date. Information on the Fair in terms of animals is revealing:-

TWO BRIDGES FAIR
Autumn – 21st August 1876
60 Store Wethers
20 Breeding Ewes
10 Steers
4 Heifers
30 good Dartmoor Ponies
at 2 p.m.
(1938 Sawdye & Harris West Street, Ashburton)

A truly remarkable inventory where sheep, cattle and pony record their place here at this time.

Nineteenth century hill farmers always called the ponies 'colts', something that has stayed up to today. The ponies were first mentioned in 1012 in the will of the Saxon bishop Aefwold of Crediton, who mentioned, 'the wild horses on the land at Ashburton'; and ponies are one of the oldest animals on Dartmoor along with the 'Dartmoor Sheep'. Perhaps some of the above mentioned are ancestors to the Coaker family's Dartmoor Ponies!

It seems a feature of Two Bridges Fair in the past was 'wrestling'. Apparently Dartmoor wrestlers wore shoes soaked in bullock's blood and baked to harden them like iron. Opponents legs could be shattered in moments! It sounds like 'a bridge over troubled waters'!

Of Widecombe this paper cutting says: 'the farmer, who in earlier days made the fair a 'Mecca' for business is well nigh a rarity – and little wonder!'

NORTHERN VISITORS

Village "Like Hampstead Heath"

While a powerful sun spread over the moorland, thousands were emptied in to this little village from hundreds of cars and motor coaches, some of which had timed their tours from the Northcountry to be at Widecombe for its greatest day of the year—the day when it ceases to be a village, and more than anything else resembles a miniature Hampstead Heath.

Widecombe Fair has remained the same in character for many years now.

MOCK AUCTIONEER.

It never ceases to attract visitors with plenty of time and inclination to stand by and listen to the blandishments of the mock auctioneer, and those other "generous" souls who frequent the green; to allow the blare of the loud speaker bellow the latest swing tune to fall on their ears; absorb the smell of fish and chips; shy at the coconuts, and eat fairing.

There can be no village in Devon that in one day holds so many people as Widecombe.

The farmer, who in earlier days made the fair a Mecca for business, is well nigh a rarity—and little wonder.

SALE OF SHEEP.

The sale of sheep that used to predominate to the extent of hundreds, has dwindled away almost to nothing. In fact this year it reached its lowest ebb.

There were not more than 40 sheep penned—three pens of ewes and a few rams.

The challenge cup for the best pen of white-faced Dartmoor sheep, presented by Miss L. Shannon, was won by W. Norrish, of Northway Farm, with L. Hannaford, of Blackslade, second.

First prize ram was shown by J. Moore, of Higher Gooseford, Whiddon Down, and the second by O. Mann, of Dunstone.

WINNING PEN.

At the subsequent sale by Mr. J. Sawdye, the winning pen of ewes realized 56s. apiece, and the remainder from 47s. apiece. Mr. Jasper French paid £7 for the prizewinning ram of Mr. Moore, £4 5s. for the second.

Mr. R. S. Fox is this year's president of the fair, Mr. C. C. Whitley chairman, Mr. W. W. Satterley hon. secretary, Mr. J. Hine agricultural hon. secretary, and Mr. T. Daw hon. treasurer.

The judges were:—Sheep, Mr. F. R. Coaker, Sherberton; ponies, Maj. Rendell, Ashburton, and Mr. Southwood, Torquay.

It is interesting to record that as a result of the fair a sum of over £80 has been handed over to charities in the last two years.

AGRICULTURAL SECTION.

One side of the day's programme that has been well maintained is the agricultural section and the gymkhana, which attracted many entries from a wide district.

The classes for Dartmoor ponies were particularly strong, and commended by the judges as fit for any exhibition.

RESULTS.

Agricultural classes, open.—Dartmoor stallions—1, E. W. White, South Zeal; 2, F. R. Coaker, Princetown; 3, Scott Bros., Chagford. Dartmoor brood mare, three years or over—1, Miss Anne Coaker, Princetown; 2 and 3, E. W. White, South Zeal. Dartmoor ponies, two years or under—1 and 2, S. Horrell, Yelverton; 3, F. Webber, South Zeal. Ponies, four years and under—1, W. J. Wedlake, South Zeal; 2, J. Dunning, Manaton; 3, Master John Coaker, Princetown. Ponies, not exceeding 14h.h., ridden by children under 15—1 and 3, Miss Cave Penny, Poundsgate; 2, J. Dunning, Manaton.

Local.—Farmers' riding class—1, T. Daw, Widecombe; 2, S. Norrish, Widecombe; 3, H. Rogers, Poundsgate. Brood mare, three years or over—1, C. Daw; 2, Miss Cave Penny; 3, H. Rogers. Children's riding pony, not exceeding 13h.h., ridden by children under 14—1, Miss Cave Penny; 2, H. Rogers; 3, D. Nosworthy, Widecombe.

Prize for best rider—Miss Verity Pease.

Agricultural horse or mare—1, F. Nosworthy, Widecombe; 2, R. Browning, Widecombe; 3, H. Chaffe, Poundsgate.

Widecombe Fair in the 1930s.
In the results section, Frank Coaker, Master John Coaker, Miss Anne Coaker etc, are mentioned.

The Coaker Family

BITTLEFORD, WIDECOMBE-IN-THE-MOOR

William Langdon, 1935–40, with Whiteface ewes, Dartmoor pony and faithful dog.

When Pat and Patrick came to visit Hazel and I to tell their Whiteface story, Patrick brought a couple of swedes. However, this can now be regarded as a root crop only grown on a very few farms around the moor as a main feed for sheep in winter and spring and, as such, has become a rare offering.

Yet in the past, hundreds of acres were 'pulled', carted, fenced and folded-off to sheep. Milder winters and grass growing all the while and the ease of conserving grass to make silage fed along with 'cake' (compound feed) has accelerated the shift away from root crops.

Swedes were prized as a feed to all stock and mangolds too when March east winds blow and cut (burn-back) the grass, as all other feed runs short, these come out of 'caves' like 'fresh oranges'. But Patrick didn't bring us any mangolds!

1705 is engraved on the fine old granite doorway at Bittleford, but it is the oldest 'settlement' in Widecombe and is mentioned in the 'Domesday'. Mrs Pat Coaker said her family, the Langdon's, are known to have farmed in and around the Widecombe area since 1830. An Edred Langdon is recorded at Lower Town in the first list of the Whitefaced Dartmoor Sheep Breeders Association members. Fern Langdon was Pat Coakers grandfather.

A very old parish directory of 'Devonshire' compiled by a certain John Hughes in 1857

Patrick and son, William; Widecombe Fair 1991.

includes a reference of John Langdon, farmer of Scobator (Scobitor) and Elijah Langdon, farmer, Foxworthy. This book belongs to Pat and Patrick Coaker now but was originally the property of William Langdon of Bittleford. So the Langdon's moved around Widecombe and were also farming Chittleford at one point, but for over a hundred years 'Bittleford' was the home farm, as it is again now for Pat and Patrick Coaker and their families.

Widecombe-in-the Moor is described together with the hamlets of Blackslade, Cator, Dunstone, Fern Hill, Linchford, Lower Town, Ponsworthy and Poundsgate (in the old Devonshire Parishes Book). Widecombe was further defined as a very large parish, 6 miles NW by N of Ashburton, with 13,165 acres of land of which 8,119 is common, 200 furze (gorse), 450 woods and 3,296 under cultivation. The population in 1851 was 974. Also called 'Withecombe-in-the-Moor' and (Wythecombe and Wydecomb) <1611, it has many lofty and bold rocks of which one is named 'Haytor'. Lintor rock it says was struck by lightning some twenty years since (approx. 1830) which shattered it very much. Underneath it runs the famed River Dart; a small river called 'Jordon' also runs through the parish. The east and west Webburns also flow 'Widecombe Way'. The East Webburn flows almost in the shadow of the Cathedral of the Moor', spanned by Northway Bridge. Lizwell Meet is where the two Webburns unite their waters, flowing on as the Webburn to join the River Dart.

Whitefaced rams at Bittleford (1930s), owner William Langdon, with the Moor rising in the distance.

Meanwhile Pat explains that her family farmed at Bittleford and were there in 1905 when it was let to William Langdon for £72.10s. However, at this time the farm was taken in hand and the Langdon's moved out to Langworthy for a short while in 1905.

In 1919 fourteen years later and just after the first world war, and after considerable new buildings had been done, the farm was let to Elisa Langdon for less money than in 1905 at £67.16s.

Pat and Patrick also revealed a fascinating sale inventory and prices from Foxworthy Sale (a farm farmed by Elijah Langdon in 1857) dated September 30th, 1844.

Interestingly, Langdon's were recorded as buying at the sale probably as incoming occupants. A cart was bought by a Mr Smerdon for £1.8s. A steer 'yarling' (yearling) sold for £3.0s. A cow and calf £7.5s and a rearing calf for £2.6s. A 2 year old heifer made £5 and a three year old steer £5.7s.6d. One Dartmoor Pony (3 years old) £4. Other property sold included a pair of chimney crooks, a corn hutch and a Hogshead (cider barrel) sold for 1s.2d. and another 1s.6d. In 1800 a labourer could expect 1s a week and a quart of cider as wages!

Number and prices of some of the sheep sold in the sale at Foxworthy 1844:

6 Wethers at 15/6 each	£4	13s.	
6 Wethers at 14/9 each	4	8s	6d
6 Wethers at 15/9 each	4	14s	6d
1 Wethers at 14/3		14s	3d
6 Ewes at 14/- each	4	4s	
6 Ewes at 15/- each	4	10s	
1 Ewe at 17/-		17s	
9 Lambs at 12/2 each	5	9s	6d
2 Ewe and Lambs at £1/2/- each	2	4s	
	£31	14s	9d

A Total of 45 sheep made £31 14s 9d

The above records a range of the sheep and their prices in the sale, also a ram sold for £1.6s (old) and 13 ram lambs made between 11–13s each and totalled £7.17s.

The total number of sheep sold in the sale was around 160 (lambs included). There is nothing to say these sheep are not Widecombes.

The Widecombe farmers' surnames at the 1844 Foxworthy Sale that purchased included a Mr Ford, Mr Hannaford, Mr Wrayford, Mr Chaff (now Chaffe), Mr French, Mr Hext, Mr Hamlyn, Mr Smerdon, Mr Coaker (he would be a bit too old now if it was Patrick!), Mr Stancombe, Mr Townsend, Mr Stockman, Mr Nosworthy and Mr Langdon. Several of these names are still active Widecombe names today, 2001, but several are missing and, as farms, were not succeeded by sons and were split up to be sold for different reasons to non-farming people, it is not difficult to see how the Widecombe sheep population declined in and around the parish over the following years. Some farmers, of course, retired and some moved away to other farms. Near to the date on Bittleford farmhouse is written 'R.T.' (Ricahrd Townsend).

Sheep returning from Winney's Down (1978) near to Merripitt Farm (Kenny Watson's). The lane leads to the 'Stannon newtakes'.

However, the Langdon family continued to keep Whitefaced Sheep and always took them up to Winney's Down and Broad Marsh which are Forest Rights of the East Quarter. Winney's Down is northward of Sandy Hole Pass; above the pass is Broad Marsh where Crossing said, Is an extensive stream-work at the lower end of which is an old tinner's building. The sheep were walked from Bittleford Widecombe to Postbridge through Merripitt Farm and Little Stannon (where the old sheep dip is sited) to Big Stannon and through a hunting gate to 'Winneys Down' which is on the left bank of the East Dart river. This involved a four hour walk about the 18th July, each summer.

The family through Pat and Patrick Coaker still graze this part of the high moor (the Forest) with Whiteface Sheep, in the year 2001, and are now the only Whiteface breeders to graze beyond the newtake walls. So as their predecessors grazed the Forest in 1830 every summer, so they still exercise their rights today, over 150 years on. 9d a year is paid to protect their Forest Venille rights.

Ewes and lambs are taken up to the moor, sometimes about mid-July and some for the Ashburton Sale are brought home around mid-August; the rest as late as the end of September. The sheepfold would be used to help sort the sheep, that graze the high moor.

'Sheepfold'. A young Clyde Coaker helping to 'fold' his grandfather's sheep at the Sheepfold, before its restoration in 1984. Sheep were being gathered from Winney's Down.

Pat's father (Bill Langdon) and grandfather, according to Sylvester Mann had several hundred, if not a thousand Whitefaces all told up to 1943, when William Langdon tragically died.

The farm was let to Sidney Trant until he died in 1960. He carried on with the same sheep and exercised the same rights. A very important photograph exists with the Soper family of Sid Trant, holding the winning cup for a ram at the second association sale in 1952.

Having got married Pat (nee Langdon) and Patrick Coaker moved back to the Langdon's family home at Bittleford on March 25, 1961. Pat said, 'We purchased the same Whiteface breeding sheep back in the previous autumn at the Trant's dispersal sale' (in fact it was Fred Trant (snr) that was then at Bittleford) originally bred by Pat's father, Bill Langdon.

The sheep purchased at the sale were added to through further buying at Ashburton Sheep Fair from Wilfred Hext (10 sheep) and from the French Bros, Corringdon, Brent (10 sheep).

A ram from Richard Coaker bought to use on the flock was bred by Leonard Ball of Axna (Mary Tavy). The ewes bought at the Bittleford Sale were in-lamb to a John Savery ram.

The flock has continued to remain pure and the Coaker's joined the Association in 1961. Patrick said the first Association Chairman (1951) was John Coaker.

Whitefaces from Bittleford were first shown at the Devon County Show in 1964 and the judge was Arthur Mann and a pair of ewes were awarded 2nd prize. Showing at Devon County Show has continued every year since. Probably the high point for the Coakers was in 1988 when one of their Whitefaces won the Interbreed Wool Competition judged on the hoof at Devon County Show, beating all breeds of sheep.

In 1973, 1979, 1986, 1989 and again in 1997 P.W. Coaker has achieved the breed champion winner with his Whiteface Dartmoor sheep at the Devon County Show.

Championships have been achieved at every show over their forty showing years; at Totnes, Cornwood, Widecombe, Ashburton etc. Yealmpton was won in 1986, 1988 and 1989 gaining the John Harris Trophy for the best Whiteface Dartmoor in the show. Also in 1989 the Totnes Show Cup (Whitefaced Dartmoor Challenge Cup) was won.

In 1994 and 1998 the Whiteface Dartmoor Sheep Breeders Association Challenge Cup presented by Miss Needham has been won for best flock of over 50 ewes.

Patrick said the sheep have improved in conformation and have kept their own characteristics; because defining with great feeling, Patrick said, 'That taking Whiteface

Breed Champion; Devon County Show 1997. Patrick with his grandchildren.

Widecombes to moor, the change of herbage keeps the sheep correct in character and health'.

I think that heavier stocking of the moor in the past with cattle and sheep and more organised swaling over days and even weeks, would have produced a far more even and sweeter pasture to graze than today. The streams and the cooling breeze of the high moor, together with a naturally manured herbage would combine to allow for contented animals agisted on the moor, and the 'sweetening' influence of the ash from the swaling' washed readily into the moorland peat.

Patrick's grandfather was one of the founder members of the South Devon Herd Book Society in 1891 and one hundred and ten years later South Devon Cattle are still kept at

A proud moment: Patrick with Champion hogg in the Wool Class at the Devon Country Show in 1988.

Bittleford and through the Langdon and Coaker families Whiteface sheep still grace the farm. So the origins of the same pedigree cattle and Whiteface sheep in the same families remains at Bittleford. Throughout this story many of the farms of Widecombe parish have boasted a 'marriage' of South Devon Cattle and Whiteface Widecombes, but not all pedigree stock, or the two native breeds, for so many years as at Bittleford.

Widecombe 1969. Patrick holding winning card and rosette. Judge Ken Soper (Gerald Owens is first from the right). Courtesy of *The Western Times and Gazette*, September 12th.

Wherever there are farms and farm animals, there seem to be 'characters' (character people) too. One such was Peter Hannaford who, at the age of 75–80 during the 1960's and 1970's, would always come to Bittleford in the spring and castrate the ram lambs. Also his pride and joy, Patrick said, was to select the best ram lambs for keeping and not castrating. He also cut off the lambs' tails and these he would take home to Ruby for her to make 'Lamb's Tail Pie'. Patrick said the next time we would see him he would return with a small bag of wool, that he (Peter) had cut off the tails before cooking! – it was worth more back then'.

Fred Trant junior now at Bridestowe, also remarked of Peter Hannaford's arrival, to castrate and cut lambs' tails. Travelling to many farms on a pushbike.

Patrick also pointed out that the lovely character ram, used as the front picture to the first Whiteface Dartmoor Sheep Breeders and Flock Book Association promotion leaflet, was at the time of photographing, in his ownership but bred by Cecil Caunter (see President's letter).

Widecombe Fair moved out of the village for a while between the two World Wars to 'Two Gates'. William Langdon on right of picture. Hameldon looks down on the scene.

Champion at Widecombe Fair, September 1966, bred by Irish Bros, 'Grendon', with Patrick and Rodney Harris.

Widecombe Fair has always been an important place to finish the years showing and the Coakers always returned with many winning trophies for their Whiteface Sheep both in the local and open classes.

Detailed in the Western Morning News after the Whitefaced Dartmoors Association Sale in 2003, the headlines read, 'White Face young ram's record':-

A 'world record' for a purebred Whitefaced Dartmoor ram hogget was established at Newton Abbot at the end of August.

The animal was consigned by P. and W. Coaker of Widecombe, and was sold following the show for 760 gns, after, it is reported, some spirited bidding, to Arnold Cole of Yelverton, another registered breeder of Whitefaces.

Autioneers Sawdye and Harris reported a tremendous demand for this popular local breed with a large turn-out of buyers. 2T ewes sold to £61 (average £49–61) for N.C. Warne and Son. Older ewes went to £51 for Phil Abel while W.F.D.-cross-Suffolk shearlings made £69 for P.R. Coaker.

SHOW RESULTS:
Best ram hoggett – P Abel (£220) Best Old Ram R.G. Tregear (£168).
Best Pen of Ten Ewes – P. & W. Coaker (£50)
Best Coated Ram – P. Abel (£550.50)
Best Pair of Ram Hoggets bred by exhibitor – G. Goddard (£385.35)
Best Pen of 2T Ewes – T. Phipps (£60).

Philip Coaker and Family

RUNNAGE, POSTBRIDGE

Richard Coaker proudly among the Coakers unmistakable Whitefaces. From the collection of John Hamlyn via Tom Greeves.

Runnage is recorded in the Domesday Book of 1086.

As early as 1304 it would have had a tenement status, as an old settlement site. Although the present farmhouse at Runnage is fairly modern, an earlier building was destroyed by fire in 1868. Its name 'Renewych' (later Runnage) was first recorded in the 14th Century. Some historians think these Dartmoor tenements recall Bronze Age habitations on the Moor. Subtle changes in name spelling also record Runnage as spelt 'Rennidge' in 1702.

The Coakers have farmed Runnage since 1843. It is the general feeling of the family that Whiteface sheep came with the Coakers, the only sheep breed kept in the past, from Cator in 1843.

Philip is the fifth generation of Coakers to work Runnage Farm. Philip and Christine's son, Richard, is the 6th in line. Philip was at school in Tavistock when his father died on January 12th 1978. The only child of Richard and Alice Coaker, the Duchy of Cornwall as landlords, transferred the tenancy to Mrs Coaker, as Philip was under age at only sixteen years old at the time.

From the start Alice and Philip pursued quality, as Richard did, for he was a wonderful stock and showman; selling their sheep at Ashburton and gaining many prizes in the show and sale. It has been said of Richard Coaker that he ran sheep from 'Darthead to Dartmouth'. Sheep were summered up the West Bank of the East Dart around Lower White Tor to Cuthill and out onto Winney's Down, using the Moor's grazing. Winter keep in the form of swedes and grass run-back, was taken away on the red soil in winter, and in other areas.

Philip's Father and Grandfather were 'agisters' on the East Quarter of the Forest of Dartmoor from around 1900 onwards (Richard Coaker, at 21 years of age, was the youngest

Mrs Coaker and Philip. Taken from the front page of *South West Farmer*, September 1985, issue no. 53. Copyright West of England Newspapers Ltd.

Whitefaces in the shadow of the redundant cartwheels.

Sheep on Runnage bridge.

Agister ever of the East Quarter.. Philip's Father was involved from a very early age with the family's Whitefaces. He was schooled at Totnes Grammar School. This meant a journey, often on horseback, to Ashburton from Runnage to catch the train to Totnes. Richard's horse was left at Ashburton to ride home for the return journey to Runnage.

Using land at Ashburton for grazing meant that sheep often had to be brought back to the home farm at Postbridge and this Richard regularly did after school using his horse. No doubt, particularly in Spring, sheep had to be driven to keep at Ashburton, and the procedure reversed in the Autumn. Hence Richard is seen wearing his school cap.

It is said Philip's Grandfather, Adolphous Coaker, used to ride his horse to Moretonhampstead and to the Plymouth Inn for stabling and then catch the train to Newton Market. Horse stabling in these old 'travellers' rest places, would no doubt have accommodated lairage, and 'Coaching houses' like the White Hart Hotel, Moreton, were also providers. Their own sheep were put out on to Broad Down up until 1976 when the practice was discontinued because too many sheep went missing and were never found again, and Richard then decided not to stock the Moor again. Philip said if a sheep could not be accounted for, his father would ride for days, even if it meant just finding the smallest of remains of wool and bone; going out to check the sheep very regularly. Access to the down was through the Stannons Newtakes (Stannon, little and big or great), beside the East Dart River and through the gates near Siddaford Tor, also pronounced 'Sittaford', at an elevation of 1,764 feet.

All hands on the wool bags (sacks) at 'Runnage'. John Hamlyn is one of the helpers.

Philip explained the sheep needed to come home before the river became too high in the Autumn. However, it seems some sheep were impatient and sensed bad weather and often came home of their own accord. The Whiteface sheep were very 'moorwise' like all animals leared on the high Moor. These rights at Runnage rising to 14–1760 feet above sea level, can see rapid changes in the weather. Fog and mist can blot the Moor out within minutes. In the past Whiteface sheep were kept in small flocks and the wethers (castrated males) were allowed to grow on for their wool over several years. They were kept until fat or the price of their wool was right. The wool clip would pay for 12 months rent to the Duchy of Cornwall. One particular old stone barn at Runnage stored the wool in the dry for many months, until the price was favourable to sell.

Richard sometimes made use of the proximity of his fields to Ashburton Market to shear some of the sheep in the old market pens.

Once the Whiteface Dartmoor Sheep Breeders Association (and originally flock book) was formed in 1951, the showing of sheep seemed to increase in interest. It's intriguing to think that only a very few

Whitefaces ever left their native county of Devon, and not many of their owners either! However, showing produced one reason to travel, and when the 'Royal Show' was still a travelling show in 1958 (before settling down at Stoneleigh in 1963), Richard Coaker left Runnage Postbridge, Dartmoor to judge the Whiteface classes at Whitchurch Airport, Bristol on July 1st–4th. C.E. Caunter was first with a Whiteface Shearling Ram and Yearling Ewes (shown in wool). First prize yielded £12, Second £8 and Third £6.

The first Royal Show held in Oxford in 1839 offered prizes of £30, and £10 for the best and reserve in each sheep class, but by 1890 it dropped to £15 for first prize, £10 and £5. In 2000 the prize money was £35, £25 and £17.

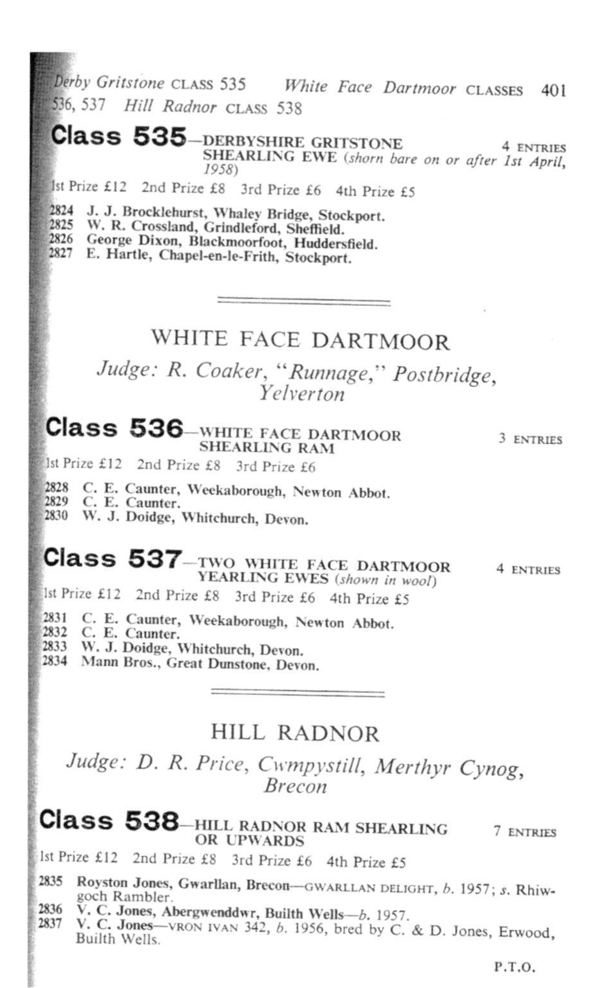
Derby Gritstone CLASS 535 *White Face Dartmoor* CLASSES 401
536, 537 *Hill Radnor* CLASS 538

Class 535—DERBYSHIRE GRITSTONE SHEARLING EWE (*shorn bare on or after 1st April, 1958*) 4 ENTRIES

1st Prize £12 2nd Prize £8 3rd Prize £6 4th Prize £5

2824 J. J. Brocklehurst, Whaley Bridge, Stockport.
2825 W. R. Crossland, Grindleford, Sheffield.
2826 George Dixon, Blackmoorfoot, Huddersfield.
2827 E. Hartle, Chapel-en-le-Frith, Stockport.

WHITE FACE DARTMOOR

Judge: R. Coaker, "Runnage," Postbridge, Yelverton

Class 536—WHITE FACE DARTMOOR SHEARLING RAM 3 ENTRIES

1st Prize £12 2nd Prize £8 3rd Prize £6

2828 C. E. Caunter, Weekaborough, Newton Abbot.
2829 C. E. Caunter.
2830 W. J. Doidge, Whitchurch, Devon.

Class 537—TWO WHITE FACE DARTMOOR YEARLING EWES (*shown in wool*) 4 ENTRIES

1st Prize £12 2nd Prize £8 3rd Prize £6 4th Prize £5

2831 C. E. Caunter, Weekaborough, Newton Abbot.
2832 C. E. Caunter.
2833 W. J. Doidge, Whitchurch, Devon.
2834 Mann Bros., Great Dunstone, Devon.

HILL RADNOR

Judge: D. R. Price, Cwmpystill, Merthyr Cynog, Brecon

Class 538—HILL RADNOR RAM SHEARLING OR UPWARDS 7 ENTRIES

1st Prize £12 2nd Prize £8 3rd Prize £6 4th Prize £5

2835 Royston Jones, Gwarllan, Brecon—GWARLLAN DELIGHT, *b.* 1957; *s.* Rhiwgoch Rambler.
2836 V. C. Jones, Abergwenddwr, Builth Wells—*b.* 1957.
2837 V. C. Jones—VRON IVAN 342, *b.* 1956, bred by C. & D. Jones, Erwood, Builth Wells.

P.T.O.

Royal Show (cover) 1958 and Whiteface Dartmoor (page 401) classes 536 and 537.

Records indicate that there were not classes for 'Dartmoor' sheep prior to 1890. The Royal Show's motto, i.e. 'The Royal Agricultural Society of England', advocates 'Practice with Science' in Agriculture, something that can't be separated even today!

Widecombe Fair, formed in 1850, was the main attraction for showing in the past in the context of a fair, and sales took place amongst the farmers on the village green, and later in 'the field', but latterly only as a show, with the Church in view. It was also staged at 'Two Gates' for a few years in its history, near Wooder, Widecombe.

The Ashburton W.F.D.S.B.A. sale allowed members' and breeders' sheep to be on view and to offer them for showing and sale.

1989. Philip at Ashburton showing his pair of Hogg Rams – John and Peter Hearn judging.

Richard Coaker was President of the W.F.D.S.B.A. from 1961–1967.

For Richard Coaker this was the highlight of his sheep year and reward for his sheep management. The Whiteface Sheep were his pride and love and leave an indelible mark on a 'born stockman'. They were even more important than his South Devon Cattle.

Philip also explained that the Whiteface Dartmoor Sheep would be the last thing to leave his farm. So he too, obviously inherited his father's passion for sheep.

Richard first won the Whiteface Dartmoor Sheep Breeders Association Challenge Cup presented by Messers Sawdye and Harris for the best pen of ten ewes in 1956. This followed W.A.F. Webber (1952), Mr C.E. Caunter (1953), Messers Mann Bros (1954) and Leonard S. Ball (1955). Richard's success was to continue into 1957, 1958 winning the above cup on four occasions. This Challenge Cup he won outright and this achievement he repeated twice more (winning three Challenge Cups) with the best pen of ten ewes.

In 1959, therefore, he presented his own Challenge Cup, won in that year by Cecil Caunter.

Some of the many successes at Runnage for the family, in the form of Whiteface Dartmoor Sheep trophies.

Again in 1960, 1962, 1963 and 1965 Richard was returned the winner and became the owner of his second Challenge Cup.

Another Challenge Cup was presented by Richard for the best pen of ten ewes. This was won in 1967 and 1969 by the Irish Bros (Grendon). Richard again won this cup four times; in 1968, 1973, 1974, and 1975, and recorded him the third Challenge Cup won outright.

In 1975 Richard also won outright the Whitefaced Dartmoor Sheepbreeders Association Challenge Cup presented by Messers Mann Bros for the best Ram Hogg, having also won it in 1965, 1972 and 1974, thereby winning four Challenge Cups at the Ashburton Show and Sale from 1955 to 1975.

Richard was to win for the last time himself the Association's Challenge Cup for the best pen of ten ewes in 1977. However, in 1979, 1980, 1983 and 1986 Alice and Philip Coaker also won the Association Challenge Cup for the best pen of ten ewes, continuing family success.

This completed the winning of four Challenge Cups for the best pen of ten ewes bred at Runnage. Philip also won in his own right, the 'Richard Coaker Memorial Cup' for the best pen of ten ewes, presented as a Perpetual Cup to succeed the original Challenge Cups won by his Father. Something he was very proud of.

Also at Totnes in 1987 the Whiteface Dartmoor Challenge Cup at their local show class, was won by the Coaker family. The sheep offered in these sales were gathered from the Moor in early August, and their lambs weaned. Mainly six-tooths were offered for sale; big strong sheep with two seasons breeding at least left in them, no doubt benefiting from their winter stay on roots. Foster, Caunter and Kerswell to name but a few, were buyers who liked his sheep and of course local breeders too!

Richard judging at Widecombe Fair, 1968.

The appearance, on odd occasions, of a black sheep is part of the true folklore of the breed. Philip said until a black sheep is born into the flock, the flock could not be regarded as being pure (an unusual anomaly!). Black spots are more usual on the ear, near to the eye and with a black leg or part black tail or black neck etc also depicting purity over many hundreds of years, they say!

To assist their welfare, summer and winter dipping took place, even more common than today, to rid sheep of external parasites and maggot fly in summer and scab in winter. Oiled winter dips help to shed winter rains and condition the fleece. Winter dipping and 'moorland clear days' (clearing the Moor of sheep for several days) ensured all sheep were dipped. Compounds such as arsenic and later dieldrin and organophosphorus were used in a water dilution. Dips built in the moorland newtakes (and on many farms incountry) all around the Moor meant sheep would not have to be moved too far during hot summer days. One such dip was built by Philip Coaker's Grandfather Adolphous inside the lane gate of Little Stannon Newtake that leds to Stannon Lodge and the Sheepfold. This dip was thought to be built around 1900 and was used as a communal dip by all the graziers of the Moor nearby. Another example is to be found at Teignhead. Philip recalls having a day off from school and regarded it as the highlight of the year to help with the dipping. Pitch mark 'M' identifies Mann's sheep (dip photo).

Some of the sheep would have been held up in the sheepfold (built in the sheep's fold newtake) to fast them before dipping. Others are shown in a photo, belonging to the Coaker family, shows Richard and others drifting sheep into Stannon newtake, now farmed by Ken Watson, before being encouraged to be dipped in the adjoining Little Stannon newtake.

Richard Coaker collecting sheep for dipping, drifting into Little Stannon from Big Stannnon. Another flock higher up in this unique photo.

The 25th July or thereabouts is a popular date for summer dipping, because maggots and ticks can trouble sheep into October and dipping before this time can mean the dip's chemical strength running out and leaving the animal vulnerable to parasites. Sheep stay in the dip for at least one minute, and their heads placed under twice.

Also a roll of netting was thrown around the dip as a makeshift pen to hold the sheep before dipping and to help keep them near to the catching pen. The dip appeared to be made of stones along its sides, and with a floor of granite stone slabs.

There was a lot of barking of dogs and shouting of people and sheep coming from all directions to get an early place in the dipping line up (some from off the Forest of Dartmoor). This was because as Mrs Coaker Snr said 'after 1200 sheep were dipped, the dip water looked like 'pea soup' and no doubt losing its efficacy'. Dipping would start before sunrise before it became too hot; and with that number of sheep one would hope that you were not last with your sheep in the 'soiled dip'. Sheep it seems appeared from every ridge, and 'yodelling-like' cries of the moormen riding their rough ponies could be heard far and wide, coming off the 'Forest' and newtakes. (says Vivian-Smith Dartmoor).

The Coaker family reserved the right of the dip and Richard was in charge of the dipping. The dip is some 15 feet long with steps up to the draining pens, but only 1'6" wide. The sheep

Dipping at Little Stannon, with a well-organised hurdle pen to contain the sheep and guide them towards the catching pen. (Ex-John Hamlyn Collection, courtesy of Tom Greeves).

couldn't turn around in the long narrow dip and had to move through. A hurdle used to be placed across the dip to stop the old wise sheep rushing past the dip bath! Richard dipping (above).

A cement inscription reads 1971 etched on the cement on top of the wall where the sheep used to exit to the original draining pens. As the sheep left the dip, someone operated a parting gate to help fill two draining pens (see photo). Once drained the first pen would be released, whilst the other pen of sheep drained off their dip, and the first pen, filled of dipped sheep again! Philip said, 'he remembers often operating the parting gate'.

These pens are just recognisable and are formed on a half circle to the boundary hedge, and two gates, one from each draining pen (at the opposite end to the parting gate) allowed sheep to run back to Little Stannon Newtake after dipping. These pens slope towards the dip to avoid too much dip being lost. Obviously the 1971 inscription was when the dip was renovated (now 100 years old), and Philip saw his father inscribe with a stick.

The original dip is a lot older and very much made of stone, built like a Moor wall and only later cement rendered, so Fred Hutchings recalled, who used to rent Little Stannon Newtake.

Kenny Watson said the dip hasn't been used for some twenty years and is filled in with earth and sand washed down from the streams that used to be diverted to fill the dip. The parting gate for shedding sheep to drain and the surrounding wall have also deteriorated and collapsed. Cattle and animals all around would also have rubbed its walls down and poached around the dip area. Now a memorial to the hard work of dipping sheep.

A Scotsman, introducing flocks of Scotch Sheep, built a fold on the West flank of Stannon Tor. The sheepfold has now been recently renovated and restored and is an imposing piece of granite enclosure, seen as one approaches it from within the sheepfold's Newtake. The wall is double-skinned and of considerable height and thickness. Every 9–10 feet a large granite post is let into the wall. From outside the fold none of these 'gatepost-like' slabs can be seen, hidden by the complete outer skin of the sheepfold wall. But they seem to support the stones carefully placed between them, and add strength to the fold.

Sheepfold (Sheepfold's Newtake) under Stannon Tor.

The fold was supposedly built in the early 1800's to shelter and protect sheep from wolves and thieves, and to make-up dung. The word 'fold' is a very old English word and found in biblical readings and suggests protection; to place or keep sheep in a fold.

Somewhere about AD900 the Saxon kings made the Dartmoor heartland a royal hunting ground and it seems that it formed a 'fastness for wolves and other wild animals'. Venison was prized too from its deer. Wolves it is said were hunted as late as the reign of Elizabeth 1st. Crown tenures, perhaps Philip's ancestors included, provided arrows to the King when he came to hunt in the Forest.

Folds could have been in evidence from very early times. The crude feature of a fold could have existed at the 'sheepfold', on this very site, many hundreds of years previous, involving shepherd and King. A tumbled, and weathered older inner wall, suggests a previous enclosure.

Also forms of agistment here at the sheepfold may have occurred before even the newtake walls were built amidst a very wild and intimidating Moor.

Over many years it has certainly provided a handling pen for Whitefaces coming onto the Moor, and when rounded up to return to their farmstead homes, while strays were found, and for dipping collection. Fred Hutchings said 'any amount of Whitefaces came up from Widecombe to summer on the Moor.'

Stannon Tor rises to 1517 feet above sea level close by the sheepfold, such is the country of the original Whitefaces, where they co-existed with raven and pony.

Whiteface (and Dartmoor sheep) have sometimes been spoken of as 'scavengers' but they are without doubt an exceptionally hardy breed and have an excellent constitution. They can thrive on very scanty fare; the herbage of the Moor (heather apart) on which they have to subsist constitutes chiefly of lichen, moss, cotton grass, small fescues and other varied and minor plants and molinia.

Runnage was undoubtedly one of the important focal points for the 'drifts', that came and left Dartmoor, and from where sheep and cattle were spread around their agisted newtakes during high summer. The lovely expression given to the movement of sheep to and fro the Moor and from Dartmoor Southwards ('down-country') is the 'White Tide' and one can imagine this wonderful 'ebb and flow' of 'white bodies' as they instinctively follow track and lane and are guided by shepherd, horse and dog.

Reserve champion, Devon County 1991.

A piece of local history relates to 'Ephriam's Pinch' near to Runnage, as recorded by William Crossing.

Ephraim's Pinch can be found following the lane to Runnage Bridge from Post-bridge, and by turning right from the main road just before it enters the common.

Following the lane to Runnage Bridge and across Sousson's Common, one can reach Ephraim's Pinch. Ephraim's Pinch is a hill, and a story relates to its name. A man named Ephraim laid a wager that he would carry a sack of corn from Widecombe to Post Bridge, some 5 miles without dropping it! On reaching this hill after completing 3½ miles of his journey, he found the 'pinch' too much for him and he had to drop the corn on the ground!

Crossing is also excited by the area around Runnage and the small group of ancient holdings around about. Pizwell for example, is just a stone's throw away from Runnage and is referred to in 1260 as a village. The old buildings and longhouse are still as they appeared in centuries past. In 1300 the name appears as 'Pishull'. A custodian of the Forest, John de Tresympel writes concerning, 'one clawe of land containing 8a. land at Pishull', (the permitted area of newtake to be added to a holding at any one time). It is also stated to be the duty of the holder, John Renewith to manure it the following year. In 1346 another enclosure was made at Pizwell by John French.

Having studied some of the fascinating Runnage history, it could be said that John Renewith gave his name to the present Runnage's first settlement, 'Renewych'.

A long way on from the above history is shown here in 1989 and 1991 with Philip Coaker.

The Exeter Ram Sale 1989. Continuing the Coaker family history of breeding rams at Runnage.

Philip winning the Whitefaced Dartmoor Challenge Cup at Totnes in 1987. In one year he won five cups.

Understandably, considering the young age at which Philip had to start farming at Runnage, through his father's untimely death, and reflecting on the almost unprecedented occurrence of five generations of the same family that have cared so passionately for this land, it has developed in him a character of immense depth, strength and sensitivity.

I can feel this myself with sheep and cattle we both keep, but for the people, I have to 'step outside', and honour, respect and remain humble and always admire!

Being conscious of this inheritance all around you, all the time, cannot be without its pressure. The responsibility is helped by experience over the years. Philip said, 'he felt this most when he went ploughing a field at Runnage; quickly his mind would flash back to when all his ancestors would have ploughed the same field, of which now five generations were Coaker's at Runnage.'

Christine Coaker, Philip's wife, also helps on the farm at Runnage, especially at lambing time and shares similar feelings for the sheep and the farm as Philip. To sustain such continuity; health, commitment, dedication and some good fortune are needed, and combine to achieve and shape this quite extraordinary history of endurance, reward and vigilance through care!

Philip talked too of John Hamlyn who came to Runnage when he was nine, and who eventually worked their all his working life (helping to lamb the sheep in his eighties). He lived until he was over 100 years old. At about that age he was still mobile. he came back to Runnage and Philip took him up in one of his fields that looked down on Philip's big stock

'That's home to Philip'. Runnage Field, Whitefaced Dartmoor sheep, Runnage Bridge, South Devon Cattle, Dartmoor Ponies and six generations of Coaker (including Philip's son, Richard).

shed; Philip remarked to John Hamlyn, 'what do you think my father would think of that' and John wryly replied, 'what do you think your *Great* Grandfather would think'!

John Hamlyn had lived to know four generations of the Coaker family: Richard, Aldolphous, Richard and Philip!!

It was a sobering thought when Philip reflected on the Ephraim's Pinch story. Philip thought the sack was full of flour and not corn bound for Postbridge, for them to bake into bread. Philip explained the journey might have been in bad snow! The fact the flour didn't arrive could have had serious consequences for the village people! The community spirit though is strong here in 'Dartmoor's heart'!

Another version of the story suggests that in order that a young man could marry a local farmers daughter, he had to carry a full sack from Widecombe to Postbridge, without dropping it! It seems he might have had to do it all over again!

The Cole Family

GREENWELL FARM, MEAVY, YELVERTON

Whiteface Dartmoors at Greenwell Farm, Yelverton by Matthew Cole, age 26, Year 2000

There are over 125 Whitefaces on Greenwell in 2000. We run about 60% pure and the rest we cross with a Suffolk. They lamb at the end of February and we lamb at between 150% and 170%. The lambs are sold fat at carcass weights of between 35 and 40kg. We maintain our flock when other breeds appear to be in favour because they occupy a niche in the market. They produce a better lamb carcass and lambing percentage than other hill breeds. If managed well they can produce 170% lambing percentage which competes with other higher performance breeds. The lambs will fatten at grass, they thrive on the very edge of Dartmoor and will summer graze the Moor once lambs are weaned. They also have a very good temperament and are very easy to work with. Indoor lambing of some of the Whitefaces takes place, and fed on silage.

Whitefaces in a shed at Greenwell.

Origins of the Flock

My Grandfather Henrie H. Cole first introduced Whitefaces to Greenwell when he used Whiteface rams on his flock of Closewool in the late 1950s. The flock was started from here. My father, Arnold H. Cole, recalls he also purchased 10 pure ewes from Ashburton Show and Sale in the early 1960s for £10–£15 each. The flock, although its origin lies with Closewool ewes, was considered a flock of Whitefaces and the ewes were as good as pure from the early 1970s. The flock was maintained at Greenwell and the flock was first registered with the Society in the early 1980s. Once we were persuaded to register our flock we became much more interested in the breeding of sheep, breeding our own rams and we started to exhibit at

Left to right: Arnold and Bridget Cole (Tim Stokes, friend) and Matthew Cole. The ram gained the Reserve Breed Championship at the Devon County Show 1990.

Verney Points Cup won by A.H. Cole in 1995 at the Devon County.

shows. We started with Devon County Show in 1988 and progressed to exhibit at all the local shows until this day and intend to do so for the foreseeable future.

In 1995 A.H. Cole won the Verney Points Cup at the Devon County Show. This was for the most points gained in *all* sheep classes. The winner of this cup (ram) was used in a photograph to promote the Whiteface Dartmoor Sheep and its Association on an updated leaflet in the mid-late nineties.

Arnold's Whiteface exhibits at the Devon County Show that year (1995) gained first and second in every class. He was only beaten in the old ram class and that was by a ram that was also bred by him and had been sold the year before. But second and third were also his placed sheep in the old ram class. A.H. Cole gained three champion winners over five years at Devon County. The Cole family added to their 1995 Devon County Show success as winners of the breed champion in 1998 and 1999.

Matthew Cole with Champion ram at Yealmpton Show 1996.

In the Flock Book record of 1979, ewe lambs were sired by a John Irish ram and the sires of 43 ewe lambs in 1985 was shared between John Irish and an Adams and Howell ram, with 50 ewes in the flock. The John Irish ram continued to sire 25 ewe lambs registered in 1986.

With 86 ewes in the flock in 1987 a Henry Bond sire was used to breed 23 ewe lambs. Thirty four ewe lambs were bred using a Norman Warne ram and at this point the flock had risen to 100 ewes.

For the age of the flock the Show success has been immense. The John Harris Trophy presented at Yealmpton Show for the best Whiteface Dartmoor Sheep in the Show was won in 1996 and 1998 by A.H. Cole.

Successes at Totnes, Ashburton and all the shows has combined for the Points Cup to have been won for overall most points including the Devon County Show and at all the shows through the year. In the year 2000 and 'Wool on the hoof', A.H. Cole won second prize for the woollen exhibit of the Whiteface Dartmoor breed.

The W.F.D.S.B.A. Challenge Cup presented by Miss Needham for best flock over 50 ewes was won as early as 1987 and again in 1996 by Arnold and Matthew Cole together that year

Champions (female) Yealmpton 1998 (also Champions Devon County, Cornwood and Okehampton). Judge: T.A. Phipps.

with the Brian and Julie Harris Memorial Challenge Cup for the best flock of ewe lambs. The best flock over 50 was also won in 2002.

The Cole family again won the best flock of ewe lambs judged on the farm in 1998 and 1999. A new 'Millennium Cup' presented by Hazel and Colin Pearse for the Champion Sheep (as a perpetual Challenge Cup) in the Whiteface Class at Cornwood Show year 2000, was won by A.H. Cole in its first competitive year.

Matthew was just 11–12 years old when he went with his father and their sheep to the Bath and West Show. He learnt the technique of showing from a very early age. His brother Neil also has considerable sheep instinct and is an excellent shearer.

Arnold recalls a Widecombe ram of theirs that left black lambs (six in all) and then one day it was run over and killed outright. These lambs were Beverley Cole's, and her brothers were afraid the black sheep were going to take over because they were increasing so fast!

Matthew Cole found a Livestock Handbook; Sheep Breeds and Management written by John Wrightson (M.A.A.C. F.C.S.) in 1913. A section on 'Dartmoor Sheep'.

I don't think the 'step-up' suggested in this article applied to the true Whiteface Dartmoor

Cyril Abel and Arnold Cole checking points for the on farm flock competition.

Sheep, either in wool or size, but with in-country management, improvements to the sheep have been made.

It is very probable, despite mentioning the Whiteface races, that the improved Greyfaced Dartmoor is the sheep he depicts and that the indigenous Whiteface remained very much the same sheep we know today, albeit through its in-country preference, some have become larger. Therefore, they are not so removed from the 'wild Dartmoor Sheep' of which Youatt speaks and are descended from the latter.

So their likeness can still be compared to our Whitefaces and 'whiteface races of sheep, with such an amount of the old nature as suffices to enure him to the severe winters of his native home'.

They were back in time small in the head and neck, small in bone everywhere, the carcass said to be narrow and flat-sided and they weighed when fat from 9–12lbs per quarter. They were the material from which the celebrated Okehampton (also Oakhampton) mutton was derived along with the Exmoor, and they carried a fleece of rather short middle-wool weighing from 3 to 4lbs of coarse and inferior quality. Devonshire's aboriginal sheep remained isolated. The Leicester in particular brought improvement to certain in-country sheep. Qualities of 'hardiness' remained just as important throughout, especially on and around the Moor.

The original Whiteface was a genuine 'Forest or Moorland' breed before any improvement took place and had wild nature and roaming habits.

The Cole family also have Scotch Blackface sheep leared in the Forest of Dartmoor away from Greenwell. These and their Whitefaces face John Caunter's Whitefaces at Green Hill.

In an old book called 'History of Blackface Sheep', by John and Charles Scott, it explains the power and reliability of learing, and agisting animals to one place. The authors explained in detail how certain ewes 'newly removed from well known to strange grounds (pastures) secretly returned to their former pastures over a distance of several miles, in one case 40 or 60 miles, in a marvellously short time, with one of Scotland's noblest rivers to swim. When these animals (as on Dartmoor) are fairly bent on returning to their faavourite haunt, they travel night and day and overcome barriers which in any other circumstances would be insurmountable.'

Sheep washing of Blackfaces in Scottish highlands took place in May and June, usually in streams and pools, as here on the Moor; the animals, when practicable being driven to a river or pool and made to leap from the bank, and swim across. The use of hot water and soap is injurious to the wool!

But some farmers said it is injurious to the sheep, and that the washing can be done cheaper after the wool is off the sheep than before, and that buyers did not pay enough for washed fleeces to pay the cost of washing, together with the shrinkage in the weight of the wool, the water having driven the grease out of the fleece!

The number of days that should intervene between washing and shearing the sheep depends partly on the state of the weather, as well as upon the condition of the fleece, but usually it is about ten days. The shearing was coarsely done, leaving a short growth of wool to protect the sheep from winter's cold, wet nights.

A practice also formerly existed in hill sheep of anointing the skins previous to the winter months. Tar and butter were used, prepared by boiling the butter and tar together. In some districts 6 pounds of butter and one gallon of tar were used for twenty sheep; sometimes more tar was used. This was done at the end of October or beginning of November. The wool was separated by the finger longitudinally from head to tail and the whole body smeared; the aim to remove insects and skin disease and defend the skin from wetness and cold with a film of grease, helping the animal through the bleak and stormy winter, as with Wethers on Dartmoor. The effect was to diminish the value of the wool by staining it with the colouring matter of the tar, which rendered the wool less fit for receiving the brighter colours in dyeing. Dipping sheep superseded these time consuming exploits!

Arnold explained that animals were put on Wigford Down, outside the gate from Greenwell, since the time of his Grandfather, William Cole, who farmed Greenwell in 1931.

The identification of animals to their owner was of utmost importance in order to trace any strays off the Moor or further afield into the 'forest'. Some quite crude practices were accepted. Arnold said his Grandfather slit the near ear and cut a halfpenny under the near ear and a top cut and slit in the off ear.

A brand was made with Cole visible in the near horn and a piece cut off the horn.

Arnold explained other marks were green behind the head, redded across the loins and maybe sometimes three red stripes on the back with sheep.

These marks identified William Cole's sheep as belonging to him. Arnold said that nowadays a 'V' is placed in the ear as opposed to a halfpenny, or penny cut that's taken from the near lower ear.

Cattle too met with similar 'horn and ear doctoring', that seemed quite drastic, but had to be large and clear, when considering identifying animals from a distance, and allowing for the ear in younger animals to grow. I've seen farmers, not at Greenwell, cut the ends off cattles' ears using hand sheep-shears! Different moorland groups, associations and agisters in the past held the information of marking relating to different farmers with rights on the Moor. Arnold referred me to a Mr Williams at 'Urgles' Yelverton, a neighbour of Arnold's, who explained that Whiteface Dartmoor Sheep were sold at Dousland Market (Sheepfair) along with the other local breeds.

He recalled Doidges of Whitchurch, Northmore's, formerly of 'Yeo', selling there too.

Mr Williams said he thought John Young was probably the auctioneer at the time, coming out from Tavistock Auctioneers. (and or Tom Brown!)

When recalling the wool prices in the past, he remembers it being worth only 1d per lb in the 1930s. He said, Northmore at 'Goodameavy' kept some wool for 7 or 8 years, but when they came to take it out it was 'moth-eaten' and of no use at all and had to be burnt.

Russell Woolcock of Ward and Chowen (Tavistock Livestock Centre) as Secretary of the West of England Blackfaced Sheep Breeders Association, records in detail on an 'Ear Mark Register', animal identification information returned by farmers for sheep, cattle and ponies. This involves horn painting and brands, ear notches, colour marking of wool and plastic and metal tags, etc. Farmers individually keep their own way of identifying their animals especially for those placed on the moor!

The Cole Family

FORMERLY BROOMHILL NOW COMBESHEAD, HARFORD

There is yet another cluster of farms in the Cornwood Ivybridge area that supported Whiteface Dartmoor Sheep in the past.

In 1934 Tom Cole farmed Pit Hill Farm and at that time took considerable interest in the sheep. John Cole said his father (Tom) used Stall Moor, joining Sherrell and Hanger Down, or just 'Hanger' as John put it! These are near to the river Erme. Ermehede 1474, refers to Erme Head the source of the Erme River. Harford Moor was also used. John said that he remembered Whiteface Dartmoor Sheep from when he could just walk.

Tom Cole was farming at Broomhill in 1949. From here he joined the Whiteface Dartmoor Sheep Breeders Association and Flockbook in 1951 and is recorded amongst a few registered breeders in the first articles of the Association printed in 1951.

About 100 ewes were kept in the past although young John Cole never did much himself with Whitefaces, farming now in his own right West Combeshead Farm. However, he said it was very much a 'horse and dog' occupation.

His father, John said, always bought a good ram at Ashburton during the 1970–1980's and paid well for his rams in the region of 200–300 gns back then.

In 1973 Tom Cole won the Whiteface Dartmoor Sheep Breeders Association Challenge Cup presented by Messrs Mann Bros for the best ram hogg at Ashburton Fair. Tom used to sell breeders and have a regular draft of 6 tooths (3–4 pens every year at the Annual Association Sale and he would show occasionally at Widecombe.

The wool clips were highly prized and John Cole sheared, having learnt through the local Young Farmers Clubs.

Speaking of the Whiteface Sheep themselves, John said both the rams and the ewes were very vicious against foxes and the ewes very possessive of their lambs.

Sheep dipping, John said, took place at Watercombe. This is above Cornwood Moor and some 3 miles 'out auver' (over). It was a communal dip used by many farmers.

Dartmoor 2001, written by Mike Brown, is a Dartmoor Diary of yesteryear recording selected episodes from Dartmoor's long and eventful history. One reference relates, I think, to Combeshead. It is dated October 5, 1564 and says that Thomas Watts of 'Tavystoke' sells Combeshead in Harford and Pethill in Cornwood to Andrew Bonnsall of Shyttistor (Sheepstor) for the 'sume of twenty marks of lawfull monye of England'.

Horace Casely formerly of 'Bozdown Farm' Rattery and now retired with his wife Mary (formerly a Hunt of Furzeleigh) at Bishopsteignton told me how, at the age of 16 years old, he worked for five years at Broomhill Farm for a Sam Horton. Horace recalled two particular stone-walled fields near to the moor, where he helped cut ferns to dry in the sun, before bringing them back to the farmyard for animal bedding to use in winter, indoors. The ferns were carted using horse and wagon. Latterly where access permitted and when not too rocky on the moors commons, ferns were also baled as small square bales, and used as the yards first floor-bedding.

Horace remarked that he had returned there recently, and to the lane he remembered, leading up to the 'moorgate'. Of the memories that he said he had of the rocks that guided him when it was foggy in the past, things hadn't changed hardly at all.

Also on his first experience of ploughing at Broomhill (some 60 years ago) with horses, he remembered hitting a rock and the plough leaping up and hitting him on the chin and knocking him out.

Horace recalled Whitefaces using the moor from Broomhill up around Redlake and of other flocks of Whitefaces around about too. Erme Pound is near to Redlake in the south quarter of the moor below Erme Head.

Horace thought that John Cole's son, John H. Cole, now farms West Coombeshead.

I actually briefly met young John Cole bringing cattle to Tavistock Market. I was struck by several sets of 'ear tagging pliers' resting above his dash-board. John remarked, 'you must have them at hand when you need them for sheep or cattle tagging'. In the past probably a pair of sheep shears was enough to take out pieces of ear, to identify different farmers animals.

Broomhill has been popular for Whitefaces for many years. Sam Pearse farmed Whitefaces at Broomhill in 1927 and Sam Horton and the Cole family that followed enjoyed Whiteface Dartmoor Sheep.

One can just imagine the Whiteface Sheep on the moor, well above the farms, speckled amongst the granite wild clatter of Yealm, Erme and Plym Heads preoccupied with their survival in searching for a feed from the moor's meagre vegetation.

Mr W.J. Doidge

FULLAMOOR, WHITCHURCH, TAVISTOCK

Bill Doidge was a very good supporter of the Association Sheep Sale at Ashburton in the year 2000 buying and selling rams and ewes over many years. He was also regarded as a founder member of its association in 1951.

Mr Doidge started his flock of Whiteface Dartmoors in 1955 from a purchase on a farm near Meavy from a Mr Pearse (possibly the Kingsett Pearse's).

In 1955 he said Dartmoor ewes were selling for around £7.2s; lambs were making from £4.6s to £5.11s. A farm workers wages was £5 for a 48 hour week, Mr Doidge explained. In 1962 at Ashburton, Dartmoor ewes sold from £6.17s to £7 and Dartmoor lambs £5.4s to £6.2s.

To make a comparison a New Super Dexta Tractor would cost £465, i.e. approximately 100 ewes. He also recalls showing at the Devon County Show and a photograph shows a prize-winning sheep being held by his son and Peter Hearn.

(Bill) W.J. Doidge, prize-winning sheep at the Devon County Show.

He remembers Cecil Harris and Ken Soper acting as stewards at Bristol when the Royal Show was held there before settling to its permanent site at Stoneleigh, Warwickshire. The motto of the Royal Show is 'practice with science'. In 1958 at Whitchurch airport, Bristol, between July 1–4 the annual show of the Royal Agricultural Society of England was held. In the Whiteface Dartmoor Shearling Ram and Yearling Ewes W. J. Doidge won two third prizes. The two young ewes were shown in their wool.

Mr Doidge makes use of Plaster Down during late summer to the end of September for a couple of months; then allowing a couple of weeks for 'flushing' the ewes on better grass keep before the rams go in to enable lambing to start around the 10th–12th March.

Lambs and ewes are sheared together. Some black sheep have turned up over the years. To ensure his sheep's wool is kept healthy all the year round, Mr Doidge favours winter dipping. The wool was worth so much more in the past at different times, but with troughs and peaks.

Up until the Second World War arsenic was used for adding to dip water to dip his sheep. Dieldrin followed and was a very persistent dip so much so, infertility in bird's eggs caused it to be banned. Organo-phosphorus dips followed, but the Ministry gave up its supervision on the farm and compulsory dipping ceased in 1991–92 as the adverse affects of Organo-phosphorus on human health gave rise to safety concerns.

Injectible products for the control of scab such as Cydectin and Dectomax and spray products such as Crovect and Vetrazin are used to help combat maggots in summer.

Reflecting on wool clip prices back as far as 1932 when the average for washed fleeces at the country sales was 6¼d per lb. All wool clipped in the UK in 1947 was requisitioned by the Home Grown Wool Order of the said year. The order prohibited the disposal of wool except to the Agricultural Ministers. Wool removed by fellmongers from skins and 'willeyed', locks, 'daggings' and 'clarts' are excluded from the requisition.

Prices of wool under control had not changed since 1941 when the average for washed wool was 20½d and for unwashed 17d. Average control prices for the five years leading up to 1947 were 23d for washed and 19d for unwashed. The price quoted in 1947 for Devon, Cornwall and Somerset strong was 16½d per lb for good clean, light, greasy wool in this case. This was the highest price for wools of specified types. There was nothing at this time to indicate a permanent marketing organisation to handle future clips.

It was reported that in 1946, 53,506 fleeces were handled, 703 fewer than in 1945. Less than 4% of the wool was washed.

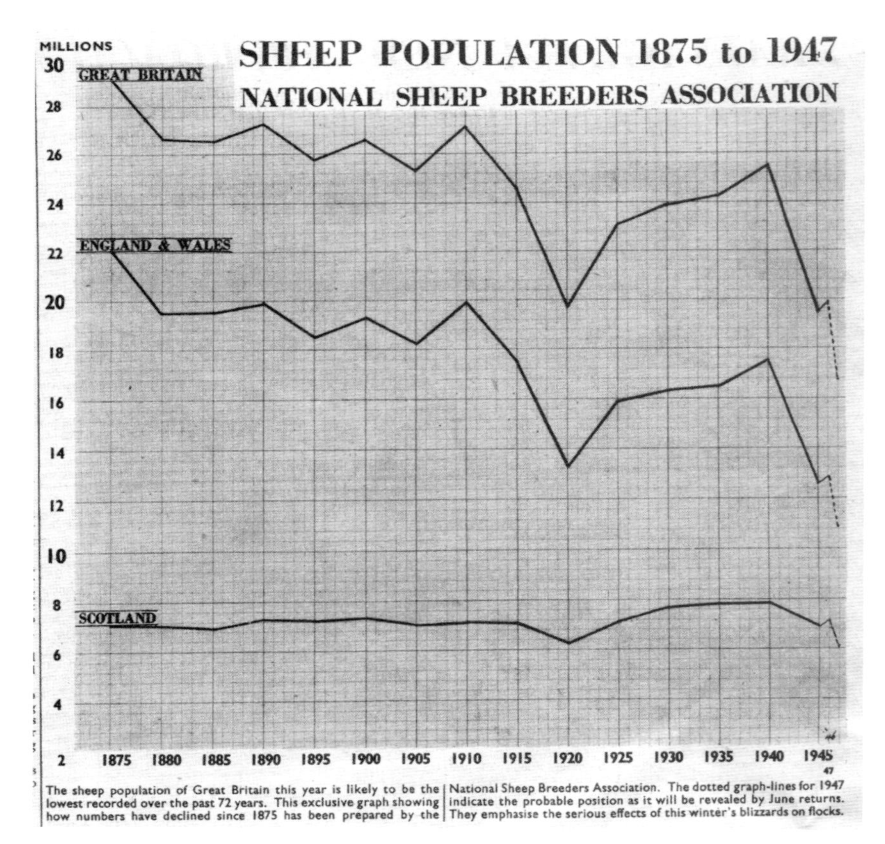

Sheep Populations, 1875 to 1947, NSBA.
The lowest recorded in Great Britain for 72 years. They emphasize the serious effects of this winter's (1947) blizzards on flocks.
Courtesy of the *Farmers'Weekly*.

The French Family

MICHELCOMBE, HOLNE

'From Scoriton, where is an inn called the Tradesmen's Arms' the Holne road runs to Holy Brook Bridge, near which a lane leads to Michelcombe, also a small hamlet. The Holy Brook comes down from Gibby's Combe Wood through Michel Combe, which gives its name to this little place, and no doubt to the French's Farm; often called by the locals "Mutchecum".'

The French family were William (Bill), John and 'Ern' (Ernest) and Henry, and Ernest was the father of Michael and John jnr.

Michael said the family had well in excess of one thousand Whitefaces at their peak. This served to emphasise the popularity of Whitefaces at this special time in their history.

His first association with the sheep was, he said, coming home from school and helping to shear them. He remembers they had lovely silky fleeces. Certainly the two-teeth hoggs and the younger sheep, or the ones having only a single lamb, would shear a lot better than poorer sheep or ones with twins. Michael said they were clean of wool on the legs and easier to shear than the Greyface. The wool clip from their large flock would have been thousands of pounds. Michael said 'as much as £5,000–£6,000 was received in the past for one season's wool'.

Michael said young Fred Trant used to shear their sheep and the whole family would come up from Blackawton.

Michael recalled Peter Hannaford from Sherwell or Sherril, Widecombe who went around the moor castrating lambs. He was picked up by the French's to come and do their lambs. Michael said Peter was an institution in himself around Dartmoor; the 'moor incarnate'!

They followed the tradition again of putting sheep away to turnips in the South Hams. His uncle (Bill) would start to lamb some of the sheep away before they came home in February. Over the years there were obviously very muddy and wet conditions endured whilst lambing the sheep, with so many huddled in the corner of fields in late winter and spring, trying to find shelter for their lambs.

Left to right: William (Bill) French, Cecil Harris, Ernest French, Reg Norrish, Michael French, Henry French and David Norrish, and the ram bought at the 15th Annual Whiteface Show and Sale, September 15th, 1965. The ram was purchased by the French family for 80 gns.

Ashburton Sheep Fair was where sheep, especially rams, were bought and several hundred sheep would be drafted out and offered for sale there every year.

Michael said he was the shepherd at one point on the farm. Michelcombe was originally three farms. John and Michael's father took on Ingslett, Michelcombe and Dodbrook, rented it in 1945 and then bought in 1959.

Common grazing rights were on Scoriton and West Buckfastleigh, that is the south Quarter of the moor.

However, Michael explained that his father was not really a 'moorman' and didn't use the moor that much.

Sheep did, however, use the newtake area on Holne and Buckfastleigh where there were also 'straying rights'. Michael said his brother John was more of a 'moorman'. The flocks history ended when the partnership ended and John (Jnr) took over in 1975 with just a few Whitefaces. Michael had a great deal of feeling for the sheep and regarded the Whitefaces as the best sheep in the world. He said they were regarded as the 'definitive sheep' where everything else was compared with the Whiteface, but all else was found wanting in the past. They were, he said, called the Whiteface and not the 'Dartmoor' because they were recognised as being special as their own breed.

He also spoke of them as enjoyable sheep, something to enjoy and not commercialise. They were, Michael said, very good mothering sheep when they lamb. Indeed very often when one picks up the lambs, the ewe is nudging away at your legs and nearly pushes you over trying to get at her lambs.

Lambing of the French's flock did take place indoors latterly and after six weeks or so, when hopefully strong enough to avoid the fox, they were put outside; (the ewe and her lambs).

Flock competition showing resulted in 1967 with the French Brothers (Holne) winning the W.F.D.S.B.A. Brian and Julie Memorial Challenge Cup for the best flock of ewe lambs. I am sure this was one of many trophies awarded for their flock in their long association with the breed.

They kept as many as two hundred ponies that used to run side by side on the moor with the sheep. The export trade in the past for ponies helped to guarantee a good income, but downhill went the Widecombe sheep, their prolificacy outstripped by other breeds as wool demand declined too. The pony trade has also fallen victim to meat and export regulations.

Moving away from the achievements of the 'show field' and happenings down on the farm, Michael French speaks passionately of the moor, and its special people that have been 'hewn-out' of its very core! Crossing also interprets accurately the feeling of something 'in-place'. On a high vantage point of the moor, Crossing says, 'there comes to the eye a most satisfying prospect of the elevated floor of the distant "Central Basin" of the moor; the lands of the Forest Dwellers.'

The French Family of Corringdon

SOUTH BRENT

In 1951 Mr Geoffrey French recalled taking his father Hermon French to the first meeting at Ashburton to help form the W.F.D.S.B. Association, and flock book, and Hermon became one of the founder members.

Speaking of the Whiteface breeders and sheep numbers actually registered, Geoffrey French recorded that on the 16th December 1950, 28 flocks were inspected, which relates to the number of breeders in the first articles of the association and 1204 sheep passed and tattooed.

Mr French revealed the photograph of the first show and sale prize-winners; Horace Nosworthy holding a cup for the first prize Ram Hogg (plus certificate) and Leonard Ball with cup and certificate for 'best pen of 10 ewes' and Cecil Caunter holding certificate and Cup for first prize 'old ram'.

Besides Geoffrey's father Hermon there were two more brothers, Herbert and Jasper French (Uncles to Geoffrey) and three sisters at Spitchwick.

Ruth Parnell's (now living at Jordan, Widecombe-in-the-Moor) husband was David French-Parnell, the son of Bessie Parnell (nee French and one of the above sisters). David was also a cousin to the French Bros' John and Geoffrey.

Percy (David's father) and Besie farmed 'Drywell', Widecombe, back in the 1920's. Jasper French farmed 'Wooder', Widecombe-in-the-Moor.

David and Ruth bought Drywell in 1956, when they purchased a small flock of Whiteface Sheep.

The French family can be traced back to 1853, but it seems there were generations of French's at Spitchwick, Widecombe. So Geoffrey French's great great grandfather is recorded there in 1853, and it seems there is no reason to suppose the family wasn't there before this date.

Spitchwick Farm was on the Spitchwick estate, but as tenants the farm after the first World War was taken in hand by a Major Fletcher, invalided out of the war.

At Christmas of 1920 the French's moved to Corringdon. South Devon cattle and Whitefaced Dartmoor sheep were always kept.

At one point in the early records it showed 135 ewes that gave 133 lambs reared.

The flock was sold to Terry Phipps around 1996. A very long partnership between the Whiteface Dartmoor sheep and a farming family manifested itself here again.

Geoffrey was also an early chairman of the Whiteface Dartmoor Sheep Breeders Association and Flock Book.

Speaking of sheep on Brent Moor, Geoffrey said, 'the use of the moor became limited by the presence of the Scotch Sheep. The Whitefaces never went up that well on to the hill because the Scotch sheep were already up ahead all the time. The Whitefaces held back and would hang along the moor wall. He said, 'the Cheviot sheep mixed far better with the Scotch sheep than the Whiteface Dartmoors'.

Whitefaces were kept at Owley in the past and Richard Coaker, John Savery, and Mann Bros' rams were used. In 1980 John French had 70 ewes in the flock.

In 1979 Geoffrey French was recorded as having 142 ewes, and sires used included rams bred by J. Northmore of Cornwood, Mann Bros, John Savery, Edward Caunter and Miss Needham.

Whitefaces at Owley, South Brent (John French, Geoffrey's brother). Flock competition being judged by Cyril Abel and Arnold Cole.

In the Woolman's Exeter and Plymouth Gazette dated Saturday, October 19th, 1850 it was announced that on the following Friday a Free Fair would be held on the Green adjoining the Church Yard at Widecombe-in-the-Moor. There would be a large show of cattle and quantity of Moorland sheep offered for sale. On Saturday November 2, 1850 the Gazette reported that a cattle fair was held at Widecombe-in-the-Moor for the first time on Tuesday last. There was a large attendance of 'Yeoman' (farmers) and gentlemen. It was thought the fair should be permanently established. 736 sheep were penned, 75 store cattle, and fatted beasts plus 4 bulls. One South Devon Cow made £15.10s. About 50 ponies were driven in. The breed and character of the Widecombe stock being highly appreciated. A future date was to be made as not to clash with neighbouring fairs.

Hermon French recalls his father taking sheep to Widecombe Fair in the early twenties where they were penned against a churchyard walk, i.e. the grass on the opposite side of the road to what is now known as the Green. It is sometimes said jokingly that the sheep were sold by the yard; but that was of course *by* the 'Church Yard' wall!

This Hermon French was not Geoffrey's father, but probably a distant relation. Bessie French said, 'the above sheep were walked from 'Rowden Farm', Widecombe.

There is nothing to say that many of the 736 sheep penned at the first fair were not Whiteface Dartmoor Sheep, and this was not an inconsiderable number of sheep for a small village fair, in the mid-eighteen hundreds.

A James Woodley of Halsanger brought 34 sheep. John Coaker, recorded as, Yeoman, from 'Bellaford', (ancestor of the Sherberton Coakers).

Geoffrey French speaks of the bad snow winters of 1947 and 1963–3 when a lot of sheep were buried in gulleys on the moor above South Brent and of course elsewhere.

He recalls being asked to go up in a helicopter in 1963 to look for sheep belonging to a neighbour called Headman who, apparently told Geoffrey, he had several hundred sheep missing.

It was the first time Geoffrey had been up in a helicopter, and he took his dogs with him. Together they were flown several miles out into the moor and they were dropped with the helicopter just hovering a few feet from the ground and then Geoffrey and his dogs jumped down on to the frozen snow. A few sheep were found on top the snow, but hundreds were buried and dead. Geoffrey said driving home sheep on foot was a bit scary if the snow was to break underfoot.

Sheep would sometimes walk into each other; they had become 'snow-blind' with the glare of the white snow.

During the 1947 winter blizzard there was a lot more ice ('ammil'), than during 1962/3, everything had a glaze of ice on it, and ice stayed on the roads for weeks; tractors with iron 'spade-lug' metal wheels, froze to the ground whilst 'ticking over' in the road, no wonder, with weeks of continual cold from the east and northeast wind. There were frequent heavy falls of snow and drifting during the winter.

So apart from losses of sheep buried under huge drifts, sheep also starved because the icing of the snow prevented them getting to roots and roughage, and longwoolled sheep because of their wool froze to the ground. Many ewes had yet to lamb, and so many sheep which survived the blizzard, were weakened, and didn't survive afterwards.

Snow was said to be still seen in the hollows away from the sun on Dartmoor into the month of June. Some roads on Exmoor (Porlock) were blocked into April and some had been cleared five times. Also digging sheep out of snow drifts is arduous, and exhausting work.

Its interesting too to follow the weather and harvests of the previous winter's and summers leading up to the disastrous winter of 1947.

In 1945 splendid haymaking weather, but little grass to cut leaving no reserves of hay going into 1946.

The 1946 summer produced plenty of grass, but only one weeks fine weather. A lot of hay and corn (sheaves) were not harvested. So here things started to go wrong; it was not just the extreme cold of 1947 (buried and weakened, hungry sheep) but a shortage of food of any kind, and with railways frozen up, difficulties of distributing food around the country, during weeks of lying snow. It is said, it took at least three weeks for the train to reach Barnstaple from Dulverton on Exmoor!

Other years not often remembered as 'bad winters' were 1919, 1928 (recorded here) 1937, 1941.

Turves or 'Vags', and cut peat on the moor could not be dried and harvested because of the wet summer of 1946. So 'peat', like ricks of hay, and corn-sheaves, normally stored 'in-hand', to start off the new winter, simply ran out. In the floods that followed the snow's thaw in the Spring of 1947, some ricks of corn and hay that did remain, washed completely away, along with vulnerable livestock that floated down swollen rivers.

The 1947 winter told here is not Geoffrey French's story, but his revealing account of conditions on the moor near him during 1962/3 winter, gave an opportunity for me to compare the two winters somewhat. Remembering that 1962/3 started near Christmas, earlier than 1947 blizzard!

David Gardener

WEST STOKE, HOLNE

David has been farming at West Stoke for fourteen years having moved down from Herefordshire in the mid-eighties. It is not uncommon for 'incomers' to be attracted to our local breeds of cattle and sheep through their easy management and temperament.

So after living on Dartmoor for three to four years, David wanted to keep something bred on Dartmoor. The Whiteface Dartmoor flock was appropriately introduced. David thought the over-wintering Scotch was in danger of being forced out due to environmental schemes and the hardy, native Whiteface were the next best thing. The flock was established from sheep bred by Arthur Brown and John Mead. Arnold Cole and Mr and Mrs Nigel Haley's rams were used.

The flock eventually numbered 80–100 ewes. The moorland rights of Holne and Buckfastleigh were not used.

David mentioned the discipline needed if one closes a flock; where one has to be very selective in the breeding which can be wasteful initially until the breed type is stamped.

It is well known that in the Domesday Book, Dartmoor is not mentioned by name. (A Pipe-Roll of 1181 has the earliest reference). It is true that the part of it forming the royal Forest would probably have been omitted Crispin Gill says. However, a list of Manors comprising Dartmoor and its immediate borders can be interpreted.

Holne was one of the larger-than-average manors and included all hamlets and farms in the parish except the Stoke farms, which formed a separate manor of their own.

So David Gardener actually reached nearly twice the number of sheep in his flock as the Domesday book recorded for the whole of Holne parish. (see History section).

David revealed a painting by 'Wimperis' painted of several flocks of sheep on Dartmoor in 1897. It shows considerable swaling of its part of the moor and horse and rider and dog guiding the sheep to a safer 'lear'. The date suggests these are Whiteface flocks.

The sheeps importance throughout the latter 1700's and much of the 1800's is confirmed by many painters of moorland scenes; people such as Widgery, father and son. Sherrin (father and son) Britain (C.E.) and others and here Wimperis. On the East Valley crest of Vennford Brook are 'Cornditches' of the 'Old Stoke Farm' settlements.

Moving sheep during 'swaling'.
Edmund M. Wimperis VPRI, 1835–1900.
'Crossing a Dartmoor Stream'.

Graham and Julie Goddard

WAYTOWN FARM, SAMPFORD SPINEY

Graham Goddard's keen interest in Whiteface Dartmoor Sheep developed into his nomination as the Association's Chairman and acceptance for the historic years of 1999 and the year 2000 astride the millennia.

To give ones precious time to meetings, shows and the annual dinner and in supporting President, and secretary alike, throughout the office years is much appreciated by all the members and our thanks go to Graham and his wife Julie for all their hard work during the lead up to the 50 years celebration of the Association.

Arnold and Bridget Cole introduced Graham and Julie to Whiteface Dartmoor Sheep in the winter of 1992. It was then suggested to Graham to attend Ashburton Sheep Fair in August of that year to purchase foundation sheep. Graham said he was grateful for the help the Abel and Cole families gave him in establishing the flock and he enjoyed the friendly rivalry that existed between the Abel and Cole families when they showed.

He currently runs a flock of 120 ewes. These lamb down in late April which, Graham said best suits the farm and the sheep. There would be less hand feeding and the grass would then be growing along with the sheep and lamb. The lambs are weaned in August and from then on the ewes run out on the moor at Walkhampton Common until tupping time. Graham's shearling ewes also keep fit and healthy on the moor.

Walkhampton is an old (the name is recorded as early as 1083) and huge parish, taking in the high moors as far east as Eylesbarrow. The common extends to some 10,000 acres.

When I judged at Graham's farm one year I remember that the sheep were out on Walkhampton Common. Graham indicated that we had to follow him. However, he

The current stock ram, sired by a Patrick Coater ram, bred by Colin Pearse.

Cattle grid to Walkhampton Common.

jumped on his Quad bike and set off at such a pace I failed to keep up with him down the narrow lanes. However, eventually we made it to the Common, but no sheep were to be seen, or to be judged! (such was the scope of the Common.)

Merrivale bridge spans the Walkham, the said river forms the boundary between Walkhampton Common and the common lands belonging to the parish of Whitchurch. Great Mis Tor (1,760 feet) rises high above the left bank of the Walkham.

On the Common nearby are deep cuttings of the tinners.

From these imposing tors of Staple Tor, Great Mis Tor, Roose Tor, and Cocks Tor etc stretches the wild part of the old forest that forms the northern edge of the moor. From whatever points Great Mis Tor is viewed it presents a grand and imposing appearance, lifting its crown of rocks above the dark ridges of the desolate parts of the moor.

Vixen Tor and Merrivale Quarry (centre) over-shadowed by the Tors around.

The Haley Family

MAYFIELDS, OAKLANDS ROAD, BUCKFASTLEIGH

Whitefaces were introduced to Mayfields in 1991. Tissa's husband, Nigel, nearly died Tissa said at the thought of having sheep and also being married.

This started some thirteen years ago with just two Whiteface Dartmoor cross ewes. However the cross bred sheep became too big for Tissa to manage and Nigel thought it would be a good idea to have half a dozen Whiteface Dartmoors as they were smaller sheep and easier for Tissa to move around. A ram was hired from the Brown Brothers. The lambing the following year was much better, no problems and no vet, Tissa remarked!

Ewe and her lambs, well into spring-time.

The ewes were found to be excellent mothers and they had plenty of milk for their lambs; a compliment from breeders that's repeated again and again.

In 1994 the flock was expanded to 12 ewes and with a further 12 ewes purchased from the Abel family at the Ashburton Show and Sale in 1995. Tissa said that their Whiteface sheep enterprise never looked back after their difficult days with the crossbreds.

A French/Mann ram was also added to the flock. Lambing time at the end of February 1996 produced 15 ram lambs and 13 ewe lambs from 24 ewes. One of Nigel and Tissas own rams was also used at this point. From the 29 ewes lambed, 41 lambs were reared in 1998. Also in 1998 two Savery rams resulted in a change of bloodline.

It seems the flock was growing and there were now 33 ewes from which to breed the flock.

It is sometimes said 'that from small acorns great oaks do sometimes grow'!

Indeed 55 lambs were produced from these 33 ewes. At around 140% lambing it is a good achievement.

Tissa is already a converted Whiteface breeder and it's not surprising that she says after seven years she doesn't want to change her breed and makes a resolute statement 'that the Whitefaces are here now and here is where they will stay'.

Interesting too that this young flock is not many miles from Buckfast and Buckfastleigh where sheep and wool production were so important, down the centuries.

The showing of sheep often goes hand in hand with sheep management.

The Brown brothers encouraged Tissa to show her sheep and between 1994 and 1996 entry in the under 50 flock competition achieved a third prize for each of these years; bettered by a first prize in 1997.

Also in 1996 Nigel and Tissa started taking their sheep to local shows.

Totnes Show was the first event and the highest prize achieved was a 2nd for the old ram class.

First prize was achieved at the Ashburton Association Show and Sale for an old ram.

Nigel and Tissa's daughter Natalie at the age of only seven was also helping with the showing.

Showing at Whistley Hill Field and the Association show and sale. (Tissa, first from right).

Since 1996 six first prizes, nineteen second prizes, 19 third prizes and 18 fourth prizes have been won with prizes at Devon County Show as well.

It has taken the Haley family just eight years to establish their flock, and they enjoy showing their animals.

The Hearn Family

OAKLEY, TAVISTOCK

In 1932 John Hearn's father (Thomas) had a Greyface Dartmoor Flock, but he found that they were not that well suited to the area. John said, 'They became inbred and if you sat them up on their ass they would die'! A Greyfaced breeder might not agree!

So a Mr Harry Rowse at Cudlipptown, Peter Tavy recommended that Mr Hearn use a Widecombe ram of his breeding. It had a goat-like 'beard' typical of the old-fashioned true to type Widecombes and the ram put vigour into the flock. Mr Hearn collected the said ram using his horse and cart, tying it up in the cart. Cudlipptown was not a million miles from Oakley near to Peter Tavy the Tavistock side of the moor.

This interchange of Greyface and Whiteface sheep, crossing first one way and then the other was not uncommon between the breeds in the past before the Association was formed. Also 'South Devon' sheep were popularly crossed with Whiteface Dartmoors.

It became easy to buy Widecombe rams in Tavistock, particularly at 'John's Fair' ('Jan's' Fair) sheep sale held in September at Church Lane. The practice he said would have gone back to the early 1800's at least.

John said 'Wagon loads of Widecombes came down from Ashburton side to the fair and from Princetown side too'. 'What John's father said went', recalls John and his father paid him 2/6d a week wages.

In 1951 they had a car and then they could go to Ashburton and buy their rams, also selling 6 tooths in 1976 and 1978. His flock was inspected in 1976 for the Flock Book by Cecil Caunter, Norman Stephens and Ken Soper. By 1979–80 he had as many as 180 ewes in his flock.

John recalls in the mid-seventies how he bought a ram at Ashburton Sheep Sale and took it home in his Austin 7 car tied up in the back seat. However, it became lively and the halter got stuck around John's leg and nearly took him out of the car door.

Rams were used over the years from many breeders; Les Barons, W. Doidge, Cyril Abel, Terry Phipps, Ned Northmore, Fred Trant, Henry Bond, F.A. Mortimore, Geoffrey French and Patrick Coaker.

In the 1970's he bought a ram from a (Frank) Nosworthy, Widecombe, and in 1975–6 the champion ram at Ashburton was bought for £45 from Richard Coaker at the Association Sale. John was very proud of his ram. He said jokingly, he was so big he would have to take back the gateposts to let him in at home!

He won at the Y.F.C. Field Day at Tavistock and John also entered a ram of Wilf Stones from Buckland, 'a good sheep', John commented.

John was born in 1923 and showed and sold Widecombes later in life at Ashburton Sheep Sale from 1970 onwards. His son, Peter, continues the tradition also selling at Tavistock Market; taking on from father in 1983. Over the years the family have showed at Yealmpton, Cornwood and Widecombe Fair with championship sheep awards during the 1970's–1980's.

Peter has judged at Westpoint (Devon County Show) and did so in the Shows' second year at Westpoint.

Peter remembers buying a ram once and it had a very long beard. He was afraid to tell his father so he cut off the beard; but his father thought it was a fine animal, hard and a survivor.

At Cornwood Show on one occasion the Hearn's won every prize and one sheep had a

John Hearn judging at Yealmpton Show 1995. Cyril and Phil won the Champion Sheep on the left and Reserve Champion Hogg held by Phil on the right.

black spot under its eye, but although the breeders say this denotes pureness of breed (black marks) others didn't agree with it winning. I think the black spots are a true mark of the breeds inheritance. Black in the tail, a black leg, black patches are still seen today.

Over the years John said many totally black sheep have turned up, but have not bred black in their turn, with the first cross. 'Wiry-haired beards' under the chin are still present!

In 1981 Peter and John judged together at the Society Sale, judging the best pair of rams and Terry Phipps won 1st and 2nd prize.

In the 1980's John recalls sending two ton of wool to Buckfastleigh and receiving as he said, one hell of a cheque! It paid for all the winter feed he bought. Also in 1981, John had the champion ram at Widecombe and Edward Caunter gave it 1st prize. However, John and a young work experience lad that was with him, went to celebrate and realised when they returned the ram should be judged for the championship as it was first in its class. Fortunately Terry Phipps had taken it out and it won overall.

John tells the story of how in 1978 the Ministry suspected a problem with his sheep (possibly scab) although only one sheep was implicated. However, with six inches of ice and a mini blizzard (February 18th–20th) he was ordered to dip his sheep. He lost 110 ewes and

Father and son judging at Ashburton Show and Sale.

lambs; they died of shock and cold because the Ministry insisted the sheep stayed in the dip for the standard one minute. But sheep dip is a dangerous product John said, and farmers should always ere on the safe side, but often put more dip concentrate in than they should, to do the job, as they think, properly. Yet here it was simply too cold!

Such has been the longevity of the breed; John explained that in the early 1970's he bought some sheep through Cyril Abel that originally had come from Leonard Ball. They were already at least 'first year full mouth' (teeth) but John kept them another two years and still was able to sell them to a Modbury farmer who always bought his sheep and, he remarked, he was pleased, and they went on to breed!

Recalling land prices John said in 1933 near him a farm was bought for £3000 and recently made 2½ million (700 acres). In 1942 15 acres beside him was offered for £1,200 (£80 per acre). But if the money had to be borrowed John said it was still too dear to buy at the time.

The Hearn's sheep are compelling, typical real Whiteface Dartmoor Sheep with small character ears. The Whiteface Dartmoor Sheep Breeders Association Challenge Cup presented by Miss Needham for the over 50 ewes flock; showing the measure of the Hearn Family's consistent breed type (smaller traditional 'Yark' – type sheep) was won by the family T. & P. Hearn in 1983, 1985, 1989 and 1992. The W.F.D.S.B. Association Brian and Julie Harris Memorial Challenge Cup for the best flock of ewe lambs was also won by J. & P. Hearn in 1985 and 1992 and in 1994 by P. & M. Hearn.

The Hext Family

PUDSHAM, BUCKLAND-IN-THE-MOOR

Wilfred Hext said there was a Hext family trio; Uncle Edwin, Uncle Lewis and Hermon Hext, Wilfred's father. At Higher Pudsham lived his father and grandfather and also previously the home of his great, great grandfather. Messrs W. and H.R. Hext were on the breeders list of the first 1951 Whiteface Sheep Breeders Association. In fact, it would seem generations of Hexts at Pudsham and generations of Whitefaces 'for as long as sheep were kept', said Wilfred!

Old Ashburton Market. Wilfred and Hermon Hext (father and son). Very concentrated faces, Cecil Harris selling. 'Dust coated' Jasper (Dealer) in Hermon's pen.

Only recently have they been crossed for fat lambs and only up to a few years ago, pure Whiteface Dartmoors were still being purchased at Ashburton to cross for fat lambs, before the Whiteface died out at Pudsham as a pure breed!

So there has been a long, long chapter (150 years) linking the Whitefaces with the same family and the same farms, and the moor, here at Buckland.

Lower Pudsham was farmed by Uncle Edwin and Beara by Lewis Hext. All these farms adjoined each other, although Beara has now been split between neighbours. In fact, Lower and Higher Pudsham have come together as 'Pudsham' and together with some of Beara is now farmed by Derek Hext (Wilfred's son). Wilfred said the past was a 'way of farming' shared by many around the Parish of Widecombe and the surrounding area.

Many notable Widecombe people were mentioned; Sylvester Mann, Bill Langdon and William (Bill) Mann at Lizwell were all into Whitefaces.

There were, Wilfred explained, 'a fair "wack" of Whiteface-sheep and it could be said we were a bit overstocked even back then'!

Sheep keep it seems was always being taken. Swedes were taken away and fenced at Chudleigh (a Mr Dymond at Batcombe). Then the first week of March the sheep came home to swedes and lambing commenced.

As the grass came in the spring they went away to keep again at places like Woodland and Denbury. Then it was back to the home farms for shearing in June and so, finally, 'out to moor' with their lambs. Wilfred said they hardly ever seemed to be home for any length of time!

It seems sheep didn't do very well on the local commons of Pudsham and Buckland. So from Pudsham and Buckland the ewes and their lambs and the previous year's wethers were driven on foot, out eventually to the Warren Inn area via Runnage and would have come up beside the leat near Stannon newtake towards Fernworthy. The keep for the summer was not in the Newtakes.

The agister was Richard Coaker's father, Adolphus, for the keep of this area, and he was paid to keep the sheep and 'look around them'!

The Hext Brothers would have kept around 100 ewes producing 100 plus lambs and 100 wethers each to take up to Dartmoor (at least 300 sheep belonging to each brother). This would account for 900 plus Whiteface Sheep altogether to lear on the moor.

Wilfred said that his father Hermon and Uncle Edwin would sometimes drive their sheep together to their lears and Lewis would follow on separately.

On arriving near to their grazing lears, Wilfred explained that it was fun to see how the ewes and lambs would eat a bit and then the ewes begin to pick up their lambs and, after about an hour, each individual brother's sheep would take up in total, their own lear; one flock going one way and the other flocks another way. (Three flocks separately to their own lears). Hermon's sheep would graze around the Fernworthy Statts Bridge area between Merripitt, Warren Inn and Fernworthy. Lewis's sheep would disperse along the main road and around the back of the Warren Inn and Edwin's sheep could be seen to head for the 'mines' opposite the Inn on the lower side of the Moretonhampstead Princetown road. This must have been overall an impressive drift to lear.

This was happening as far back as the 1920's. The sheep seem to sense the time of year and were always ready to go to the moor lear in the summer and, equally, some would begin to make their way home before others in the autumn, as if to say 'we want something better now'! (A pattern of movement already explained by other moorland breeders).

However, on the whole when they were gathered later in the year, they would still be in their separate lears and 'hardly a sheep out of place', remarked Wilfred.

Sheep, it seems, were also driven early in the morning to Ashburton Sheep Sale from Buckland; this included Trants, Nosworthy and Hext's sheep in order to pen the sheep for a good selling number at the old Ashburton markets.

Other Whiteface sheep keepers, Wilfred mentioned, were Bill Caunter at Sweaton, John Hannaford at Southcombe and Leonard Hill at Lower Uppacott.

The Hext's used to sell sheep on the Green at Widecombe Fair. However, Wilfred pointed out that the dates of the fairs were changed. Traditional Widecombe Fair used to be before Ashburton Fair. However, Ashburton was brought forward and took place before Widecombe as a sale. Wilfred said this really 'killed' Widecombe because if you didn't sell your stock at Widecombe there were no other sales following to draft out ones stock before winter.

Talking of wool, Wilfred said, that before the 2nd World War broke out in 1939, the family had 10 years of wool in store. This wool was probably only worth 3½d a pound, stored in so called 'ricks' in their barns. During the war, 'the War Ag' commandeered wool on farms and wool and its price was controlled. However, eventually prices rose from 7d to 1s 3d a pound!

Sheep dipping just after the war took place at Little Stannon, and the Coakers dip was used for some four to five years, by the Hext family.

Derek recalls a black sheep turning up on one occasion in his Whiteface flock.

However, it was turned away to 'turnips' with its company and went missing presumed pinched!

It is interesting to reflect on a reference made in the 'News in Moreton' in 1855; 'Policing the Parishes of Chagford and Moreton'. Before a policeman was appointed sheep stealing and every species of petty theft were carried on with impunity and now we rarely see anything of the kind.'

Derek also said he can remember from a very early age holding sheep at Ashburton Sheep Sale for showing, by his father.

Leonard Hill[1] and Reg Hill[2]

[1]FORMERLY OF LOWER UPPACOTT, WIDECOMBE-IN-THE-MOOR
[2]FORMERLY OF GRIMSTONE NEAR BLACKAWTON

Len Hill is recorded as one of the first twenty seven members to join the W.F.D.S.B.A. and flock book in 1951, farming then at Uppacott, Widecombe-in-the-Moor. His brother too was a great Whiteface Dartmoor enthusiast and Reg is seen as part of the original Inspection Committee at Cudlipptown, Peter Tavy (Harry Rowse's farm) during the early days of tattooing sheep for the Association to identify the registered Whitefaces. Roy Hill, is a son of Len Hill and now lives at the School House, Leusdon, Poundsgate.

Roy's father Len, began farming at Lower Uppacott in around 1929. In the Devonshire Parishes Book of 1857 a James Warren, farmer and mason farmed Lower Uppacott and a John Warren farmer and mason farmed at Higher Uppacott.

Roy's Uncle Reg lives at Grimstone and farmed Whitefaces at Blackawton in quite a hard farming area that seem to favour Whitefaces.

Reg Hill's sheep were summered on the moor near Hexworthy, where the Smith Brothers (Jim and George) as moormen agisted the stock and money changed hands for keep and attention. The Smith's agisted over a big area, extending to Holne, Greenhill and the Erme Valley etc. So George and Jim Smith agisted moorland around where Len Hill also put his Whitefaces on their moorland lear to Hexworthy.

Reg Hill's sheep were walked up to the moor from Grimstone, Blackawton using dogs and horses. Edwin Pearse, sadly now passed away, who used to shear at Grimstone said, 'When it was near the time to putting the sheep on the moor from Blackawton they became restless and would, no doubt, even travel from Blackawton to Hexworthy virtually unattended remembering their way, from the fields at Grimstone!' This being not an uncommon story told by other Whiteface breeders in the South Hams who used the moor in summer.

Roy Hill explained the journey the sheep took from Grimstone, which he said one wouldn't attempt to take today, because of more traffic and faster roads.

He said the sheep would have come up the Totnes road from Grimstone, were slipped in at Buckfast and up towards the moor via Hembury over Holne Moor and finally to their lear at Hexworthy, a journey of some twenty miles or more!

Len Hill used to sell and buy Whitefaces at Ashburton and also judged Whitefaces at Widecombe Fair and Ashburton. In 1956 Reg Hill judged the Ram Hogg and old Ram Classes at Ashburton on September 6th along with Hermon French of South Brent. In the old Ram Class this particular year his brother Len Hill, Uppacott, Widecombe achieved second prize (first in this class was Cecil Caunter).

On September 5th, 1957 at the 7th Annual Show and Sale at Ashburton, Reg Hill judged the best-coated Ram, won by W.S. Steer of Dockwell, judging in company with T.H. Cole and M.J. (Jack) Bowden (Manaton) also Reg judged the best pair of ram hoggs, when C.E. Caunter and French Bros, Corringdon tied the class.

Also at the 9th Annual Show and Sale of Whitefaces on Thursday, September 3rd 1959, Peter Hannaford ('Sherwell', near Widecombe, also spelt 'Sherril') and Reg Hill, Grimstone, then judged all the sheep classes:

Ram Hogg	Ball	
	Mann Bros	
	French Bros Corringdon	– Rams in this class made to 25 gns
Old Ram	Coaker (Richard)	
	F. Nosworthy	
	C.E. Caunter	
Best Coated	Ball	
	Richard Coaker	
	F. Nosworthy	

Dipping from Uppacott used to take place at Hatchwell, Widecombe near to Langworthy Farm. Originally a John Hannaford in 1857 farmed both these two properties.

Edwin Pearse used to 'live in' when shearing at Reg Hill's farm at Grimstone, he said, 'The sheep were wonderful big Dartmoors (Whitefaces) like donkeys and sheared very good fleeces of wool; coming off as one fleece in many cases using the hand shears.

There were four or five hundred Whitefaces at Mr Hill's at that time and Edwin said 'They would come in day after day as a very even flock of sheep, all looking the same'.

Edwin also recalled that Reg Hill had big Whiteface rams that he sold, but Edwin said even back at this time it was difficult finding different lines of sheep to help mix the breeding. However, it seems Reg Hill used to breed dozens of rams for sale at Ashburton Fair and sold rams privately as well. Edwin Pearse travelled to many farms away from Bowden (his home) and into the South Hams to shear sheep.

He used to shear 50–60 sheep a day using just hand shears, starting at Kingsbridge and finishing up at Bere Alston. In one season he would shear around 3000 sheep.

He explained that the hand shears were made of solid steel and were very strong and firm. When sharpening them it was as much as Edwin could do to press the shears down on to the grinding stone, turned by someone else, to help put an 'edge' on them.

Sheep shears as part of a stand and turned by hand by someone other than the shearer came before electric shears. Apparently Edwin used to cut his brother's and sister's hair with such a gadget! This happened over 67 years ago and must be one of the oldest individual stories of working with Whitefaces.

Edwin was good with dogs and with Edwin just directing a particular dog from the farmyard, it would gather sheep three or four fields away and bring them back to him in the yard at Bowden. When keeping Whitefaces himself he gained first prize at Dousland Sheep Sale with sheep he took to the sale, and they also achieved top price.

There were Whitefaces all around Widecombe and Holne and Edwin stayed and sheared at places like Combestone ('Cumpson') with Harry and Polly Norrish.

The wool was very important and lots of money paid for it and Edwin talks about how the staple strength was improved by encouraging two strands thickness of wool and this was more likely to be achieved on in-country farms. Here on the moorland farms thinner strands were more likely to be seen. The result of 'two-strand wool' was to produce heavier fleeces.

Edwin even recalled having to sleep on the wool in some cases in the barns where he sheared and there was 'shift-working'. Also wool might have to be kept for years to achieve a half-decent price.

At one particular farm where he went in for dinner, because being given dinner was part of the shearing job, he remembers being given 'dumplings' (suet cooked) with his stew, but Edwin joked that, 'they were so hard that if you drilled a hole in one you could make a hammer out of it!'

When Edwin sheared lambs he said he would put the shears in water before sharpening them to achieve a different 'bite' and this helped him to shear lambs faster.

Shearing was hard work because on most occasions the shearer had to catch the sheep and tie up the wool as well as do the shearing. So all the work had to be done and wool left tidy and not thrown out of the door, Edwin recalled.

Sometimes he sheared lambs wet to get the job done and then drying the wool later outside on a fine day.

Edwin said the Monks of Buckfast, Buckland and Tavistock had sheep and used the moor and the Buckfast Woollen Mills were very important.

He also said that the Dartmoor people were the only ones that put Whiteface Dartmoor sheep 'to moor' in the summer with their lambs.

It seems the Monks at Buckfast 'depastured' the moor with many sheep near to where the Avon Dam was built. Once the area was flooded and given over to the dam, their grazing here was gone forever.

The catchment area above the dam consists of 3,125 acres of moorland with no dwellings upon it except Huntingdon Warren. It was said Moorland sheep, cattle and wild ponies graze in the area rising to '1850 absl'. It is said, sheep wanted to go back to their lear after the land was flooded! 'This, to a piece of land that was no longer theirs'!

Whitefaced Dartmoors – A New Society's First Fixture.
Judges at the Ashburton Show and Sale of the Dartmoor Whiteface Sheep Breeders'Association.
Messrs. W. J. Mann (*ewes*, left) and R. (Reg) Hill (*rams*), 1951.

Miss June Howell (Associate Member)

IVYBRIDGE – PREVIOUSLY L.J. ADAMS AND J. HOWELL

The Adams and Howell team became very much in evidence with their Whiteface Dartmoor Sheep, especially in the 1970's and 1980's and Leslie Adams managed Miss Howell's land and animals. Their flock was started in 1976 provided by Jack Lambshead and others and a Ron Norrish ram.

Miss Howell recalls Prince Charles on a visit to the Devon County Show speaking to Ned Northmore. Leslie Adams was stood beside Ned at the time because he was showing sheep on this occasion too. Prince Charles came as President of the show in 1979.

In 1978 Leslie and June won the Reserve Breed Champion award at the Devon County Show for their Whiteface Sheep (ram).

'Savery' Ram – 1981.
Champion at Devon County, Widecombe Fair and South Brent.
L.J. Adams and J. Howell.

The Devon County Show on one occasion was very muddy (probably 1981), like 'liquid mud', Miss Howell recalls. Their male champion in the show classes had to be led by Leslie to the main show ring in all this mud! It was a Savery bred ram owned by the team, also winning at the Devon County Show, the Lloyds Bank sash and Money prize as well as the Championship in 1984 (Also their hoggs won wool prizes (two tooths) as a full mouth; (J.S.9/R1), its sire was bred by F.J. Trant.

At the Society Show and Sale the best pen of two-tooth ewes, sired by a Philip Coaker ram, won first prize on one occasion. Flock Competition success was also achieved before the Miss Needham Cup came into being. Also local showing at Cornwood and Yealmpton, for example, and South Brent in the 1960's, and here on one occasion Ned Northmore judged. Adams and Howell also won at Brent in 1981; and The Mann Bros Cup at Widecombe for best ram was won in 1981.

In 1982 and 1985 at Yealmpton Show, Adams & Howell won the John Harris Trophy for best Whiteface Dartmoor Sheep in the Show, and also in 1985 winners at Totnes, of the Whiteface Challenge Cup.

But like all competition showing, Miss Howell remarked, 'One minute you are riding a crest of a wave and the next minute down again'. However, she said the house was plastered with rosettes won by their Whitefaces.

In 1982 and 1983, 90 ewes were recorded in the flock and ewe lambs and ram hoggs consistently reared, kept and shown.

She recalls at the Devon County Show on two occasions how her sheep got pneumonia in the tent housing a lot of sheep and the sheep had to be taken home. (It seemed the flaps of the tent remained closed). Permission had to come from the Chief Steward and at the time he was in conversation with the Duke of Kent. Apparently at the old County Show Ground at Whipton, because it was on top of a hill, there was, Miss Howell commented, either a howling gale blowing through the sheep tent or it became too hot inside if the flaps were closed.

She entered the Ciba-Geigy 'Golden Fleece' Competition, where wool is sent away for judging, winning prizes. The last ram was sold in 1994.

In 1985 Adams & Howell presented a Challenge Cup for Best Old Ram at the Association Show and Sale; having won the Savery Cup outright with a Savery Ram in 1982, 1983 and a Patrick Coaker Ram in 1984, at Ashburton.

A trait commonly seen in rams; the rams were expected to have beards. A crest of hairy wool under the chin and on the neck denoted hardness and allowed the water to run off!

She recalls buying sheep from the Ogles at Skerraton. Grass keep was rented at Ermington and Burrator etc in an early grass growing area.

The Irish Family

GRENDON, WIDECOMBE

When we think of Widecombe and Whiteface Dartmoor Sheep, it is inevitable not to think of the name Irish and farms like Grendon that holds the heart of the breed's home and a history of dedicated farmers.

Gertrude Irish affectionately holding one of the families highly valued indigenous sheep.

Wherever a sheltered valley can be found for the home enclosures farming can be kinder than on the open moor; such is Grendon. It is interesting to find chronicled in 'Dartmoor a New Study' by Crispin Gill 'that shelter-belts were also made in the 1860's and 1870, notably

The whole family,hoeing the 'turnip' field at Grendon.

at Grendon across Cator Common and at Princetown, by convict labour, though the belt known as Long Plantation was formed a little later.

Most of Colin Irish's aunties and uncles were born at Bellever, Postbridge (seven children in all). Of these relations, Wif, Jack and Gertrude kept Whiteface Dartmoors at Broadaford during the early part of the 1900s. They moved from Broadaford in 1907 to Grendon, but were farming both farms for a time.

The uncles that farmed Grendon along with Colin's father, Austin, before the war were Wif and Jack (Wilfred and John). During the war Colin's father was involved with Dunkirk and the Army Police.

Colin said 'when the move to Grendon was made the Widecombes went too, learing on Grendon Common'. The family used to show at Widecombe Fair and sell Widecombes on the green when sheep and cattle were sold there along with ponies.

Colin recalled his grandmother walking to Ashburton with butter in a market basket and then coming home to help hoe mangels!

Wif Irish did not drive a tractor or car and would go away many miles from Grendon to view farms to assess winter keep, such as swedes, on his bike. Corn (barley or oats) after 'folded' turnips on these farms with all the fertility from the sheep would crop well the following year.

Colin and his uncle used to drive Whiteface sheep to 'Venton' near Rattery (Tom Hodge's farm) from Grendon on many occasions and walked their sheep home in June via Buckfastleigh Race Course, Blagdon and Summer Hill; some 20 miles, on to the Newtakes. Their moorland grazing was Spitchwick Common and the East Quarter of Dartmoor and the back of Riddon Ridge.

Colin said 'Wif used to take his bike so he could ride home from Rattery when the autumn "drives" took place.' This 'drift' Colin said took place in November after the rams had been put in at home (around the 8th October) so as to start their lambing in March.

As a young boy I can just remember them passing near to my father's farm at Glebe, Rattery only a couple of miles from Venton.

John, Wilf and Colin at Grendon, hand shearing their 'Widecombes' (1965).

Colin explained the breed characteristics are a strong curl to the coat or wool of the sheep, broad, black-tipped nose, good bone and thick body. However, he feels today that the breed is losing the bone size.

The sheep of Colin's grandfather were pitch marked, S.I. (Sidney Irish). The black pitch mark can be seen on the sheep's wool in the photograph with Gertrude.

In 1964 the Irish Brothers won the W.F.D.S.B.A. Challenge Cup presented by Richard Coaker for best pen of 10 ewes which they also won in 1969 with their Whiteface Sheep. The last ram the Irish Brothers bred was sold to Terry Phipps.

It was not uncommon, Colin said, to come back from Ashburton Sheep Show and Sale as late as midnight in the past, because there were so many sheep to be sold and on getting back to the Tavistock Inn it was dark and the only way to see home was to guide oneself between the tall lines of beech trees at Grendon.

Colin remembers being dragged out of bed at midnight by his uncles during the bad snow blizzard of 1962–3 to help stop the sheep being 'snowed-in and lost'. Sheep, the opposite to cattle, always seem to want to go *with* the snow wind and become buried in deep drifts. So with a lantern and a dog called Sharp, Colin had to try and keep the sheep where the snow was drifting the least (some 60 Whitefaces). Later, if unsuccessful, dogs would mark buried sheep.

Near to Blackaton, Colin recalled how the bulldozer trying to clear the roads later, piled the snow some 26 ft high, but it 'caved' back into the road like a frozen mass and the road was impassable for weeks.

Colin said at lambing time Wif might not sleep for a whole week because he was also helping neighbours like General Sturges and doing the Irish's own lambing.

Another story emphasising the bond between man and dog was told by Colin. When out in the fields at night a particular dog of Colin's would come back to rub his legs to indicate a fox was nearby. It would also catch foxes as they came out of the withy (willow) beds at Grendon.

Colin highlighted how Wif Irish used to wear white heather on the lapel of his jacket at

Reg Aplin and 'Wif' Irish at Widecombe Fair.

Widecombe Fair. He said 'Wif would go looking for the white heather weeks before the Fair at a particular spot on the moor'. It has also been mentioned that in order to be sure of some white heather Wif used to cover over some heather that might be red and deny it the sun to change its colour to white!

Colin used to help with the 'swaling' on Hameldon in the spring so that re-growth of the heather in future years would be enhanced by the ashes remaining from the burning and this helped to nourish the recovering heather and grass aided by stock grazing and treading. Obviously the burnt areas were sweetened by this 'swaling' routine; almost like a coat of lime!

The Irish Family

CATOR, WIDECOMBE-IN-THE-MOOR

Betty Hicks (nee Irish) explained that there had been five generations of the Irish family going back 150 years at Cator. Great Grandfather was Edmund Irish and father was Walter (Edmund) Irish. The original settlement was a longhouse dwelling (13–14th Century) with a cobbled yard used by John Irish for cattle.

The pattern seen so many times around Widecombe, repeats itself at Cator where there were always Whiteface Dartmoor Sheep and South Devon cattle. As Betty said, 'everybody went on the same!' So their farming system changed little over the years.

Betty said that Uncle Walter, Grandfather's brother, used to go out when it was dark and plough by lantern. The lamp was attached to the 'hames' of the horses' harness. 'Crossing'

Yealmpton Show in the 1980s. First for ewe lambs (and other prizes on the day). Showing John and daughters, Angela, Susan and Clare.

was moved by the remoteness of this part of the Moor and spoke of the air of 'semi-wildness' worn by its heathery downs (some new reclaimed) and intermingled with little irregularly shaped 'crofts' (farmsteads) many of them very ancient, and which speak of a time when the early farm settlers forced their way into these upland valleys! Maybe of Celtic and Saxon heritage born by name too in tor and ford!

As far as Whiteface sheep were concerned, Ashburton Sheep Fair was always used to sell and trade sheep and rams. A new Whiteface ram was bought usually every two years.

Betty Hicks' brother, John Irish, explained that sheep were always driven to Ashburton Fair and laired the night before in a field near Great Bridge ready to take into the sale the following morning. John said he used to meet up with Wif Irish from Grendon at 'Three Gates' near Broadaford and all their sheep would be driven to Ashburton together. Betty was quite upbeat about the names given to moorland gates; like 'Two Gates', 'Three Gates' and 'Bluegate' (Hill) etc. and there is 'two crosses' too!

George Shillibeer at Bellever, Postbridge made the comment that there were always 'a cracking lot of Whiteface sheep' to be seen beside the old Widecombe road near to Cator belonging to the Irish's.

Malcolm Whiteside (whose mother's maiden name was Warren; a very old Widecombe name) explained he did a lot of shearing at Cator with John. He also said that Joe Mortimore used to help by 'bellying' out the sheep and opening up the neck of the 'tied' (close knotted wool) sheep to make the shearing with electric shears easier when removing the rest of the fleece. Joe would use his handshears to tease away the wool. This happened in the early days of electric shearing machines. The longwools would have been more difficult to shear off with untidy areas of wool around their body.

John Irish shearing a Whitefaced Dartmoor, securing the sheep with his legs splayed across the sheep's neck, to finish the shearing!

On this day the Widecombe sheep were penned in a steep-sided pen (as shown) and three sheep were suffocated and trampled in the bottom corner and died.

All farm tasks involving the movement and collection of sheep either for shearing, dipping, drenching and feet trimming etc can result in accidents as the sheep are often tense and frustrated by handling, and dogs present can be unpredictable and over-excited by the occasion.

Cator is a farm from which the rights on Spitchwick Common can be enjoyed from Newbridge to Cator Gate coming through to the farm. This is the East Quarter of the Moor. Venville rights were paid to Richard Coaker.

Many of the moorland gates (Cator Gate etc) were replaced with cattle grids in the second half of the 1900's.

As an open common Dartmoor is of most value when worked in connection with in-country farms; 'the great drawback being that unless for a very hardy stock, the place is so very exposed and the winters so long!; a livelihood is hard won!

To this end Betty and John's father Walter Irish used to take winter keep away. Together with Joe Mortimore they used to take roots at Tom Hodge's, Venton Farm, Tigley near Totnes. Margaret Rogers recalls the big drifts leaving 'Sherril Green' in Spring.

W.F. Miners (Bill) was the haulier from Widecombe for sheep that went away to keep from Cator. John remembers hoggs lorried to Stoke Gabriel for wintering. The lorry was open top and the back ramp used to slide under the lorry for transport, and was pulled out to load the animals.

Amusingly it seems the lorry was washed out in order to take locals and young farmers to dances!

Neighbours too came to mind, and John spoke of yet another family farm cared for by brothers; – the 'Leamons' at Dury and Cator Court; Herbert ('Herb') and George. An ageing bowler-hatted Herbert can be picked out in the centre of the old Ashburton Market photograph showing a market full of sheep near to Ned Caunter, and other faces are familiar to some too! (see Secretary's letter).

John continued with the Whitefaces after his father died and the flock book records show he had 130 sheep in 1985.

An interesting mix of breeders sires were used, e.g. M.K. and J. Widdicombe, Norman Stephens, John Savery, Edward Caunter, Philip Coaker, Henry Bond and Terry Phipps. All these breeders rams were used after 1979.

In 1952 Henry Brown said his father (Arthur) bought a good Whiteface ram from Walter Irish of Cator.

In 1983 John won the best flock of ewe lambs judged on the farm by the Association judges. Also in 1984 the Whitefaced Dartmoor Sheep Breeders Association Challenge Cup presented by Miss Needham for the best flock of over 50 ewes, came to Cator.

John always had good dogs around him witnessed by the photograph. Even today he has requests for sheep dog collies from contacts up country. His father and himself always bred the same strain, and the same breed year on year, and there were nearly always a couple of 'bob-tail' puppies (short quarter-length tails) in a litter!

For John the memories of the 1962/63 snow winter were still very vivid. The sheep were nearby, but didn't move for weeks and weeks, staying on the same circle of snow. Great balls of snow attached to ponies tails as they dragged their tails along the drifted tracks. Hay was the only available feed, as all the roots were buried and couldn't be reached. The milk lorry it seems was buried near Broadaford with no chance of collecting milk at Riddon, Broadaford, or Shallowford etc for a long time to come, during the coldest winter for one hundred and fifty years.

Charles Vancouver's 'General View of the Agriculture of the County of Devon (1808)' says,

Flock judging at Cator.
A neat agile young ram with 'clean' Whiteface character, typical of John's sheep, and his sheep dog keeping an eye on events.

'from the number of sheep annually summered upon Dartmoor the ewes and lambs are brought down into the country on the approach of winter, together with the preceding year's hogg sheep. A large proportion of sheep stock is always found to occupy the surrounding districts during the winter season. The greater part of these flocks, being wethers and chiefly preserved for their wool, are left upon the forests during winter. This right doubtless originated with a tenancy in Venville. The leading object Vancouver says with all the flock-masters is over wintering for the wethers wool; but under such harsh conditions considerable losses are sustained'.

The broken-mouthed sheep were culled at shearing time and some, if not fit to sell, are fattened at home. The 'caw' or liver rot wasn't picked up on Dartmoor, but sheep 'scab' was a problem on the Moor, and spread amongst sheep. It seems if a severe winter was in prospect the wether flocks were removed from the heights!

Vancouver also says, 'the usual consideration paid to those who rent the different quarters of the forest of Dartmoor directly from His Royal Highness the Prince of Wales, is 3s 4d per score annually; a sum considered sufficient to exempt them from all liability of having their sheep impounded or taken up as 'estrays'!'

William Marshall's 'Rural Economy of the West of England' (1796) says 'rights are secured on respective commons with a few pence annually under the name of 'Venville money', to the Duchy. The Duchy reserve the right of agistment, preserving the right of flocking the forest lands.

Sheep breeds vary on the 'Southern hangs' and on the upper mountain parts here the polled breed of the South Hams are mostly feen (seen), and on the Northern and Western fides' (partially horned breed). The partially horned breed are prevalent, corresponding in general appearance with the established breed of the Cornish mountains, with Whiteface connections. In winter these sheep are drawn down to the inclosed (enclosed) country where the ewes drop their lambs and return with them in the Spring to their mountain pasture.' Hence, 'the leading object of the "Moorside Farmer" is to "raife" (raise) fodder enough for his cattle, and to preserve "graff" (grass) enough for his sheep, to supply them during the winter months; depending almost wholly on the commonable lands for their summer maintenance.' (Working Oxen it says are everywhere fed on the commonable land, their work though under this treatment it says 'was moderate!')

Walter Kernick

FORMERLY OF ISAFORD FARM, WIDECOMBE-IN-THE-MOOR

I found Walter Kernick's name on the first list of the Whiteface Dartmoor Sheep Breeders Association as a registered breeder among 27 names. I traced his son, Brian, and found that Walter was still alive and retired in Cornwall. He drove to Tavistock where his son and daughter-in-law now live. At the age of 90 years old he came to tell me his story.

He was born in 1910 and will be 92 years old in October 2002. At the age of 14 years old he left school and worked at Brook Farm (Coombe, Buckfastleigh) for a Walter Abbot. Greyface Dartmoor Sheep were kept at Brook. Walter Kernick eventually became the horseman at Brook.

He recalled at a very young age having to plough and till ground with horses and harvesting crops in different ways according to its condition. He remembered a cornfield that had gone down flat on the ground with the weather and he had to help cut it with a scythe so as not to lose the heads. However, his boss lost patience and just pushed it up into a rick with a horse and sweep and promptly lost a lot of the ears of corn after all the hard work of cutting the corn by hand!

On another occasion Walter was left to drill a field of oats with horses; however, on finishing the field he had one bag of seed over. On arriving home his boss made him drill the whole field again, cutting the drill back to cover the whole field with the remaining bag of oats.

In 1926 he recalled having to take 30 of his boss's sheep to Ashburton Market at 4 o'clock in the morning with his dog named, reassuringly 'Help'. Then he returned to Brook at 9 o'clock to get the bullocks ready for market too.

John Sawdye's father sold the sheep, but on arriving back at the market, he found that his boss, Walter Abbot, had only sold 2 pens of sheep and so the remaining 10 sheep had to be walked home.

Walter lived at Hawson Court in 1935 and from there he rented land from a Miss Codd at Scoriton Gate and other land at New Park, Buckfastleigh. Also up until 1945 Walter was contracting (agriculture).

He said, however, that after the 2nd World War farmers started getting their own tractors and only had contractors where they could not go themselves, so he sold his business in 1945.

Then he bought a 'fergy' tractor, or was, in fact, persuaded to hire purchase this tractor and with the change he had over (from the £333 tractor value) he bought 30 sheep at St John's Fair, Tavistock in 1945 (total price £207) and these were Leonard Ball's Whiteface breeding.

Commenting on why he chose Whitefaces, Walter replied that 'a Dartmoor was a sheep that could live on Dartmoor all the time' and that's why he liked them!

In 1947 these sheep he said 'were up against the moor near to Scoriton Gate and when the snow came in late January, he could not get them away. The sheep he said, somehow had to dig back the snow to try and get at the grass, and stayed put. It seems they all lambed against the moor and when the snow went he took them down to New Park.' On passing Owen Mann's at Scoriton Farm, the latter remarked, 'on how well the sheep had survived compared to his that had been given a lot of attention.'

During the earlier blizzard winter of 1927 and when still at Brook, Walter recalled helping the Pearse family at Bowden farm to dig out sheep, and even moving some in a wheelbarrow!

In 1951 the Kernicks moved to Isaford driving their sheep from Hawson Court by road and Brian Kernick said the journey was often 'repeated' in reverse because they kept on Hawson Court for a while when at Isaford. Brian was only 15 years old at the time. Colin Slade and his family now farm Isaford without sheep!

At this time, Walter remembers Cecil Harris forming a committee to start the Whiteface Association. Walter, then at Isaford, was one of the first registered breeders of Whitefaces.

Remembering the moor as he did in days gone by, he remarked that it was managed differently in the past. When swaling, for example, they used to keep fires going day and night but now there is too much bracken and the whortleberries are smaller! His best days in farming were he said, 'when driving horses'.

There were he explained 'Moormen on Dean, Buckfastleigh and Holne Moors, Edmunds, Eden etc. to tend the agisted stock, but farmers only kept what the farms could hold!'

Wool was he said 'hoarded till it was worth something'. At Brook Farm, the wool was stored in the 'Wagon House' and Walter remembers periodically having to pour water over the wool, presumably to prevent it drying out too much!

When at Isaford, Widecombe, Brian said dipping took place at Northway (Bill and Reg Norrish). 'The Norrish's would dip them in for you' he said. That is put your sheep in the dip for you. All the neighbours descended on Northway to dip their sheep; people like Ned Northmore from Kingshead. The road had to be right (clear of other sheep) before going home so as not to meet other farmer's sheep on their way to be dipped. Walter's sheep had to be let up in the higher yard at Northway before they could be moved home. Dipping when living at Hawson Court for the Kernicks was at Brook Farm.

One particular ram bought early on in their breeding programme with the Whitefaces came from Sid Trant, but one day it knocked Walter over and Brian found Walter upside down, kicking his feet in the air and up against the hedge. Brian had to pull the ram away to avoid Walter being hurt. The ram, it seems, was later sold to French's of Michelcombe, but it was put in a footpath field and the Post Mistress at Holne was attacked when she was going across the field!

During the late twenties, Walter said Edwin Pearse used to help with shearing (60 sheep a day with hand shears). I suggested this was a lot of sheep to get through with hand shears, but Walter remarked that Edwin had to get through so many because he needed the money, but I feel he must have been a competent shearer. Edwin would charge 2/6d a score during the late twenties.

In the 1950's Walter's sheep were dispersed at Ashburton and were the last pens to be sold on the day by Cecil Harris for £4.10s.

Iron-shafts that attached this horse-drawn 'scuffle' to a working horse; handles are visiable for the 'Farmhand' to guide the implement, walking from behind.

H.J. Lentern (Archie)

COCKINGFORD MILL, WIDECOMBE-IN-THE-MOOR

Having started his career in agricultural contracting with the Whites of Broadhempston in 1953 Archie Lentern moved to a farm of thirty acres at Cockingford Mill, Widecombe-in-the-Moor.

His flock of ten sheep (Whiteface Dartmoors) originated from Joe Mortimore when he farmed at Shallowford.

The flock was built up to 60 sheep using a 'Savery' ram early in the breeding programme. Some showing took place at Widecombe Fair and he gained first prize for lambs at the Autumn Show and Sale held annually in October at Ashburton Market. The judge was Philip Coaker.

Summer and winter keep were always used because his acreage at home was so small. His ewes and lambs were put into Stannon newtake. This was a natural lear because the original ewes came from Joe Mortimore's flock that also leared in this area. The sheep came home in September/October.

Lambing time was in March and mainly outdoors. Winter keep was at Gordon Stones at Ogwell.

Talking about the use of trains conjured up memories for Mr Lentern. 'He vividly remembers horns two or three foot long sticking out the sides of cattle trucks as the trains filled up with animals that had been sold at Ashburton Fair' There were special loading pens for these animals at the market near to the trains. The fairs were a regular occurrence throughout the year and many animals changed hands. The trains moved on down to Totnes via Staverton, where many animals were reloaded and sent up country to dealers premises for sale onto farmers again, in places such as the Midlands and Yorkshire, to fattening pastures and wintering yards. This practice is by road now, because the branch train lines closed, but the trade is a mere shadow of its former self.

It seems from Ashburton little movement of sheep took place on the trains.

Mr Lenten remembers a distinct division of the cattle market at Ashburton, with Rendells selling in the 'Top Market' and Sawdyes in the 'Bottom Market'. The 'Railway Inn' opposite the west end of the Top Market became renamed as the 'Silent Whistle', no doubt appropriately when the trains stopped and the station closed in the late 1950s!

Ashburton Market has not reopened since Foot and Mouth, and may never do so on its present site. A market charter dated 1310 exists for Ashburton, but a series of unprecedented events have come about in the last decades of the 1900s; the implementation of quotas on production, an escalation in tuberculosis in cattle, and with BSE and Foot and Mouth removing millions of animals not used for human consumption, all this has combined to starve the markets of animals and so of revenue!

The Mann's Family

GREAT DUNSTONE, WIDECOMBE-IN-THE-MOOR

Three 'Manns' on right side of photograph. Right to left: Richard Mann holding the first prize rosette at Widecombe, in front of his father O.S. Mann (Oliver Sylvester). Beside them A.W. Mann (Arthur William) – 'Mann Bros.'.

It seems almost unreal that generations of the same family over at least some one hundred and fifty years can succeed in keeping the same breed of cattle and sheep on the same family farm. Yet this is repeated on many farms on and around the Moor where families have never moved and South Devon Cattle and Whitefaced Dartmoor sheep have always been kept with a great deal of family pride!

The pasturing of stock, cattle and sheep, on the Moor is a very family blooded instinct, and tradition bonding, unquestioned, man to his beast, and both to the Moor. Also, such is the expectancy of this situation continuing, family Christian names are inherited too! One such family is the Mann's at Great Dunstone (four generations), where a form of birth right is established that envelops the farmstead and the animal with the people.

William Crossing reveals that in the 'Court Rolls of the 10th of Henry VI, 1432–3 a Robert Manna is mentioned; in 1579–80 Anthony Man of 'Wydecomb', surrendered the 'morety' (share) of a tenement at Babeny, then held by Leonard Man (note the presence of only one 'n').

Sylvester said the Mann family have lived in Widecombe as far as records can show. A copy of the Devon Historian shows a Sylvester Mann in 1645 on the burial register. In 1702 Richard Man is named as one of the forest tenants at Dunnabridge. The Churchwardens in 1786 were Peter and Sylvester Mann in Widecombe.

There is probably little doubt that the family's ancestors shepherded the 'wastes of the

Moor', and were 'leared to the farmstead like their sheep were leared to the Moor!' Though not it would seem out of obligation but borne out of a love for the animals, the place and the people and their families inheritance; not challenged by outside forces!

As one enters the steep drive that at Great Dunstone leads down to the farmstead, the house is seen to be thatched, and the old porch and living room face the cluster of tors above the Widecombe valley, and 'pil tor' in particular, is visible from the house.

Sylvester Mann's Grandfather, Richard, came to Great Dunstone on his marriage to Betsy French and rented the farm in around the mid-eighteen hundreds (rents were about £1 per acre).

Very strict rules governed tenants:- there was to be only one mowing of grass a year; no sale of corn, or 'stay' turnips, no sale of manure. The only dogs to be kept were sheep dogs. Animals had to be prevented from grazing woodland; also birds, their nest eggs and their young were to be preserved, and any game preserved. A conveyance between landlord and tenant seem to have one page relating to the Landlord and seven pages of duty for the tenant to strictly adhere to, whilst carrying out his farming, and strict rules applied on how the farm's condition is left on relinquishing the tenancy back to the Landlord at some later stage. Gladys Mann met and married Sylvester as a Land Army girl from Kingsbridge, and then settled into Widecombe. To start with she thought the farming on Dartmoor was old fashioned and behind the times and the sheep very small, as 'Dartmoor Widecombes' could be in the past. Her native South Hams sheep were the bigger 'South Devons', thriving on the red, and better soils of South Devon. But she loved Dartmoor and along with Sylvester she used to visit Leonard Ball and his wife at 'Axna' and the compliment returned, and sheep were always on the agenda! Gladys also spoke of her journeys with the pram in their van, on taking sheep to keep at Torbryn.

Sheep also used to be walked to Widecombe Fair where the farmers got together buying and

A picture dated 1906, 'Widecombe Fair'. Whitefaced Dartmoor Rams tied to carts, offered between farmers (an old reason for the ancient fair).

selling their stock in the past to one another without an auctioneer; two or three sovereigns would buy a good ewe, dropping to just one sovereign for a plain ewe (about 1 gn).

The Mann's also walked their sheep, accompanied by horsemen, some sixteen miles to the Marldon area, Edginswell and Coffinswell. Nearly all the farmers and their children rode a Dartmoor pony, usually with nothing more than a sack for a saddle, and binder-twine traced for a halter. Also these ponies were safe to ride carrying a farmer all day over the Moors, sure-footed over the rocks, and avoiding the mires (bogs) (Dartmoor Magazine, No. 38 – C. Seward).

Sylvester and Arthur, who also knew the South Hams like the back of his hand, sometimes took 'keep' in the Kingsbridge area, and starting from home, farmers on horses controlled the flock. They used to rest up at Totnes, where local farmers would put up the flock of sheep and horses and the men for the night, and then the journey continued the next day. In-country wintering of sheep by moorland farmers was common practice, and a way of life.

It was in 1955 that 'Mann Brothers' bought Great Dunstone Farm; Oliver Sylvester (O.S.) and Arthur William (A.W.). So again this strong partnership with brothers running their farm together comes to the surface, both with stockmanship in their blood, and all round farming skills that were self-taught and handed down family to family.

Sylvester judged mostly at local shows but enjoyed judging at the Devon County Show, and Arthur liked showing too. Richard used to help Uncle Arthur 'trace ropes' to halter sheep to show.

1990 – Sylvester judging at home at Widecombe Fair.

Richard Mann, Sylvester's son and his wife Caroline, have continued to farm Great Dunstone up until this day, and have a young family (two sets of twins and eldest daughter).

Mann's sheep used the newtake keep at Stannon. Historically it is said from around June to October the open moorland and newtakes of the Forest of Dartmoor and its surrounding commons became the grazing ground for thousands of beasts. All evidence suggests (Dartmoor Magazine issue No. 43. 'Red Tide' by Tom Greeves.) Dartmoor was highly prized as a grazing area three and four thousand years ago, if not earlier, and that it was used far more intensively than in either the Medieval period or present day. The great 'territorial

Hand shearing at Dunstone.
Left to right: Sylvester Mann, Arthur Mann, Sam Cannon and William Oldrieve.

reaves', some of which run for miles across open moorland, appear, it is recorded, to be dividing areas of grazing. The High Moor was open country at least by 1500BC. The soil and hence the quality of the grass was probably better than today. Richard said his father often spoke of the 'big drifts' of cattle and sheep to Dartmoor, and Sylvester said this happened in the summer on every Saturday in June, and the animals returned in early autumn (1800–1900s).

In the early part of the 20th Century, there were several flocks of Whitefaced Dartmoors within Great Stannon Newtake. Some belonged to Richard Mann of Dunstone, William Mann of Linchaford, Owen Mann of Bowden, Buckland-in-the-Moor, and Hannaford and George Hext of Tor, Poundsgate. The story remains with history as only a handful of sheep (i.e. Whitefaces) keep up the tradition. (Freda Wilkinson).

The Mann's sheep were leared around Lade Hill (Lad'll) Bottom in the above Newtake. Animals were identified by iron pitching (of sheep) to mark their owner's initials and saw branding of the horns of cattle, and the specific quarter mark was also branded on the horn using a heated iron (East, West, South and North – E.W.S.N.)

When the Scotch sheep arrived on the Moor, there was it seems a 'no nonsense policy' to help separate these sheep from the Widecombes using the sheep dogs. Amusingly at lambing time if the sheep dogs saw a different colour lamb from a 'Widecombe' Whiteface in the flock, they would try and separate it out from the Whitefaces, because they were used to separating the different adult breeds on the Moor.

Wool was regularly graded on the farm, and was also held over if cheap until the price went up. At Dunstone it was stacked like a 'rick of hay' in a barn in the yard.

There was often fun amongst farmers, and on one occasion a guessing game went on as to the 'weight of a fleece', which at the time did seem quite heavy (20lbs would not be unusual for a Whiteface Dartmoor Ram to shear). The guessing game went on for some time until the fleece became ragged and one day a ploughshare fell out! Game over!

Richard explained how his father Sylvester rode to Kings Ash Hill, Paignton, leaving early one morning to tail-lock out 60 sheep with handshears; the wool was placed in bags, and put on the horse either side of the saddle and he rode home via the Rising Sun Inn; a round journey of some 30 miles, and all in a day's work! Some shearers valued their shears so much they even kept them under their bed! Anecdotes and stories of endeavour abound. The enthusiasm that greeted me everywhere for the breed was stimulating and made one want to go home and put the rams in with the ewes, be it summer or winter, and increase the flock!

Richard felt whatever the prices for their sheep through the year, there was a real sense of pride that existed back in the old days, both the sheep and the people explicitly presented, and showing too, was a special day out.

The presence of black and rust are acceptable traits in the Whiteface. Black spots of varying sizes on the ear, and a big round black spot was said to be worth a guinea, and is a strong identification regularly seen on sheep today.

'Rust' or a tortoise-shell colour is prevalent too on occasions, found on the top of the tail, on the rump, and on the back of the neck and ears. When the sheep is shorn, it can show up as round patches on the rump.

Wool on the sheep's head is less common today, where 'clean hands' are the norm! Also more noticeable than today, and in the past a hardy straight area of wool down the flanks was evident; goaty beards (of historic significance) and sharp high shoulders on rams was supposed to denote milk in the offspring female.

Sylvester remarked 'that breeding for more wool you will lose the true type of Widecombe sheep, and lose their hardiness, so much prized on the Moor in the past'.

However such was the price and demand for wool in days gone by that the wool taken off a wether would pay for that wether's keep for a whole year!

It seems tails were grown shorter and of three-quarter length in the past!

Treatment, it was said, for ailing sheep, was to bleed them in the 'olden days'; before penicillin and modern drugs a farmer knew it was either try bleeding, or watch them die! Richard was told by his Uncle Arthur about taking sheep to Ashburton Market, probably to the field called 'The second Meda' (the Meadow) on Whistley Hill. When the Auctioneers opened for market, no pens were allocated, so farmers like Arthur would quickly grab one of their sheep to put in a pen to reserve that particular pen for the rest of their ewes in order to obtain a decent position in the sale. Obviously a lot of sheep overall would have been sold and a full day's auction took place. Many of these sheep fairs occurred in the street in the past, and near to railway stations to help move animals away . . . The sheep dog seems to often make its way into the photo's! I said to Richard, 'What did your father call the dog', and

Ashburton Market (Vealenia Terrace). Sylvester Mann receiving a winning trophy from Cecil Caunter.

Richard said 'Ben'. I remarked, 'how did you remember that', with his Dartmoor humour, he replied, 'they were *all* called Ben!'

Richard recalls memories of dipping the Mann's sheep that grazed 'big or Great Stannon'. The sheep were dogged down through 'Little Stannon Newtake', to the sheep dip in the said newtake. Sometimes Richard said it was pouring with rain, and you couldn't see the Moor or the sheep; but it seems whatever the weather the sheep had to be dipped! Sylvester used to round up his sheep in Stannon. It seems on one occasion that others collecting sheep from the Forest and Winney's Down when it was blowing and raining came back to the dip drenched, only finding a thorn bush to shelter under on the moor!

Relating to the weather again, the drilling of swedes in a sloping field was always a gamble, and sometimes in June, early July a thunderstorm would wash them out into the road, and down the farmyard lane if it was nearby. The date of drilling was always strictly observed, and sayings handed down were followed by generation after generation. Richard gave an example: in relation to when to drill swedes, it's said 'every day *after* the 21st of June is a week too late! Re-drilling after a catastrophe would mean the swedes will never be as big as if the crop was successful in mid-June, when drilled the first time.

The snow winters surface again, and in 1947 Sylvester told Richard, 'mangolds were loaded onto carts, in such bad winters, and taken out to the sheep.' The mangolds were covered with hessian bags to avoid the frost penetrating the mangolds whilst on the carts, and only a few were given to the sheep at a time, because if they weren't eaten quickly, they would be frozen like concrete to the ground and become wasted.

Richard's Whiteface rams at Ashburton. (Photo: Chapman).

Gladys Mann recalled walking in the snow with bare feet to feed the sheep because her wellingtons became full of snow walking through the drifts.

Some of the ponies not used to hay would not eat it, and some hay was pushed down rabbit holes to tempt ponies into eating from the hedge.

A sign of bad weather (gales and snow) was indicated by the movement of the ponies down off the Moor into the moorland villages for shelter and hopefully food; the moorgates were often open to allow this to happen and cattle grids were not around back then.

On references to the Association's Flock Book of 1979 a Dr Greep of Cornwood recorded 14 ewe lambs tattooed, and their sire was bred by Mann Bros. Following this breeding back to the Mann Bros flock revealed in 1986, 55 ewe lambs (M.G.6) were sired by J. Savery and Dr Greep's rams and also in 1987 and 1988 at Dunstone. From this it seems the importance of not going away from, or losing altogether their valuable breed lines, the Manns recovered their breeding from Dr Greep, having sold sheep to him in the first place.

This ability to breed fairly close in flocks or between flocks, emphasised the constitution of the Whiteface sheep as a breed, even when line bred. Also one could begin to read the way the breeders mind worked in relation to holding their Whiteface type.

The tar-pitching of ewes and rams in order to help identify sheep, especially on the Moor, became unacceptable to the wool trade as it stained the wool and the practice ceased.

For 'tar-pitching' (pitch-marking of sheep) tar was melted down and applied with a hot iron; it could apparently 'take the skin off your hand'! It was placed 2–3 weeks after shearing on the wool of the sheep. Richard explained that economics have dictated the sheep's decline and crossing resulted with different breeds of terminal sires in some flocks, and less pure bred sheep have been produced as a result.

The subsidy structure and management levels varied and families own preferences.

However originally, all the farms had Whiteface Dartmoor sheep and because many of the families themselves were related, rams circulated readily amongst farms.

Richard selling his Whiteface Ram in the ring at the Association sale in Whistley Hill field, Ashburton. (Photo: Chapman).

It's quite humbling in the context of much of farming today to think that Richard still keeps the Whiteface Dartmoor sheep where generations of his family farmed before him.

'Manns' sheep is synonymous with Whitefaces and most breeders will have tapped into their precious gene pool to improve their flocks.

The display of Cups (5 won outright and four in just one year at the Ashburton Show & Sale in 1999) were on show when I visited Great Dunstone; a testimony in itself to the Mann's Flock.

Cups won by the Mann family.

Five Won Outright

1 Presented in 1953 and won outright in 1960 by Mann Bros. 'The Widecombe Fair Challenge Cup' for best pen of local Whiteface Dartmoor Sheep.
2 Presented in 1952 by Miss Needham the Whiteface Dartmoor Sheep Breeders Association (W.F.D.S.B.A.) Cup for the 'Best Ram Hogg' won by Mann Bros outright.
3 Presented by John Savery in 1962 at Widecombe Fair for the 'best Whiteface Dartmoor Ram', a cup again won outright by Mann Bros (1962, 1963, 1964).
4 Presented by John Savery in 1956, the W.F.D.S.B.A. Cup for 'the Best Ram' again won outright by the Mann Bros in 1965–6.
5 Presented by Cecil Caunter in 1972 a Cup for the 'best Pair of Ram Hoggs' (W.F.D.S.B.A. Show and Sale) won outright by the Mann Bros – 1973, 1976, 1978 and won outright (any four years) in 1980.

1 The Manns then presented a following Challenge Cup themselves in 1981 again winning this in 1998 and 1999 (Richard) for 'the Best Pair of Ram Hoggs' at the W.F.D.S.B.A. Show and Sale.

2 Presented in 1977 by Richard Coaker the W.F.D.S.B.A. Challenge Cup for the 'best Ram Hogg' and won in 1996 and 1999 by Richard Mann. Richard Coaker having won this class outright himself four times, hence the new cup.
3 The W.F.D.S.B.A.; 'The Cecil Caunter Memorial Perpetual Trophy' awarded for most points at the Annual Show and Sale (ewes and rams) (presented in 1981) won in 1998 and 1999 by Richard Mann.
4 Presented by John Savery Jnr. in 1999. John Savery Perpetual Challenge Cup 'Champion Whiteface Dartmoor Ram'. Won in its first presentation year by Richard Mann.

The above four cups were won by Richard at the Association Show and Sale in 1999. Also the best Pen of Ten Ewes competed on many occasions; won in 1954, 1961, 1985 etc. Again 1968 and 1971 winning the best Ram Hogg at Ashburton.

The Sylvester Mann Memorial Cup awarded for the best ram running with the flock at time of inspection. Whiteface Dartmoor Sheepbreeders Association annual Flock Competition. It was won in its first year by Terry Phipps (2002) and in 2003 by Colin Pearse. A beautiful 'styled-handle-Cup' in silver, given by the family of the late Oliver Sylvester Mann.

Many familiar faces. Sylvester is seen on the immediate left. Whitefaced Dartmoors penned at Whistley Hill field for the Association sale (late 1960s).

John Mead

BULHORNSTONE, SOUTH BRENT

John moved to the farm after his uncle in 1939. The Greyfaced Dartmoors has one of the oldest flock books and its association was formed in 1908. The interests of the Greyfaced Dartmoors were very much at John's heart.

However, he felt as he spent considerable time taking his Greyfaced Sheep around the shows in the area during the summer, with a lot of success, he would buy some Whitefaces to show alongside the other Dartmoor breed.

Widecombe Fair. Jenny holding two sheep, centre of picture. The unmistakable rocks of 'Bone hill' are in the background.

His showing expertise and enthusiasm and knowledge for all types of stock, soon won him success with his new breed of sheep, with daughter Jenny very much in support in preparing and helping show their Whiteface Sheep.

At the Devon County Show he achieved the most points overall awarded for sheep and cattle, with his Greyface and Whiteface Dartmoor Sheep in 1992. John won the Championship for both breeds and with it the points Cup (Verney). This must have been something never achieved before with our two local breeds of sheep by one exhibitor at Devon County level!

In 1999 he won first prize in the interbreed ewe class at Kingsbridge Show and his ewe won reserve to a Border Leicester Ram that received the Championship.

John's Great Grandfather moved out of Corringdon when the French family moved in around 1918–20, again a family with a long Whiteface Dartmoor history.

John always commended the wool potential of the Greyface Sheep and it is not uncommon for a Greyface Ram to shear 30lbs of wool. But he also remarked that the Whiteface is a wonderful wool breed.

In 1998 he made £60 of 'two-tooths'. The following year he sadly took them home, and in recent years the Whiteface has been marketed on a falling trade for breeding ewes and ewe lambs.

As a result, generations of Whiteface breeding is very much in the balance at a critical time for all livestock farming around the moor and further afield. The very poor (a few pence a lb) wool trade has not helped the future of our breed.

During his time with the Whiteface Sheep, John has showed and won prizes at many local shows.

Cornwood 1991.
Left to right:: Jenny (daughter), John Mead, Philip Coaker, John Savery, Dennis Robins and John Savery Snr.
(Courtesy of the Savery family).

John has sold Whitefaces as far afield as Cheshire (a ram and two ewes) to establish a new flock.

The Welsh Mountain breeders of sheep have used Whiteface Dartmoor Rams on their breed in the past to retain hardiness; both breeds have very similar characters suitable for survival on the hills.

It was quite a success story for someone to be farming Greyfaced Dartmoors and to win breed Championships with one longwool breed and then also to achieve a Devon County Breed Championship winner with another longwool breed as John and daughter Jenny did with their Whitefaced Dartmoors.

As an indication of sheep prices in 1946/7 at South Brent; The farmer and Stock Breeder reported 'Dartmoor Lambs up 40s' on the previous year of 1946. Ewes made from 8s to 18s, more than in 1946. Top price for the registered rams was 54gns. E.W. Mead and Son achieved 1st for Old Ram and 1st for coated ram or ram lamb and S. Mead was second.

Messers R.H. Luscombe and Sons sold 471 breeding ewes (Av £5.2s.6d.) Ewe and wether lambs averaged 85 shillings.

Messers John Maye and Co offered 827 sheep (including 187 wethers) The wethers averaged 107s.8d.

Messers Rendells offered 830 breeding ewes and other store sheep and 42 registered and unregistered 'Dartmoor and South Devon rams. Here it is said Whiteface rams would have been sold.

Messers John Pearse & Sons had on offer 859 sheep. Wethers sold from 76s to 143s (92s). Lambs av. 83s.7d. and 'Dartmoor' rams made from 3½ to 10½gns.

Ann Monro and Simon Butcher

WHITEFACED DARTMOOR SHEEP AT CORNDON FARM

In 1992 David Webber at Scoriton near Holne sold up his flock of Whiteface sheep and Ann Monro, who was by then farming the land at Corndon Farm with Simon Butcher while still living at Smith Hill farm near to Dunnabridge and not far from Two Bridges, made the decision to keep a small flock as the number overall of Whitefaces seemed to be dropping fast. So two pens of four-tooth ewes were bought at Mr Webber's sale, these joining some older ewes previously bought from Eileen Abel and a ram bred by Arnold Cole. In all this amounted to no more than 30 sheep, which was ample at the time, as they would have to lamb outdoors and far enough from home.

Ram Power.

The farm of Smith Hill (Smithill) is north from the road running Westward to Two Bridges. The house stands on the right bank of Cherry Brook. On Smith Hill between Cherry Brook and the Moreton' road a small stream rises, sometimes referred to as the Smith Hill Brook; at 1200 feet above sea level it is a really moorland patch giving little back until midsummer passes.

Although the risk of lambing outdoors was very apparent Simon found the Whiteface ideal for this, as they were found rarely to lamb overnight, preferring to deliver their lambs at first light, so having been seen at around midnight no more attention was given until dawn the following day and few if any lambs were lost to overnight visitors! This is something Simon commented on and I feel it probably relates to the sheeps wild instincts. The lamb born at first light is then up and sucking and should be quite strong when darkness comes around, and before the sheep is teased by the forces when they are at their most hungry and shielded by night-fall; but unseen losses there probably are especially with one lamb of a double birth.

Simon and Ann kept all the ewe lambs back either for replacements or to be sold as breeders and the wether lambs were mostly kept into their second year and sold straight to the customer, having been slaughtered and hung at Henry Lang's in Ashburton. Simon said that they have persevered with the Whitefaces, especially because the wether meat is so sweet and has a ready market, and the meat proved a big success with all who bought it. More recently, older wethers and ewes have been bought by local butcher Rodney Cleave, who has 'cold smoked the meat,' and found a ready market at a local gourmet restaurant.

Spitchwick Common is used for sheep after weaning but it can be a very dry common in a drought year. Ann is the only registered breeder with Whitefaces using the Common. Yar Tor and Corndon North Tor were used from Corndon when Herbert Chaffe farmed Corndon.

Simon remembers Walter Chaffe, whose family had farmed Corndon for several

'PHONE: 369 9599

DR/ TO **TOM LANG**

FAMILY BUTCHER

28 EAST STREET, ASHBURTON

July 1960

Mr Sawdye

	A/c RENDERED	£	s	d
2	6x Tongue		14	2
4	Chicken 19/6 D meal 3/5	1	2	11
7	Lamb Liver		5	3
9	D meat 3/4 Chops 7/		10	4
11	Top Side Beef	1	5	6
	Chicken £1/2/2 Duck 19/6	2	1	8
14	Lamb Liver 5/ D meal 3/6		8	6
18	Leg Lamb £1/3/8 D m 4/7	1	8	3
21	*Sweet Bread 1/5 Lamb Liver 5/		6	5
24	D m 3/6 Lamb Liver 5/6		9	–
		£8	12	·

*Sweet bread

Paid with thanks
T M Lang

Granite-stone built Creep hole.

Whiteface ewe hoggs moving fields on their own through a granite 'Sheep Creep hole', built with granite lintel stones and granite-stoned sides to form a tunnel the width of the hedge and just wide enough for one sheep at a time to come through. (Photo: Colin Pearse).

generations, telling him that the wool from the farm was kept in the upper floor of the Cider house. A small stone barn sandwiched between the threshing barn and the Shippen. The latter barns were always buzzing with activity, and were the hub of farmyard activity for around one hundred and fifty years on many moorland farms.

The upstairs room of the cider house measures 10' by 15', and was often referred to as 'the bank', for the wool was the real value of the sheep in those days. Walter's forbears had bought the farm from their landlord with wool from 'the bank' and there was still wool left over (and from a small barn too)!

In those days, wethers were often kept into their third year and beyond as the wool on their backs was their greatest asset. If only wool was as valuable today Simon remarked!

It seems that the Whitefaces have a mind of their own on Corndon and are apt to find a gap in a hedge, so Simon is re-introducing some 'stone creepholes' or 'sheepholes' in the field hedges for the sheep to access the adjoining fields.

Creepholes became fashionable with the advent of turnips in the late 18th and early 19th centuries, built into field boundaries i.e. the hedges of adjoining fields, allowing sheep to access the root field, from an adjoining field, and therefore given priority over the cattle, which might be 'carted' their roots to another grass field nearby.

Ann speaks of a ewe she called 'blindy'. She was given her name as a result of getting on her back during the Foot and Mouth outbreak; as a result she lost both her eyes to birds pecking at her, (magpie or crow). Normally, without movement restrictions and controls brought in to contain Foot and Mouth she would have been slaughtered. However, reprieved from this fate she has since coped very well and Annie says her offspring every year 'act as her eyes', and their smell, contact, and 'bleeps' guide her everywhere!

Simon captured the humour of Alec Turner in another story about sheep. He was asked to lunch one Sunday to a family that had lived in the Parish for several years, but were not of the local 'ilk' and in passing conservation Simon was asked why it was that nobody kept the local breed of sheep anymore? Simon explained that he could think of about four farms within walking distance that kept flocks of Whiteface Dartmoor ewes; 'Oh no', came the reply, they meant the 'Red Devon Sheep'. Simon told the family that there wern't any sheep called 'Red Devons', they were cattle!

It seems the family several years earlier had been walking past Corndonford Farm, and the fields were full of 'Red Sheep'. Alec Turner the farmer, had told them that the sheep were a very old breed that no one kept anymore called 'Red Devons'!

However Alec with his saucy dry humour must have been laughing that his joke had lasted so long. It seems his sheep had just come back from grazing on Red Soil land 'in-country'!

"Just act naturally..."

The Moorman

The Coakers of Runnage at Postbridge were 'agisters' for the East Quarter of the Forest in the late 19th and 20th Century, notably Adolphous Coaker. The present 'Quarterman' for the East Quarter is Ivan Mortimore of Shapley Farm (Higher) Chagford, whose father farmed Lettaford Farm, Collihole, and Fernworthy Farm, with Ivan's Grandfather. Later the family moved to Corndon where Courtney Mortimore farms today, with his family.

Remembering the Whiteface Dartmoors on the Stannon Newtake and around the Warren and Statsbridge, Ivan also recalled the story told by Philip Coaker's mother that she remembered as many as 1200 Whitefaces being dipped at the sheep dip in 'Little Stannon Newtake' near the entrance gate to this part of the moor. The dip is no longer used and now remains derelict. Previous to Ivan as the East Quarterman was Fred Hutchings of Yardworthy Farm. Back in history at one point the moor was divided into only three quarters.

The presence of people still regarded as 'moormen' today recognises a concept of slow change to the moor, for people like John Perryman, James Rowe, William Endacott and William and George Hutchings in the past carried out this duty on Dartmoor, from different parishes. They 'over-saw' the moor's stock and had the interest of the moor at heart and were well acquainted with different portions, with Dartmoor in their ancestry. George Hutchings was also farming nearby Teignhead Farm and his father was a moorman.

Ivan and Courtney Mortimore's Father and Grandfather farmed Fernworthy Farm, Chagford. Philip Mere's family once farmed Fernworthy Farm too.

'In place names of Dartmoor 1931' Fernworthy is spelt Vernaworthy in 1355 (Ferne – in 1377) and Fernworthy Yeat 1579 – 'Bracken Wordig' (Fern homestead).

The move to Fernworthy was made away from Lettaford Farm, where George Mortimore was born and, for a while, the Mortimores farmed Collihole Farm.

The move to Fernworthy Farm in a sheltered combe beside the River Teign (the South Teign) was around 1910–1920 and is really intriguing because the enclosures then (newtake)

The reservoir at Fernworthy where the old packhorse bridge and clapper bridge are exposed during drought times – Autumn 2003. (Photo: John Midgley).

was a prize grazing area said to be of around one thousand acres before all the conifer trees were planted and before the fields were flooded in the early 1940's to allow for a reservoir at Fernworthy. The farmstead is now in ruins. Some of the newtake area and enclosures were 'walled in' during the early 1800's and late 1700's. N.T. Carrington wrote in 1826: 'the air of Dartmoor being healthful and bracing, its inhabitants are commonly called 'moorsmen'.* The moor farmers cultivate with great labour the 'few acres around their habitations'. They are used to the climate and become attached to the soil.'

Harold Wonnacott drifting a 'mixed flock' across Thornworthy Farm fields beside Fernworthy Reservoir (1992).

Animals were taken in and agisted at Fernworthy Farm and Ivan and Courtney's Father and Grandfather used to ride to Paignton on horse back to meet cattle assembled there, and then help to drive the long-horned 'bullocks' up to Dartmoor and to their newtake at Fernworthy for summer grazing. This drift took place in the early 1920's.

Ivan spoke of Cyril Dadd's father who kept big horned steers, some until they were four or five years old, that grazed Fernworthy enclosures. Mr Dadd was asked in the autumn what he was going to do with these big South Devon cattle. He replied 'that he was going to sell 'em and not drive them home'. They were sold in Chagford Market for ten pounds each!

Crossing explains that Fernworthy is an old settlement and formerly consisted of three farms and is referred to in the seventeenth century as a village. It is not, however, one of the 'ancient forest tenements' nor is it strictly a part of the forest although it lies within its boundaries, and so it is in the Lydford parish. The 'Jury of Survey' in 1609 mentions the estate. A considerable portion of the land was enclosed during the eighteen hundreds, defined originally by a 'tin bound' extending along both banks of the Teign.

Wilf Hutchings (son of Fred Hutchings) is farming Yardworthy Farm, on the moors edge below Fernworthy Reservoir. He is one of Dartmoors excellent wall builders and restorers. Wilf is not short of work, for jokingly he said to me 'it would take 100 men 100 years to restore Dartmoors walls'! Joking apart, he knows the walls must be kept up.

*The name 'moorman' seems to come from that of 'moorsmen', an old name given to the moor's people.

William Crossing said Fernworthy is a good example of a moorland dwelling sheltered by some fine sycamores, promoting a debate as to why these trees in particular; (perhaps deeper rooting than the beech), but the shade they afford in summer is also significant for the farmstead and the animals.

Ivan spoke of the rams being approved that were put on the moor by a ministry run inspection scheme to try and improve the standard of the rams used. Rams approved for use on the moor were given a green 'A' mark and those rejected a red 'R' that was painted on the rams, (practiced in the mid nineteen hundreds). Philip Meres says there was a sheep dip at the farm. The farm settlement was knocked down in the 1950's. Philip's father used to collect rushes for rick thatching from Fernworthy.

Ivan spoke of bulls used in newtakes, and where heifers were separated into a newtake of their own away from the bulls.

Jim Endacott was the Reeve of Dartmoor, born at Bold Venture, near Chagford, and appointed Reeve (a type of Moorman) in 1910 when he was just twenty-one. For more than fifty years, he rode the moor 'everyday up Dartmoor for the Duchy'.

So the Endacotts of Fernworthy managed the North Quarter of the moor early this century. (William and Jim). They are also seen in wonderful archive photos leading waggons, loaded very high with probably 'turf vags', and pulled by a team of horses, working on the moor. The slabs of turf were cut for fuel on those parts of the commons around the forest where there was little peat. Farmhouse hearths used to be piled high with peat!

The jurors of 1609 said that Venville tenants have a right to take from the moor, 'turves, vagges heath stone, cole, and other thinges to their custombes'.

Michael Mudge was formerly at 'Moorlands Farm', Prince Hall, but is now an agister for the Southern portion of the West Quarter of the Forest, farming Huccaby, a Duchy tenement. Michael's father farmed Brimpts, near Hexworthy, and leared six flocks of sheep in the six hundred acre newtake. Michael explained that his father spent hours learing his sheep to keep the flocks separate.

Michael speaks of many farmers who, in the past, used the Quarter he agists; from the Caunter family, the Browns and Webbers at Holne, and some of these families still lear stock here today. The Caunter flock probably holds to being one of the oldest leared flocks!

Some of the Weekaborough sheep still use the moor and run up against Whiteface and Scotch sheep at Green Hill belonging to the Coles of Greenwell, learing the West-Southwest side of the moor – above the Erme. Sheep from Staddicombe too still use their rights on Holne Moor.

Alison Coaker speaks of wonderful Whitefaces 'out on the South Moor'.

Walter Chaffe, when he was at Huccaby, helped agist the same quarter as Michael Mudge agists now. Michael also referred to Jim and George Smith as moormen at Hexworthy and of the changes in the way the moor is managed today, in particular of how the 'swaling' of the moor in the past wasn't so constrained as it is today. Plots he said were rotationally burnt and John French worked on the quarter Michael now agists with the swaling. Today Michael commented the burning is not planned in the right way.

Although Michael had mainly Closewools at Moorlands Farm, he recalls an interesting story about Whitefaces. Apparently the tale comes from a Tom Easterbrook who worked for the Whitleys and Bill Mann at Lizwell. The story explained how there used to be a lot of sheep walked away to winter keep, as said in many breeders' stories, to in-country farms. Tom told Michael how that many sheep 'being walked home from winter keep via Woodlands, Ashburton, were still crossing the A38 (before it was a dual carriageway) when the first sheep in the procession were well on ahead over the top of Ashburton towards the moor'. There were many sheep in any one drift owned by different moorland farmers.

Not far from Hexworthy as the crow flies William Crossing recorded that 'close to Lough Tor is a rectangular enclosure known as Lough Tor Pound'. The gateway is on the side nearest the Tor and the walls are high. This the moormen used to speak of as a 'sheep measure'. So its capacity being known, when it was filled with these animals, there was no need to count them more than once to ascertain their number'! (Just a question of counting the number of measures and the multiplying by the number of sheep in the first measure.) Presumably their size was consistent, as the Dartmoor sheep in the past were, it seems, a lot smaller and this measure just gave a pretty close estimate that too many weren't missing when the sheep left their pasturage on the moor at the end of the summer.

Peter Hutchings, whose family work, farmed and drift the moor's stock, conveyed an amusing story about counting sheep; some farmers' sons were forced at an early age to work on the family farms and so schooling was at a premium. Peter tells of one such person who could only count up to 12, so when his boss (or father) sent him to count the sheep, he would return and say he had counted, for example, three twelves, and four sheep in a field. Numbers might prove all over the place if the ministry subsidy count was forthcoming!

Dunnabridge Pound is not far from Huccaby and its enclosure has long served as a drift pound.

In 1342, there is mention of it in an account of the 'bailiff of Dartmoor' where the sum of threepence is shown as having been expended for a lock for the gate!

Disturbers of the peace during the time of the drifts were put in stocks (leg and arm holds) here accounted in 1620 by the Reeve of the Manor of Lydford laying out money for the repair of the pound walks, gate and stocks at Dunnabridge.

Tenants were summoned to the day of drifts by the blast of a horn, blown on the hilltop with the horn held against granite to bounce the sound across the valley. Four moormen supervised the driving of the quarters of the moor.

Mr John Edmunds of Gribblesdown, South Brent, has been agister for the South Quarter of the Forest since the 1960's and comes from a long family line of agisters stretching back to 1843 and the early part of the nineteenth century; they paid the Duchy and, in turn, farmers would pay the agisters for looking after their animals whilst they were on the moor.

In the past the Forest was let as a whole before being quartered. A few shillings would have been paid as 'venville rights' on the Forest and stock could not be then 'empounded' (pounded). This could incur a charge for their removal. Venville sem to start when the wolves were driven off Dartmoor, say around the 1600's. There were no physical boundaries of the moor at that time.

It is said that Totnes and Barnstaple were exempt from Forest Rights (Venville) because they never helped other parishes to drive wolves from the Moor, that were ravaging the flocks and animals! It seems the last wolf was caught at Brimpts! Perhaps the last *bear* at Beardown!

The French Brothers at Corringdon, Williams Barons at Charford, Nr Avonwick and Tom Widecombe at Cutswellcombe had their sheep agisted by John Edmunds at the end of the Second World War. However, John Edmunds said 'seemingly apart from John Savery, Whiteface sheep are now only little seen as part of the animals on the South Quarter'.

John remembers the importance of wethers acting as good snow ploughs through their tracking across the moor in snowy winters and kept by farmers until three to four years old and even as broken mouth sheep. They had good coats with wool on the ground, withstanding heavy rains and good mutton resulted.

In the late 1920's farmers would pay the agisters of the East Quarter between ten shillings and twelve shillings and sixpence per head of cattle for five to six months on the moor (June–October) depending if they were put on the open moor or in one of the newtakes.

The Edmund's family of South Brent were responsible for beasts in the area of the South Hams stretching from Kingsbridge to Start Point. This happened when these animals had to be collected at Moreleigh (six miles from South Brent) before being driven via Diptford and Avonwick to a 'moorgate'. John Savery (Zeal) held the title of 'Moorman'.

Courtney Mortimore at West Corndon, Chagford, remembers lots of Whitefaces coming to Dartmoor to be summered. He also explained where the Forest boundary of the moor came in relation to Chagford Common and said it was as far east as 'Kings Oven' behind the Warren dip and across to Fernworthy. 'Moormen' left their names to the moor; e.g. 'Leaman's Mead' and 'Little Man'.

Colin Endacott formerly of 'Jurston' said 'there use to be any amount of "Dartmoors" up over from Jurston and along to the Warren Inn.'

Fred Hutchings, before he died, spoke of how he tendered for Little Stannon Newtake and his tender was accepted. However he said 'how the army had trampled the newtake to death during the Second World War'.

Fred's daughter, Doreen, had a photograph of Prince Charles in the early 1980's when he was helping to put up walling stones by one of the gates that helps to enclose the sheepfold.

A shepherd/Moorman once said 'that to test if the walls of a field were high enough to contain sheep, he placed one in the field. It ran he said, around the field desperate to join the flock, where it paused was suspect, where it decided to jump was the weakest point!!'

Old time farmers would not pay the builders of stone-walls until a sheep had run the walls and found no point weak enough or low enough for a 'breakout'.

Usually one animal on its own spells trouble and its more likely to knock itself out on the wall than actually get over the obstacle!

Michael French wrote (in Dartmoor Magazine No 40) on 'Memories of a Moorman' (Harry Norrish) who had 'a thousand years of history that lived all in his head'!

He was a master Moorman of the moors life he worked, says Michael. Michael wrote this very amusing story that is generous in the affection that Harry held for the moor, and his knowledge and instincts that were obviously born of his ancestry, and nurtured by his enthusiasm for life.

William Henry Norrish one of four brothers and one sister born in 1888 at Combestone Holne.

Harry, Michael says, was a stockman and farmer of repute, but it was on the high Southern Moors, much of which is known as the 'South Quarter' that he came 'into his own and where he established himself as master'.

At Dockwell South Brent, having left Combestone, the threesome took over from an elderly brother; here Harry established his own brand of moor farming.

Although sheep and ponies were Harry's mainstay, cattle were important too, with some of his steers kept to 'Oxon-like' proportions, topping markets at Ashburton, Newton Abbot and Exeter.

Once though Michael records, when loading an elephantine 6 year-old on a Cattle truck, Harry broke down and wept, so attached to his beasts did he become.

On one occasion to really get the feel of the moor Michael went on an Erme Valley excursion with Harry 'out Au(w)er', (out over) as the Moormen called that part of the moor, that only they knew about!!

Harry always carried a flask of not so diluted whisky he named 'fire-water'.

When 'sticked up' (waiting) for someone to arrive with some sheep or the like) at such places as 'Little Aune', it had a powerful and longstanding effect.

The sheep gathering forays was an exacting game known as 'Waiting for Harry'; patience is an essential of shepherding sheep in any situation.

Harry used to wear an ankle-length army great-coat and with cap pulled over his eyes, and he would post say Michael French, at a certain point on the Moor, and then himself disappear over the skyline.

It seemed ages, and nearly dark and then Harry would appear with a group of wayward sheep, that for some reason hadn't wanted to be rounded up.

So Michael gathered 'waifs and strays', or ones Harry overlooked from his position on the ridge.

Then he would wave his cap in the air to signal there were sheep escaping to the left or right, or that he could see some from his vantage point that Michael couldn't.

When all three situations prevailed, the cap would be tossed in the air, or hurled to the ground, depending upon the degree of the impending disaster!

Also Michael described the canny way Harry separated 'strangers' from the flock.

Often other sheep 'tagged on', belonging to other people, so in order to avoid sorting them back in the yard, employing great stealth (which usually meant standing motionless for ages) with a prod or wave of a long stick he would dispatch the great unwanted into the heather!

But Harry Norrish was, Michael said, 'a single minded man with a peasant frame, and with insights into a world unknown to most, far brighter to him, was the 'back-country hills, from the distant Neons that he had no time for!

Venville rights over the forest are still exercised. J.L.W. Page wrote in 1892; Venville appears to be a corruption of 'fines villarum' meaning probably boundaries of the vils (though many think the word a corruption of fen field), Vil being the Norman name given to the settlements, or perhaps the manors bordering the Moor, now represented by the parishes. From time immemorial the inhabitants of these vils have claimed the right to take from the Forest and its commons around (Devonshire Commons) anything that may do them good, except vert or green-wood and venison. Thus do all 'tenants in Venville' as they are called, pasture their flocks and herds, cut turf and fuel and take stone and sand from the surface. Venwell rights as the peasantry called them, are nothing less than a right claimed by the inhabitants of a certain district of pasturage and turf from the fens, free of all cost, (a few shillings a year later) a privilege handed down to them through many generations as a reward for services done by their ancestors in destroying the wolves, which in early times, so much infested the Forest of Dartmoor. It is said that wolves were hunted upon the Moor as late as the reign of Elizabeth.

In consideration of all this the Duchy of Cornwall exacts certain services from Venville tenants. The latter owe suit and service at the Forest courts and are always liable to be called upon to take part in the 'drifts'. Formerly the practice was to hold two drifts in the fall of the year, for bullocks and ponies respectively, and in each of the four quarters into which the forest is divided.

On the day appointed the moor-man for each quarter gives notice to the inhabitants of parishes lying in Venville, and to others, to collect the cattle or ponies, as the case may be, and drive them to some spot appropriated to that particular quarter where they may be claimed by the tenants. There is no direct payment to the Duchy, but the moor-man who farms the quarter gets so much per head. The beasts of strangers must pay a fine. Every animal has to be branded with the mark of his quarter and, however far he may roam, the fine payable is due to the moor-man of the quarter where he has depastured. Animals not claimed are confined in Dunnabridge Pound and after the lapse of a given time, if no owner arrives with a satisfactory title, sold. The old pound for such strays was Grimspound, although not its original purpose.

Duchy Regulations for Swaling

These regulations are recorded in the Reverend H.H. Breton's Beautiful Dartmoor.

These he said had been explained at a recent prosecution of someone for 'firing' the forest at Moretonhampstead!

Capt Scott James, the deputy forester, stated that he was instructed to superintend the burning of the moor, which was only allowed to be done in accordance with the following regulations issued by the Duchy authorities:

1. No swaling will be allowed within the Forest of Dartmoor, except by persons duly authorized by warrants issued by the Duchy of Cornwall.

Whatever swaling is necessary shall be carried out by the moormen under the supervision of the deputy forester.

2. No swaling whatever will be permitted after the 31st of March in any year.

3. A provisional plan has been prepared, each quarter of the forest being divided into ten parts, and a tenth part will be swaled every year in regular rotation.

4. Warning notices will be posted in different parts of the moor prohibiting the burning of the heather gorse, or fern-growing lands within the Forest of Dartmoor.

5. A watch will be kept for unauthorized burning on the moor. This says Breton had increased, because of more tourists on the moor, so much so that a more rigid enforcement of the regulations had become necessary for the protection of the pasturage of the moor for the Commoners, the presentation of birdlife, and the natural beauty of the moor.

It was emphasised that unauthorized fires had frequently caused great damage of the moor and had been known to burn hundreds of acres and even at times to set fire to the earth itself, in which cases it took years for the pasturage to recover, as opposed to a fast burn, more regularly organised on the moor.

Moormen and the Abbot's Way

'Abbot's Way' has been called a spurious name of a southerly trans-Dartmoor route in 1794, two and a half centuries after the dissolution of the monasteries.

Buckfast to Nun's Cross, crossing the Avon was not its best route. If the Abbot of Buckfast did sponsor a way, it was by Holne and across Holne Ridge, says Worth.

Crossing remarks, the name of the above way he always heard it called by the Moormen, was the 'Jobblers' or 'Jobber's Path' used by 'Yarn-Jobbers' in former days.

The monks of Buckfast were extensive traders in wool and this commodity and yarn spun from it, no doubt often formed the loads which were carried on the backs of horses on this old road. The Moormen's allusion to the route 'Jobber's Path' relates to that portion eastward from Broad Rock. If the name 'Abbot's Way' had been used historically, the 'Moormen' would have preserved the name. 'Jobber's Path' seems to pre-date 'Abbot's Way' by name!

Moorlady

These stories seem to put forward the place of the 'Moormen', but entwined very closely here is the contribution of the 'Moorladies'.

Such an example of a 'Moorswoman' is Pat Coaker of 'Bittleford'.

She said the moor gives her 'fresh air and freedom', and with her knowledge of the moor, its dogs and ponies, and later its sheep and cattle, it defines her as a true 'Moorswoman'.

F.A. Mortimore (Archie)

GRATTONS, WIDECOMBE-IN-THE-MOOR – FORMERLY OF LIZWELL FARM

Archie Mortimore arrived at Lizwell via quite a roundabout route with his family moving farms several times along the way.

Flock at Lizwell (used for the first Association leaflet).

From some of the fields at Lizwell Farm one can look down on an imposing canopy of mixed deciduous woods that conceal 'Lizwell Meet' where the two Webburns unite their waters, one of the beauty spots of the Dartmoor borderland and then 'the Webburn joins the River Dart.'

Looking down onto the farmstead, on the high eastern side of the Widecombe Valley, is an impressive array of Granite tors.

Looking from right to left – Buckland Beacon, Rippon Tor, Haytor, Pil Tor, Top Tor, Mil Tor, also Buckland Beacon casts a shadow over Pudsham.

Also from Lizwell, the jagged looking Bonehill rocks, Bel Tor, and the striking Chinkwell Tor can be seen. The fine group of rocks known as Honeybag Tor is the northern most of a range extending for two and half miles southward.

The high land from which these rise forms the eastern side of the deep Widecombe Valley, the head of which is a little to the north of Honeybag where the branches of the East Webburn meet. This stream was anciently called 'The Niprell' runs through the valley, together with a road coming down from Heatree Cross.

Hameldon forms the long high western side of the Widecombe Valley.

In 1955 the Whitley estate was sold off, of which Lizwell was part.

Archie's father, Mark Mortimore, was born at Langdon Farm, North Bovey. He was a brother to Jack Mortimore at Higher Jurston, Chagford, (Archie's grandfather was also at Langdon). Mark Mortimore persuaded his relations to take on Whitefaces. These were crossed with the Greyfaced Dartmoors and Archie said good results were achieved.

Widecombe Fair 1970.
Left to right: Terry French (holding P. W. Coaker's sheep), Richard and Arthur Mann, Maurice Mortimore (Archie's father), Archie Mortimore, Tom Nosworthy. Miss Needham was the judge in the white coat).
(Courtesy of P. W. Coaker and H.R. Rivers, Market Street, Newton Abbot).

In 1900 Archie's father moved to Beetor Farm, North Bovey. Then Mark Mortimore married away from Beetor after the First World War and in 1924 moved to Lamerton, Nr Tavistock. It was here at Heartwell Farm that Archie was born.

In 1933 the family moved to Hazelwood Farm, Marldon. South Devon Longwools were farmed here, but the Whiteface was introduced to cross with the South Devons.

The neighbours said 'the Whitefaces will "break" if you have them at Marldon'! (breakout). However, Archie has a liking for the 'crosses' his father bred and felt they were lovely sheep, 'tempering' the size of the South Devon and a much tidier sheep with more milk was produced.

South Devon cattle were kept too! Archie recalls milking a particular cow by hand and filling a three gallon bucket in three minutes (a gallon milked per minute) but as soon as the cow felt he had finished milking her, she would let fly and try and spill the bucket of milk!

However, in 1947 another move was made to Cuming Farm, Buckfastleigh situated parallel with the Old Totnes Road and the River Dart. Archie worked with his father there for five years until he retired.

Then Archie moved to Lizwell, Widecombe in 1952 and married Audrey Vallance. On the porch at Lizwell a date reads 1631. Lizwell was once part of Jordan Manor and part of the house is 14th Century and has longhouse features. The farmstead has the feeling of a very old settlement, with water and shelter its greatest advantages.

Before Archie came to farm Lizwell, a Francis Nichols had one thousand Exmoor Horn Sheep; he managed them as 'hind' to Wallace Whitley.

Between 1907 and 1937, a William Mann had one thousand Whitefaces at Lizwell and he took winter root keep in the South Hams. The sheep almost 'ate' their way down to the South Hams, because having been only gone a week away from Widecombe, they would have to move on again to another farm.

Tom Easterbook who, with his wife, were servants of Lizwell, was told on one occasion by William Mann 'To tip his sheep out to Prince Hall', Archie explained. This meant that several hundred sheep had to be walked over the moor many miles of a night by Tom Easterbook to relieve the home farm. It is interesting to find in an old Devonshire Parishes book dated 1857 that a Nicholas Easterbrook actually farmed Lizwell.

Lloyd Mortimore describes how the old buildings in their yard once housed the

'Thresher' (and generator in the round house), for threshing corn and a 'wool chamber' for storing wool. Lloyd, wife Rosemary, son Peter and daughter Sarah farm Lizwell today.

However, Lizwell was proving to be a good farm for sheep and Archie said 'Whitefaces always answered well to Lizwell, did well there, and are wonderful sheep to work with'. These are words of real satisfaction and praise for our local sheep. The story goes that William Mann (Lizwell) on moving sheep on Newbridge Hill, met a stranger, who helped move the sheep. William gave the person a ha'penny (old halfpenny). He refused saying: 'Your need is greater than mine'!

Judging the flock at 'Lizwell' inthe old yard.

Archie introduced Whitefaces again to Lizwell in 1956. He said everybody around had Whitefaces. Archie spoke to Fred Trant at Bittleford who was he said, a wonderful showman of Whiteface sheep at Ashburton and the local shows. The sheep were perfection and held a 'Dartmoor look', and they had a 'charcoal tint about their fleeces', no doubt, from the remains of the burnt vegetation that is 'swaled' in March. It leaves charcoal and ash on the moor's floor and black gorse sticks are left, only half burnt and rising from the ground like a series of antlers; these the sheep rub on as they are attracted by the young shoots that soon appear amongst the blackened areas that have been swaled. They soon adopt a charcoal colour and become quite strongly 'leared' to these areas as they scavenge between the rocks.

However, when showing his Whiteface Sheep, Fred Trant use to rub a handful of the burnt charcoal onto the sheeps fleece to help achieve a blue-grey charcoal tint on the sheep and make them look natural and appealing to the judges!

Audrey Mortimore recalled Sid Trant pasing Lizwell at haymaking time and Archie had just finished building a loose hayrick. Sid said, 'he'll be down by the morning' and, sure enough, Audrey said, next morning the rick had tilted and they had to get poles and prop the rick!

Archie remembers judging sheep with John Savery and explained how meticulous John was about breed points, noting particular faults in different flocks.

Tattooing lambs at Zeal Farm, John said to Archie, 'we have to go upstairs to find the sheep'! This was outside of course in the yard. The sheep would go up the granite steps that led to the big barn floor above which was once the old granary store. One could just see agile, lively young Widecombes scampering up these steps thinking they were jumping walls on Dartmoor!

Archie is still helping out with Terry Phipps and tattooing members ewe and ram lambs. Black ink is used to rub on the ear, after the date and members prefix is stamped in the left ear of the sheep.

Archie holding the ink at Barramoor Farm, North Bovey, with Sylvester Mann (right of picture) and Colin Pearse (holding sheep).

Archie vividly remembers Miss Needham coming to the Whiteface meetings on her motorbike and on one occasion when it was pouring with rain she would have a hessian sack on her shoulders and on her knees and would still be saturated when she arrived at Ashburton for the meeting. The first association sale Archie said was in the Cattle Market in Vealenia Terrace, Ashburton.

Archie also spoke of Wilf Irish who would sometimes lead a horse behind the Irish's (Grendon) sheep going away from Widecombe to their keep at Rattery and then ride the horse home again (and sometimes a bike!)

Archie judging at Widecombe Fair. Phil and Alison Abels champion (year 2000).

More snow winter memories are recalled by Archie. In 1947 Archie said the weight of the Ammil (ice) on the trees brought them down and trees could be heard 'cracking off' everywhere. However, he said 'that animals survived in Luscombe Woods for weeks because the weight of the ice brought the trees down with ivy on them that the animals ate'.

During the snowfall of February 18th and 19th 1978, Archie said 'he remembered dragging sheep racks over hedges not seen because there was so much snow'. (Roads and hedges can be hidden by a heavy fall of snow very quickly. The blizzard of 1962/3 lasted ten days before it eased, with chilling temperatures. 'A storm *in* Dartmoor bears little resemblance to storms in general. It can be awful perilous, astounding and pitiless for man and beast,' so writes N.T. Carrington in 1826).

Recording an earlier age in farming. Ash poles, wheelbarrow and sheep hay rack.

Archie used long bean sticks to find sheep buried in the snowdrifts; some sheep came out steaming after ten days or so under the snow, but were OK! Certainly the snow wasn't frozen so hard as in the bad winters of 1947 and 1962–3. For others have recorded lambs just frozen to the ground where they were born. Trees and telegraph poles just snapping off like 'cannon-fire', weighed down with ice. Coils of ice just on the telephone wires were as large as pipes!

Recounting his success in showing Whiteface Dartmoors over the years, Archie said, I have won the Whiteface Dartmoor Sheep Cup several times at Widecombe Fair, also the Sidney Trant Cup for the most points in the local class eighteen or nineteen times (all breeds). At Totnes Show Archie won the Whiteface Challenge Cup in 1982, 1984, 1990 and 1991 and probably on occasions, the previous cup, presented for Whiteface Competition at Totnes. Archie also won in 1974 and 1979 the W.F.D.S.B.A. Cup presented by H.G. Woodley (George Woodley) for the annual competition, the best flock of under 50 ewes. Archie has

Breed Champion at Totnes Show in 1990. F.A. Mortimore.
(Photo: *Herald Express*, Torquay).

also shown at Cornwood and Yealmpton Shows.

He recalls buying a good Whiteface ram as a two-teeth from John Irish (Cator) at the Ashburton Show and Sale (its sire bred by Cyril Abel). He had several championships with this ram at shows. Archie said he sold it as a full mouth at Ashburton Show and it was purchased by Philip Coaker of Runnage.

Archie said 'several two teeth ram hoggs sold at Ashburton registered sheep sale have gone around members flocks over the years. Following the flock record from 1979 to 1988 rams used on Archie's flock were bred by Mann Bros., Stephens, Savery, Adams & Howell, Richard and Philip Coaker, Irish's Grendon, R. Woodley. The flock number 40 ewes in 1980.

Archie explained with great feeling, that despite Suffolks having been bred in the family (and Lloyd Mortimore still breeds rams at this time), for sixty five years he always enjoyed his 'Registered Whiteface Sheep; a very good sheep and they always done well on Lizwell'.

No story about Widecombe would be complete without a photograph of the 'Widecombe Wag', Tony Beard, farmer and broadcaster and entertainer seen in the glasses in this picture.

Left to right: Television personality Leslie Crowther presenting the trophies. Archie Mortimore with more than a handful of Cups, Jim Hine over-seeing the cups (previous Chairman and President of the Show) and Tony Beard officiating.

Joe Mortimore and Family

BEACON, EAST SHALLOWFORD AND DOWN PARK

May Mortimore's father farmed Bowdley, Ashburton. She marrried Joe Mortimore in 1944 whilst he was still in the army and later they both moved in 1946 to Beacon Farm, Buckland. The farm lies just under Buckland Beacon and was rented from a private landlord. May's father, Arthur Caunter, had Whitefaces at Bowdley.

Joe started at Beacon with Greyfaces in 1946. In the blizzard winter of 1947 all the Greyfaces were buried and lost. At this point Joe was already unhappy with the breed. May remarked that Joe said 'they didn't have any milk and didn't rear many lambs'. It was not uncommon to lose a lamb, and find on post mortem a ball of wool matted inside the intestines causing the lamb to die. The long wool would have been sucked by the lamb looking for its mother's teat. May explained how severe the 1947 winter turned out to be; 'the ice tingled on the manes of the horses frozen to their hair'!

According to May, 'Beacon was not a very *fat* place and they survived on a shilling a day because Joe came out of the army with little money.'

A change to Whitefaces took place in 1948 purchased at Ashburton. J.S. Mortimore's sheep were registered and included in the 1951 Association list with Beacon Farm recorded on the first members list.

William (Bill) Mortimore, Joe's father, in the meantime was farming at Down Park, Chagford.

East Shallowford. Late 1950s. The old traditional stone wall gives shelter from the keen wind of spring, as welcome sunshine casts their shadow.

Another move took place for Joe and May and 'Toots', Joe and May's daughter, in 1952 to East Shallowford, Widecombe-in-the-Moor. A farm around 100 acres, but May said 'it was run down with rabbits, especially the hedges'. Common grazing was enjoyed on Rowden Common mainly for cattle. Sheep were driven with horse and dogs (Floss and Sharp) to Stannon. May said Joe always used his 'hackney horse' (cob type) called Tom for hacking around. Two other horses were kept for work on the farm. Stannon was the sheep's summertime lear.

A stroll leads to Rowden Down, the summit of which is known as 'Rowden Ball' where there is a small tor. The enclosure gives rights to East Shallowford. Near the northern edge of the down is Rowden Farm on the road leading to Lower Cator (nearby is Jordan Ball).

East Shallowford's entrance is passed descending Jordan Ball to the Webburn. An old stone with its centre hollowed out is seen in the wall of the farm's entrance. The top of a gates back would swivel in the hole, facing to the ground, with the rest of the stone laid across the top of a hedge. Thereby the gate would open rotating in the stone's hole, (probably top and bottom). A practical idea using the assets of nature around the farm; (wood and granite).

Just below here the 'Shallow ford' on the West Webburn, which gives name to this farm, and to West Shallowford, which lies on the further bank of the stream. Above here the road from Ponsworthy, Poundsgate and Dartmeet via Locks Gate Cross runs onward to Cator and the Forest. West Shallowford too, and the Nosworthy family form a partnership with Whitefaces.

Dipping also took place at Little Stannon and Joe would ride out often from Shallowford to see his sheep at Stannon. 'Toots' would take her dog to Stannon when driving sheep, and her father would pick her up with his tractor. May remarked that 'Joe lived for his sheep and obviously he had sheep in his blood'.

Recorded in the Ram Judges Book of 1954–1960 at the 4th Annual Show and Sale in 1954, the old ram class was won by John Savery. His ram was bought by Cecil Caunter for 23½ gns. Second, was the Mann Bros, third was Cecil Caunter and reserve J.S. Mortimore, but Joe's ram made more than the first prize at 25 gns, purchased by Maurice Widicombe at Brent. Joe

Joe Mortimore (Judge) and Miss Needham (showing) at Devon County.

was again reserve with his old ram in 1956 and third behind the Manns and Leonard Ball in 1958 judged by W.J. Sprague of Chagford.

Reported in a local paper in November of 1961, the headlines read 'Better Quality in Whiteface Sheep'. This was addressed to the under fifties Flock Competition won by Dave Webber of Hawson, Holne with Joe Mortimore of Shallowford, Widecombe in second place. George Woodley of Ivybridge was third. It is interesting to see the area spread over from where the Whitefaces were judged, in this case from Holne and Widecombe down to Ivybridge. At Widecombe in 1963 Joe won third prize with his ewe *hoggs* at the Fair.

Winners in the class for Whitefaced ewe lambs at Widecombe Fair. Right to left: J.S. Mortimore (Widecombe), Mann Bros. (Widecombe) and L.S. Ball (Mary Tavy).

Black sheep owned by Doreen and Ken Soper went on to help in 1958–59 to 'found John Sawdye's black flock' and these were sired by a Joe Mortimore ram.

Joe liked to see that the ram's horns were right because horns growing in tight to the head can rub and cause sores in the summer, attracting flies and causing maggots. He also liked to see, as so many did in the past, wool with a tight curl.

Totnes root sale was an important milestone during the year as precious winter food had to be found and bought. At Tom Hodges, Venton Farm, Tigley, roots and grass were often taken and animals lorried together with Walter Irish's (John Irish' father at Cator) to Venton.

Joe used to lamb his sheep in February, earlier than many breeders. Joe, along with Richard Coaker and Miss Needham, was involved in the tattooing of sheep.

May recalls the terrible blizzard of 1962–63 at East Shallowford. She said on Boxing Day they returned from a trip to Shaugh Prior and the car never went out again until the second week in April. Also half the thatched roof of the house caved in under the weight of the snow. May explained that Toots and Joe walked to Ponsworthy to get food and they walked over a milk lorry that was trapped beneath several feet of snow and hadn't realised it was buried under their feet. However, the yard barns at Shallowford gave protection to their sheep. In Joe's time there was a big barn and stables, a Shippen, cart linhay, pig houses and a traditional layout in this piece of Dartmoor's backwaters. A stone trough in the yard receives a spring supply of water.

Joe's father, William Mortimore, on retiring at Down Park resulted in May and Joe leaving

East Shallowford and taking some of their Whiteface sheep to Down Park in 1968. Surplus sheep were dispersed of at Ashburton.

Then in 1986 retirement came about for Joe and May from Down Park to a bungalow in Chagford in June of that year. Joe had a farm sale in May after the farm was sold. Down Park was advertised as a typical small Dartmoor Farm with southerly facing land. It had been in the same ownership for 60 years with William and Joe Mortimore. May said Widecombes didn't do so well at Down Park as at Widecombe.

May spoke affectionately of many of the Whiteface breeders, in particular Leonard Ball at Axna who she said was one of 'Dartmoor's People'. All this when, May said, 'Dartmoor was Dartmoor and Whitefaces', in those days gone by.

Speaking of Albert Caunter, May's father's uncle when he farmed Tor Farm, Poundsgate, she said he had wool stored in two bedrooms of the farmhouse. Probably during the depression years of 1930's when wool prices, as all else, slumped and wool was only making a few pence a pound. This meant wool had to be stored over, somewhere on the farm, waiting for a better price!

Chris Murray

PENNYWELL FARM AND DEVON'S FARM AND WILDLIFE CENTRE, RATTERY, NEAR BUCKFASTLEIGH

The farm opened in 1988 as Devon's Farm and Wildlife Centre. Pennywell stands at 650 feet above sea level on the northern boundary of the Parish of Rattery, with spectacular views towards Hembury Woods, Leusdon and the Three Barrows on Dartmoor and also extensive views eastwards taking in Broadhempston and Staverton.

Whiteface sheep at Pennywell all started with a chance meeting one Sunday in Buckfast Abbey with Quentin Rae. Quentin's own enthusiasm for the breed rubbed off onto Chris.

However five sheep bought out of Exeter Market from Robert Partridge initiated the small flock in 1992.

A further 12 sheep were purchased from Quentin Rae in 1994 and again in 1998 before Quentin left to live in France.

Rams were purchased from the Ashburton Association Sales.

Chris Murray admitted he loves history and continuing something that has been around this area so long and putting it on view to the public was very important to him. Chris Murray's enthusiasm for Pennywell, its animals and the enjoyment in entertaining people is very evident in his vibrant nature and character. Away from Pennywell in 1973 he was the first person to open a farm to the public in the UK.

Chris finds the traditional Whiteface sheep 'attractive and easy to care for'.

At one point at Pennywell, Chris said he assembled all five of the local sheep breeds, both the White and Greyfaced Dartmoors, the South Devon (later merging to form the Devon and Cornwall Longwool) the Devon Closewool and the Exmoor.

However the difficulty of keeping different breeds of sheep apart with the visitors walking around the farm was to prove impossible.

So Chris settled for one local breed in the Whitefaced Dartmoor at Pennywell. He remarked, 'they look like a sheep'.

Chris initiated 'Dartington Foods, and speaking of marketing produce to sustain a demand for a type of meat and a particular breed of animal, Chris said, 'we need to use specialist labelled products with breed names'; for example, simply as 'Whiteface lamb', and so encourage a demand for their meat to give the breed a lifeline in future and encourage more breeders.

A video playing at Pennywell shows among other things sheepdog trialing, but Whitefaces are not being used, because Chris said he has real problems with the rams in particular, standing up to the dogs, and driving them away and also visitors are sometimes attacked! Their wild and restless survival characteristics are hard to keep down! A one-eyed ewe that acquired the title of 'Hawkeye' on losing its eye to a hawk is still breeding. Also a sheep with milk one side still quite remarkably rears two lambs. Chris lambs the sheep in polytunnels in February; I imagine they might think the tunnels are some sort of hollowed out granite tor!

The 'guinea spots' (black spots) can be seen on the feet and faces of some of his sheep, also Chris referred to the ears as 'egg cup shaped', as mentioned by Ned Northmore!

Chris had a smallholder from Berkshire visiting Pennywell on one occasion and he persuaded Chris to sell him four to five ewes because the Berkshire farmer thought they were 'a proper sort of sheep'. He still has some of the breed on his farm.

I think it indicates that the breed can be adaptable away from Dartmoor and if it did spread its wings it could extend its numbers.

Chris spoke of the monasteries and how they favoured certain breeds of native sheep, e.g. Tavistock Abbey attracted the Greyfaces, at Buckfast the Whitefaces were kept and the Devon Closewools could be found at Tiverton. So, some of the abbeys could be identified by their breed of sheep.

Chris and his wife entertain as many as ten thousand children a year. He says he loves entertaining, education, learning and sharing with others and has developed a form of 'Devons Living Heritage' at Pennywell.

Jokingly Chris said that he was told that Dartmoor farmers were a preserved species too, was that, he remarked because of subsidies or just because their roots are firmly planted where their forefathers were before them?

So although Pennywell is not a rare breeds farm it does exhibit some of the lesser breeds. Yet despite all the work that has been carried out in this country to conserve wildlife of all descriptions, it was not until 1968 that a working party was set up by the RASE and the Zoological Society of London to preserve the rare and in many cases, ancient breeds of British Farm Animals.

Individual enthusiasts like the Whitefaced Dartmoor Breeders maintain their own flocks and herds but many of the interesting and historic species of livestock were seriously endangered or extinct. There were no pure ewes left of the 'Norfolk breed' of sheep once so influential and prolific. Many breeds could be numbered in their tens not in their hundreds and thousands as of old.

Hele Farm, North Bovey, using the 'Rare Breeds Survival Trust', once collected together a wide range of rare breeding stock. It would be a tragedy if the older breeds were allowed to disappear; who knows what commercial requirements will prevail in future years. The rugged qualities of the island, hill and mountain sheep and their hardiness and economy in wool and meat. For such advantages future generations may well be thankful.

The Whiteface Dartmoors as an ancient breed was exhibited at Hele Farm (the sheep once covering a large area of Devon as we know it and West Somerset). However; with the coming of the enclosures they were driven back to Dartmoor and are now a localized breed.

They are naturally very hardy and can flourish on poor pastures in summer and at high altitudes.

RICHARD AUSTIN

Sheepdog Spot has the smile of spring

SPOT the sheepdog attentively watches over newborn lambs Larry, Libby and Lily.

Spot is well known for nurturing lambs at Pennywell Farm wildlife park near Buckfastleigh, South Devon. His owner, Chris Murray, said: "If lambs are near Spot, he mothers them by snuggling close to them, keeping them warm and out of harm's way. He loves shaking hands with children and is very affectionate."

Larry, Libby and Lily have all been brought in from the fields to be given extra milk. Mr Murray and his staff bottle feed them by hand.

Mr Murray said: "Spot is such a loving dog that he licks the lambs clean after they have dribbled milk over their faces."

At Pennywell, Spot, a former champion sheepdog, helps Mr Murray explain the life cycle of sheep through the shepherd's calendar, and performs sheepdog displays. So far this year 40 lambs have been born at Pennywell, and Mr Murray expects 80 more in the next few weeks.

Whitefaced triplets and a friendly paw! (Photo: *Western Morning News* by Richard Austin).

Miss S.C. Needham

DIPLEIGH, WIDECOMBE-IN-THE-MOOR
FORMERLY OF SOUTHCOTT, MANATON

Miss Needham has been Treasurer of the Whiteface Dartmoor Sheep Breeders Association (and previously flock book) since its inception in 1951, now fifty years ago, and was one of its founder members. She is now the Association's President.

Her early childhood memories are that every farmer around Holne kept Whiteface Dartmoor Sheep. A local sheep and she says it must be one of the most ancient breeds of sheep in the Western Peninsula.

She told me she has farming in her blood and attributes her interest in sheep to her Grandfather who farmed in Worcester and was a well-known sheep breeder.

She says the White Dartmoor sheep are a very important longwool sheep extending their territory into Tavistock and Cornwall and certainly regarded as one of the oldest indigenous breeds in England today.

Jim Smith holding Widecombe lambs with such affection and pride (Photo courtesy of Miss Needham).

So she grew up with 'Widecombes' around her, she remembers Widecombe Fair purely as a visitor from Holne as early as 1922, when she was just eight years old, with the sale of Whiteface Dartmoor sheep along with other livestock on the green.

She recalls a band coming out to the fair in the early years of her connection with the fair, called the 'SILVER THREAD BAND' from Bovey Tracey. The band played a lot of hymns and so the pony Gymkhana was often performed to the tune of 'ONWARD CHRISTIAN SOLDIERS' among others!

Her love of handling sheep came through being dropped in at the deep end in 1941 on Mr Jim Smith's Forestoke Farm at Holne, where she put her gift for lambing to the test and was self-taught in applying this delicate skill! She also recalls riding on Holne Moor twice a week checking leared stock.

As a common factor a lot of farmers traditionally kept South Devon cattle along beside Whiteface sheep and owned a horse to tend their stock. Miss Needham's own South Devon cattle had lines going back 200 years.

In 1944 she said Jim Smith made eight pound four shillings each of eighteen month old Wethers; an unheard of price for Whitefaces!

In 1945 she farmed her own farm at

Manaton called Southcott. Unfortunately, the sheep didn't like it there; she thinks because during the 'War Ag' period, potatoes were grown all over and the real old pastures were lost under the plough. This, she said, made the soil deficient in minerals.

It is not uncommon for sheep or cattle to have a preference for certain areas (as already highlighted) especially our native breeds like the Whiteface Dartmoor sheep and South and North Devon cattle. Sometimes it is said the Whiteface Dartmoor sheep won't survive very well North of Chagford and, similarly, that South Devon cattle shouldn't be taken north of the A30 road.

However, Miss Needham wanted to farm stock and her own Whiteface sheep flock at Southcott numbered 20 and the first ewes cost eighty-four shillings each. There were ten four-tooths from Jim Smith in 1945 at his 'selling up' sale, she recalls.

In 1949 she bought ten six-tooth ewes at around £8–£10 each from Leonard Hill, Lower Uppacott, Widecombe. Miss Needham remarked that these sheep were very wild and one particular sheep got away and spoilt its wool for showing, by becoming hung up in brambles.

One of her first sales with 'Widecombe wethers' was in 1949. She said at this point that in general the Whiteface sheep were a very motley lot and the ewes were better than the rams.

At this time Cecil Harris, an auctioneer and our present Secretary's father, took a lot of interest in the breed. He agreed a new policy should be followed and that an Association and flock book should be formed, a constitution shaped, and to select and register better sheep. Some of the Greyfaced Dartmoor sheep's constitution rules were borrowed.

Miss Needham became one of those founder members and despite the scepticism of the male fraternity, helped to turn things around for the breed.

The showing memories of Miss Needham go back to the Bath & West Show where she won the breed championship in the early 1950's, when *three* ewes and lambs had to be found for showing (quite a task with a small flock). In 1967 she was the winner of the Breed Champion at the Devon County Show and also was awarded prizes over the years at Devon County too. She recalled that Seale-Hayne hosted the Devon County Show in the late twenties or early thirties.

Breed champion at Devon County Show 1967 at its showground at Whipton. Joe Mortimore judged.

Miss Needham remembers the problem of having to shear ram hoggs for the Bath & West Show, after the Devon County Show, where they had to show ram hoggs in their wool.

On one occasion she took her sheared ram hoggs to Liskeard with Miss Coney Boddington when the Bath & West was held at Liskeard in its 'travelling show days', only to find competition from unshorn hoggs. The unfortunate judge was John Savery!

It was also 1967 that this photo was taken at the Association sale at Ashburton in Whistley Hill Field. As ever Miss Needham is supporting the Whitefaces at ring side.
Blackawton is quite 'hard keep' country and these lively rams reflect the area that suits them well.

Miss Needham mentions how important the moor at Holne could be in respect of grazing. She said hoggs were put on the moor in April. Ewes and single lambs were put up after shearing. When the ewes were removed the wethers stayed until November before going on to turnips for the winter.

She said, 'Holne Manor had a Lady of the Manor and a Reave to say when such and such had to be done on the moor; like drifting, swaling, fern cutting and turf cutting (peat) all within certain dates'.

Miss Needham spoke of the unfortunate problem she had herself of a slipping kneecap at Forestoke during the war. She was lambing a ewe a quarter of a mile away from the farm in two big seven or eight acre fields; riding her cob horse she tied him up to the gate and a particular ewe was having a double. She took off the second lamb and, on rising, her kneecap slipped out and she had to crawl to somehow get on her horse and it was March and very cold. Back at Forestoke she had to have it manipulated back and this was sadly a common occurrence.

She was also very renowned for riding her motorbike to the Whiteface Dartmoor sheep meetings much to the amusement of the men! But on one occasion she arrived absolutely wet through with just an old hessian sack wrapped around her shoulders and trying to protect her knees from the unpredictable autumn rains!

She explained she sold three old ewes to Mr Fred Trant and, very pleasing to all, they produced seven lambs. Miss Needham commented that Mr Trant was fully aware of the antiquity of these ewes. The one that produced the triplets was the sole survivor from the ewes bought from the late Mr Leonard Hill. She was toothless, but all three lambs were reared.

Miss Needham's showing achievements were numerous. Compounded through winning the W.F.D.S.B.A. Cup presented by H.G. Woodley for annual competition for the best flock of under 50 Whitefaces in 1986, 1990 and 1992.

Fleeces and Spinning came up in Miss Needhams memories. She explained fleeces were rough washed for spinning and lots of families were keen on home spinning. Wool was knitted and Tweed was popularly made using Whiteface wool.

Black wool is often sought after and she recalls a black lamb she called 'Coal dust'. She spoke in depth of the nature of this lamb. Miss Needham felt the gene inherited from the mother had a special characteristic and could be nature's way of transferring more vigour. The lamb it seems was a huge character that seem to transfer intelligence and was psychologically different as a mutation (the act of being changed) from the other sheep.

A gene undergoes mutation and as a result produces an offspring differing from the parental strain, an heritable alteration of the genes that in this case produced a black lamb.

12 Advertiser/Post, Friday, September 3, 1999

A 'great lady' says farewell to farming

By Richard Davies

Sylvia, 85, bows out as she would wish – gracefully, and with a prize for the last ram she took to market

Staff

THERE was consolation for Miss Needham as she took her last white-faced Dartmoor ram to Ashburton market – it won a prize.

The year old animal won first prize in the best coated ram category, just an hour before it went under the auctioneer's hammer.

Miss Needham walked into the ring with her ram as auctioneer John Harris began the sale. Well wishers and photographers gathered round to watch the end of an era for the woman Mr Harris described as 'a great lady'.

After a number of brisk bids the ram was finally sold for 70 guineas, one of the best prices of the morning.

Miss Needham, who is pictured with shepherd Clyde Coaker, said afterwards she was 'very satisfied' with the sale price, and the best-coated prize (worth £10) was 'lovely'.

Asked if the day was a sad one she said: 'Yes and no. All things come to an end. The important thing is to let go gracefully.'

WHEN Sylvia Needham first went into farming as a young woman on her own, people scoffed. They gave her six months to survive – 12 at most.

But on Friday she sold her last ram at Ashburton market and, at the age of 85, had a chance to look back on a lifetime on the land, an extraordinary woman in a man's world.

She had worked on a farm during World War II but when, straight after hostilities finished she decided to set up on her own, it was, to say the least, an unusual job for a woman.

But she had always loved animals and had farming blood in her veins. It wasn't so much a question of why should she farm as why should she do anything else?

'It was a terrific challenge, an adventure. Life is an adventure, really,' she told me at her bungalow home which overlooks some dramatic scenery around Widecombe-in-the-Moor.

She read books on farming, especially haymaking, but accepts she was terribly green and naive. With her self-deprecating manner she makes it all sound very simple, but of course it wasn't. There were tough times but she tends to skate over them. That is very much her way.

She was born in Tiverton, the elder daughter of a clergyman who went on to become vicar of Holne. Her parents never tried to talk her out of farming, being country people used to country ways.

The farm she started was at Manaton, most of it on very steep ground, full of rocks, with only four or five flat meadows for her handful of cows. To begin with she was on her own, then after a year 'a dear chap' called Sid came along to work for her, and together with his older brother they got the place in shape. Once they had finished there wasn't a weed to be seen.

She stayed there 11 years before moving to Broadford across the valley from where she now lives in splendid isolation.

At Broadford life became easier, yet strangely more tedious. There may have been a milking machine, but it had to be washed, and she hated that.

'I haven't really ever been lonely. Of course there have been moments of loneliness, but I never felt like giving up. It was something I'd taken on and that was that.'

She never married, but has always been surrounded by great friends. The job was her first and only love.

Godchildren often came to stay and when they did they were immediately put to work on the farm. She saw some of them at her 80th birthday party and they told her how much they had enjoyed staying with her – and just how hard she had made them work!

One of her earliest memories was of her younger sister being born. She was taken to see her in a private home and can re-live the journey up the stairs into the room where 'this little pink thing' was.

'I wasn't best pleased,' she ruefully admits.

She accepts her early life was privileged but she has never sought riches. 'There is poverty in the country these days, a lot of it and terrible economic pressure. But a lot of poverty relates to poverty of the spirit.'

She is clearly happiest talking about the old days, but strict with herself as if her razor sharp memory is somehow rationed. 'My heart is living 60 years ago, but my head says live in today.'

Change has swept across her beloved Dartmoor, not much of it to her liking. There are two communities now in Widecombe, she says, the old ones and the incomers.

'It's so very sad when the young people of the area can't get houses of their own,' she said. Some of the new people in the country can't tell a bull from a cow, she added dismissively.

To meet this indomitable woman of the moor I have to leave my car on the edge of the main road and walk a quarter-of-a-mile along a rough track through gorse and fern, and around rocks.

She greets me warmly – though she claims to be a bit of a recluse – wearing a faded check shirt and beige trousers. She makes me a coffee which keeps warm on the Aga and throughout the interview feeds me delicious ginger biscuits.

As we talk squirrels come to the window, peering cheekily in. She has a regular collection of animals she watches, rabbits, sheep and birds of all kinds, including jays.

'It is a beautiful spot,' she said, and the peace is blissful. Try as you might – and I did – there isn't a sound to be heard beyond that of the birds in the trees.

I ask her about the future. 'Of course I am living on borrowed time, I recognise that. So many of my contemporaries are dead. But still you've got to go on.'

The bungalow has no mod cons and definitely no television, though she has a great friend who not only allows her to watch what she wants but keeps her informed of what is worth watching.

She does have a radio though, through which she keeps herself informed.

Perhaps predictably her favourite programme is *The Archers*.

She became a founder member of the white-faced Dartmoor sheep association and last week was an end of an era for her. She has concern for the future of farming, but not for her own in this life – or the next.

'It's the end of one thing and the beginning of another. I've no sloppy idea of heaven and crowns and harps,' she said.

Her eyes grow distant as she tells of the past camaraderie of the countryside, how neighbours rushed to help her get hay inside before bad weather set in, how their action helped to save the lives of her stock for the coming winter.

She pulls a face, clearly meaning she cannot see that happening these days.

She still retains fields across the valley where she will keep a few sheep as pets. There will still be animals at her window, her friends, her history society.

Damaged knees mean she cannot walk as much as she would like, but she drives and meets people. Whatever happens you sense she will make the best of it.

As I say goodbye she looks across at her fields, lying baking in the August sun. She is lost in thought for a moment, then she says: 'I didn't really think about being a farmer, I just did it.'

This very moving letter was written at the height of the 'Foot and Mouth' Epidemic in March 2001, from Dipleigh, Widecombe-in-the-Moor, by the Associations President, Miss Sylvia Needham.

White Face Dartmoor Sheep Breeders Association

Affiliated to The National Sheep Breeders Association

President :

Chairman :

Hon. Treasurer : MISS S. NEEDHAM, Dipleigh, Widecombe-in-the-Moor. 621227

Hon. Secretary : J. E. HARRIS, A.R.I.C.S., 13, West Street, Ashburton. 652304

Dipleigh Widecombe-in-the-Moor

19.3.01.

My dear Fellow Member, with your Family,

I write to you at a time of deep distress and trauma in our lives. We all feel desperate, caught up in circumstance over which we have no control, which, perhaps creates in us feelings of helplessness, & even hopelessness.

As President of this Association, I feel it's my privilege to commend to you all; the thought, we be aware of the sense of friendship and unity in our ranks; and in our unity find strength to endure our great trouble at this time.

I want you to know, how much you are in my thoughts in these dark days of anxiety.

God Speed you, & your Flocks & herds.

John joins me in these thoughts.

Yours sincerely

Sylvia Needham

My dear Fellow Member, with your Family,

I write to you at a time of deep distress and trauma in our lives. We all feel desperate, caught up in circumstances over which we have no control, which, perhaps creates in us feelings of helplessness, and even hopelessness.

As President of this Association, I feel it's my privilege to commend to you all; the thought, we be aware of the sense of friendship and unity in our ranks; and in our unity find strength to endure our great trouble at this time.

I want you to know, how much you are in my thoughts in these dark days of anxiety.

God speed you, and your flocks and herds

John (the Assoc' Secretary) joins me in these thoughts.

Yours sincerely.

Sylvia Needham.

Miss Needhams feelings at this time, would almost certainly have gone back to the cancellation of Livestock Classes due to a Foot and Mouth outbreak, when the Royal Show took its place at Newton Abbot (on Tuesday 1st July to Friday 4th July) 1952.

Along with Leonard S. Ball, Cecil E. Caunter, John Coaker, French Bros, (Corringdon) Mann Bros, John Savery (Higher Lincombe), and W.A.F. Webber. (A Challenge Cup was offered by the W.F.D.S.B.A. for the best exhibit in the Shearling Ram and Yearling Ewes classes), Miss Sylvia Needham then of Southcott Manaton entered the White Face Dartmoor Classes, but was not able to compete!

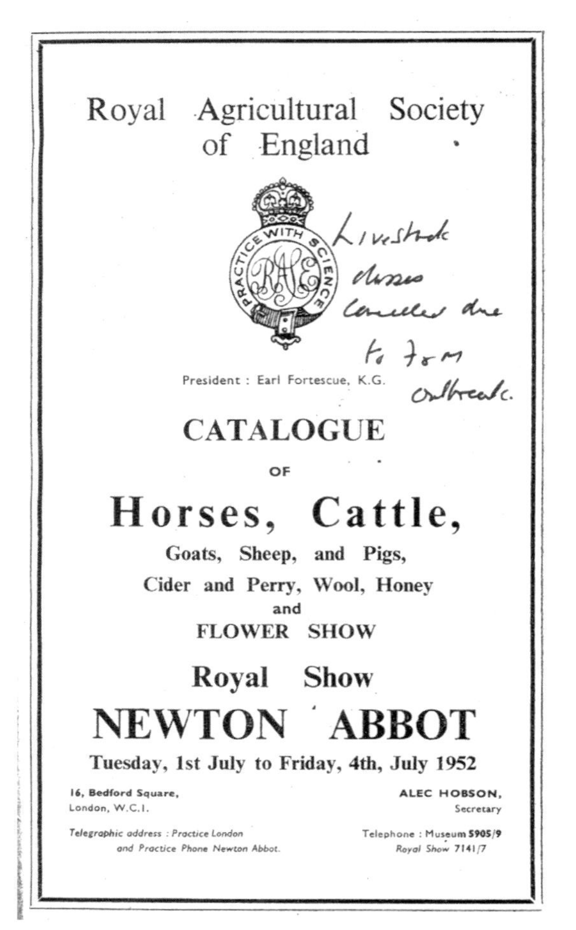

Royal Agricultural Society of England

PRACTICE WITH SCIENCE

RASE

Livestock classes cancelled due to F&M outbreak.

President : Earl Fortescue, K.G.

CATALOGUE

OF

Horses, Cattle,

Goats, Sheep, and Pigs,

Cider and Perry, Wool, Honey

and

FLOWER SHOW

Royal Show

NEWTON ABBOT

Tuesday, 1st July to Friday, 4th, July 1952

16, Bedford Square, London, W.C.1.

ALEC HOBSON, Secretary

Telegraphic address : Practice London and Practice Phone Newton Abbot.

Telephone : Museum 5905/9 Royal Show 7141/7

228 *White Face Dartmoor—Classes* 534, 535.

WHITE FACE DARTMOOR

JUDGE :

W. J. MANN, "LIZWELL," IPPLEPEN, NEWTON ABBOT.

Class 534—WHITE FACE DARTMOOR SHEARLING RAM.

FIRST PRIZE, £12. SECOND PRIZE, £8. THIRD PRIZE, £6. FOURTH PRIZE, £5.

5 ENTRIES

2459 Leonard S. Ball, Peter Tavy, Tavistock.
2460 Cecil E. Caunter, Ipplepen, Newton Abbot.
2461 John Coaker, Sherberton, Princetown.
2462 French Bros., Corringdon, South Brent.
2463 Mann Bros., Gt. Dunstone, Widecombe-in-the-Moor.

Class 535—TWO WHITE FACE DARTMOOR YEARLING EWES.

FIRST PRIZE, £12. SECOND PRIZE, £8. THIRD PRIZE, £6. FOURTH PRIZE, £5.

8 ENTRIES

2464 Leonard S. Ball, Peter Tavy, Tavistock.
2465 Cecil E. Caunter, Ipplepen, Newton Abbot.
2466 John Coaker, Sherberton, Princetown.
2467 French Bros., Corringdon, South Brent.
2468 Mann Bros., Gt. Dunstone, Widecombe-in-the-Moor.
2469 Miss Sylvia C. Needham, Manaton, Newton Abbot.
2470 John Savery, Higher Lincombe, South Brent.
2471 William A. F. Webber, Hawson, Buckfastleigh.

s535A A CHALLENGE CUP is offered by the White Face Dartmoor Sheep Breeders' Association for the best EXHIBIT in classes 534 and 535.

The Norrish Family

FORMERLY OF 'SHERRELL', IVYBRIDGE
NOW AT FIRCROFT, WOODLAND ROAD, IVYBRIDGE

John and Bertha Norrish at Shewell with the sheep (1951).

Ron Norrish's father, John, was one of the founder members of the Association in 1951. Ron Norrish's wife, Agnes, was a Colton and her family roots were at Holewell Farm, Walkhampton. The mother of Ron was a Woodley and they originally farmed at 'Webland' South Brent. Also George Woodley, a cousin, was a son of Hermon.

John Woodley with his sheep. This photograph probably taken in the early 1900s.

John Woodley (also family with George and Hermon) was born in 1853, his daughter, Bertha, was to marry John Norrish. A very old photograph shows John Woodley in a field with Whitefaces and the sheep are quite big for 'Widecombes' at the time. The photograph was probably taken in the early 1900s.

This time warp of life embracing the Whiteface sheep, their owners, ponies, dogs and the moor, repeats itself yet again and all this starting so far back in time.

The Norrish family, including Roger and Ann, also showed me a wonderful picture of sheep stretching out over Hanger Down, Ivybridge, being gathered through a lot of ferns that are just dying back in the Autumn. The sheep probably coming into 'flush' for the rams. Ron's father, John, is the horse-rider with 'coat and legs', and hessian bag under the saddle and his dog seen working too, alongside the sheep. There is too quite a flock of sheep in view. The Woodley's would not have used the moor much, if at all, from Webland. South Devon cattle were again in place with both families.

Great grandfather, William, and grandfather, Harry, were forerunners of the breed as explicitly explained by Roger in the 'gift of a three-legged sheep' all at Combestone ('Cumpson' Holne).

Ron Norrish sold and showed his sheep at Ashburton. A Mr White from Dartmouth bought his sheep year after year from the Association fair. These he crossed to produce fat lamb.

John Norrish sold his Whitefaces mostly at Brent and Bob Kerswell was a regular buyer. Sheep around the early 60's made about £15 a piece. Also again revealed by Ron that a lot of Whitefaces were purchased to go to Cornwall; Tamblyn and Dunn by name were the buyers.

'Hanger Down' to the Stall Moor, was the run for the sheep on their learing patches. Taken through a lane near the moor from Sherrell (not to be confused with Sherril, Widecombe) to Yadsworthy waste to Wisdome Waste and Waterscombe, in the Cornwood area, out to Broadrock some 8 miles from the boundary farm wall and the open moor.

John Norrish on Hanger Down, Cornwood, Ivybridge.

John Norris had a cob called Bluebell who, when you let go the reins, would part the Scotch sheep from the Whitefaces, given his freedom to twist and turn.

Ron recalls the story of the ram being brought home from Tavistock and how the ram fell back off the cart and hung itself on the way home. Using these high-wheeled carts must have caused many hazardous journeys for sheep straining at their makeshift halters!

Ron also recalls when he was seventeen-years-old he stayed at Alan Helmer's, a neighbour of John Tucker's, where Ron's 'away keep-sheep' had to be lambed due to snow. He also told the story of one occasion when he was threshing corn at Sherrell and how, usually, all his dog liked doing was 'ratting' normally around the rick and threshing machine, but he disappeared, probably he thought, because of the noise of the threshing machine. In fact, he disappeared 8 miles away to where Ron and the dog had walked his sheep a few days before.

The day following the threshing, Ron went to see the sheep, and his friend said to Ron, 'Why did you come in yesterday? Because I saw your dog here rounding up the sheep.' Of course, the dog came on it's own and Ron then realised where it had been.

In the *Dartmoor Magazine* (Autumn 1995) and an article written by Michael French (Whiteface Breeder) called 'Memories of a Moorman', Michael writes candidly of Harry Norrish of Dockwell, South Brent (formerly Combestone Holne) and how one of Harry's last sheep dogs 'Yip' – was a strangely useless creature to whose collar his master would occasionally tie a short stick. This was meant to control the beast and slow it down, but more often the ploy contrived to trip it up – the stick flying in the air around its head and legs, causing the animal to wind up in a tangled heap. If Harry had counted the number of times he'd had to dismount in order to unwind it, he might have pondered the economy of it all.

Ron and Agnes Norrish, Devon County Show.

Ron and Agnes presented to The Devon County Agricultural Association in 1973 the:

W.R. and A.R. Norrish Perpetual Cup
Presented by Mr & Mrs W.R. Norrish for the Best Exhibit.

It was presented as recognition of the best exhibit at the Devon County Show and to encourage flock book members to put one of Devon's original sheep breeds in the public eye at the Show. They were winners of the Breed Champion at the Show in 1974, 1978 and 1980. Also in 1973 W.R. and A.R. Norrish won the over fifties flock competition, securing the W.F.D.S.B.A. Challenge Cup, presented by Miss S. Needham for the best flock of over 50 ewes. Roger Norrish himself won the best flock under 50 in 1976 and the winner of Breed Champion at the Devon County Show in 1977.

Ron's random memories: Ron said that John Savery used to drive his sheep through the square at Brent to the sale field. Also Ron bought a ram from a person called Tucker at Fenn Farm, East Allington (an original flock book member). It turned out to be a good choice of sheep.

Ron also spoke of the problem of getting to shows on time. Les Adams picked up Ned and Patrick with his lorry to all go to the Devon County Show on one occasion. On another day at Widecombe in 1977, Ron was judging and the rain, he said, 'was chucking it down'.

Ron remembers picking out sheep with his father when they were not selling very well. There is a saying that if a Widecombe has a black spot its worth a guinea. Ron picked out a sheep with two black spots and convinced his father it must be worth selling!

For a bit of fun at the Devon County Show, Patrick Coaker ordered an ambulance for one of John (Jack) Mead's sheep that started puffing and panting in the main ring at the show. It was a big Greyface sheep and someone turned up with a bottle of O2 (oxygen) gas. They said to John, the sheep's too big and fat to make lambs!

Roger Norrish started showing when he was only 14 years old. Three years later he had the Devon County Show Champion Whiteface ram.

Roger Norrish, Devon County WFD Breed Champion.

The character breed points Ron likes to see in the Whitefaces is sheep fairly short on the leg, a black tip to their nose, a thick ear and a curl to their wool.

In 1973, H. George Woodley won the under 50 flock competition and was to present the H.G. Woodley Cup still in circulation for annual competition for the best flock of under 50 Whiteface ewes.

Hermon Woodley dipping at Sherrell: a remarkable old task of sheep husbandry now practised less and less as injectionable preventatives and spray dipping (mobile dips) takes the place of on farm dips.

Mrs Ron Norrish (nee Agnes Colton) speaks of the 'small moorland farm', Holewell, on which her father William Henry Colton (Bill to his friends), ran about 50 Whitefaced Dartmoor sheep and South Devon cattle with followers. The neighbours, one on each side of Holewell, were Mr Harry Hillson of Eggworthy Farm, Walkhampton, and Messrs Dawe Bros. of Dittisham Farm, of the same parish, kept around 100 Whitefaces.

Agnes explained that 'dipping sheep' each year as a matter of practice was a time consuming process and the only 'dip bath' was at a Mr Fice's of Hall Farm, Sampford Spiney, a few miles from the Coltons. There was no transport then, so sheep were walked to the dip. They had to be rested and then dipped, drained, and walked home. Agnes said each farmer took his own dip chemicals and helped to clean up ready for the next flock!

William Henry Colton had the first Whitefaces in the Colton family back in 1913. When he married, they bought some for 2/6d each at Widecombe Fair and took them to Holewell Farm.

If there was ever a story of hard work, dedication and sheer thrift on the fringes of Dartmoor and down its deep winding lanes working with Whiteface sheep and South Devon Cattle this is yet another example, seen in this tale all through!

So another cluster of farms in the heart of Devon keeping Whitefaced Dartmoor sheep is revealed around Holewell and Peek Hill in the Parish of Walkhampton and Yelverton, the sheep obviously finding it to their liking in the valleys and on the hills around about.

Agnes commented that draft ewes and store lambs were sold at Dousland Sheep Sale which used to be held in August/September time. John Colton (brother to Agnes) remaked that Dousland in the Sheep Sale field would have seen a lot of Whitefaces sold and brought, especially pre-association times. John Young and Tom Brown of Tavistock Auctioneers would have sold the sheep.

Peek Hill and Brent Tor (and Church) left of middle distance. (Photo Colin Pearse).

A move to Peek Hill by the Colton family in 1936 was to a farm of better stock feeding quality, and a change to Greyfaces took place crossing these with the Whitefaces for ten years.

The Whitefaces can handle better than the Greyface on the harder keep farms and on the natural vegetation of the Moor in summer, and keep fitter in larger flocks, thereby helping to avoid them 'running to fat' which on good land can cause them to roll on their backs.

David Colton (John's son) said 'the most annoying fact about Whitefaces is that unless you have sloping fields they do get on their backs after a shower of rain, followed by hot sun, and they start to roll!' Then the crows and magpies can peck their eyes out or drill a hole into their stomach whilst they are still alive, if not 'righted' quite quickly!

John Colton recalls wool being stored in the past (a recurring story) and worth 2/6d a pound when a good price, but dropping as low as 4 pence in 1937. John also talked about some reasons for wool becoming less popular, washing wool in washing machines can be a problem and hand washing is too time-consuming, and also less wool carpets are laid today!

John Colton also referred to the practice of 'sheep-washing' in the past. Sheep put away to keep in winter, and their fleeces red-soiled on turnips would have come home to their Dartmoor farms very muddied, and so before shearing they would have had to be washed.

Otherwise wool would be down-graded, and also it is likely 'stoney-grit' could blunt the hand shears. The clear waters of Dartmoor were ideal for sheep-washing.

In some areas sheep were literally driven through a particular river to help wash them, and others manhandled into a river pool.

David Colton also spoke of 'the demise of the Whiteface Dartmoor'. He explained why he thought the 'Whiteface' had fallen from favour: low wool price was probably a major reason commercially that has fuelled their decline and hitting all longwools the hardest. Also fat colour, and an overall lack of conformation in carcass quality, and as already explained the problem of seeing and also losing sheep getting on their backs.

In conclusion, David felt the decline in the Whitefaced Dartmoor was because too much of its output had been channelled into wool production, and not meat, giving poorer quality carcasses. Also, more importantly, reducing too their hardy and thrifty character so valued in the past on the Moor, and for its headage-based system! (A function and combination of keep, hardiness and size).

The Gift of a Three Legged Sheep by Roger Norrish

Somewhere on the southern foothills of Dartmoor, in the half forgotten corner of a granite walled house lies a photograph. It rests there in it's dog-eared shroud of ancient newspaper, a sepia washed relic of a bygone age, a treasure brought out infrequently to inspire the mind on evenings of fireside tales. A barometer of social change.

Combestone Farmhouse. Harry Norrish's family. An inspired piece of writing and photograph to match, where family and animal survival was a 'tunnel vision' in the moors heart. N.B. 'Ash House' (thatched) left of farmhouse! (Courtesy the 'Sherrell', Norrish family).

It is an unremarkable piece in some ways and of no particular interest to anyone perhaps save the family to whom it has now passed and to those who may wish to share it's memories. It's wooden frame bears witness to the loving craft of dark nights long since out of mind and the faces that lie within stare out austerely, unflinching in the cold stare of the camera's eye.

Nobody knows exactly when it was taken and few will know the names of the family standing proudly at their back door, unaware of we who gaze at them from another century. Their brief moment in time a vignette of an age now nearly forgotten.

In the early 1870's, William Norrish took Beatrice Mann for his wife and settled with her at Combestone Farm, a small granite pocked steading that even now clings to the side of a valley above Home like moss on a gatepost. It was hard sour land, spread with bracken and yellow flashes of gorse, stunted scrubs of blackthorn and white drifts of 'Widecombe' sheep that grazed the high moor and the steep sides of the vale down to the river.

William and Beatie had arrived like pioneers in a new land with no more than their few basic possessions strapped in a rough cart, a couple of South Devon cows brought from their savings and the prospect of a lifetime's hard labour. Like so many who trod the same path out to the moor they knew that it could not be broken like the vast plains of far off countries, it could not be tamed and turned solely to their use, it merely tolerated them, as it always has.

There beneath 'Cumpson Tor' they set their lives, moving to the moods of the countryside and working with its' seasons. They lived from the land by selling cream and butter from their cows, cutting faggots from the woods and the payment in cash or in kind for William's work on neighbouring farms.

In the manner of these small legends it is said that one day, by chance William came across a Whitefaced ewe amongst the trees at the river's edge, her leg caught in a poacher's snare that had broken it beyond all mending and held her there for uncounted pitiless days. He carried her back to the farm and tended her, removing the rotting limb and binding the stump with cobwebs and linen.

The unerring tread of time has left behind the name of that unfortunate animal's owner, but it is said that he was struck by the hard work and compassion of his young neighbours and that be promised them should the wretched creature survive it would be theirs to keep. They made sure it did! And so unwittingly by an act of kindness and the grateful thanks of a neighbour began a line that would last for over one hundred years in the name of William and Beatie's family and the hardy blood of that poor ewe that must still flow somewhere in the veins of maybe just a few Whitefaced Dartmoors. It's own small dynasty. The gift, if youlike, of that three legged sheep.

In the spring of that year the ewe gave birth to their first lamb and by the autumn they had saved enough money to buy six more from Ned Caunter and his father over at Hexworthy. Life began to take shape at Combestone Farm, and there they stayed in the side of the hill, nurturing their South Devon cows into a small herd, their ewes into a flock that would eventually boast an even number of legs, and their own family of four boys and a girl, each of whom would one day have their own Whitefaced Dartmoors.

By the early 1900's the family began to spread. Harry and Polly, the two youngest, remained at Combestone, while 'Farge', slightly the elder, married and moved to Seal Stoke. But it was the two eldest sons Frank and John who carried the flock forward through the long years of the 'Great' war. John, as straight as a die and as cussed as a mule in the face of fools and bigheads and Frank, truly born a shepherd who at the age of thirteen during the great blizzard of 1891 was sent down to Ringmore to look after the hoggs in keep above the cliffs where, armed only with a lamp and a sack around his shoulders he spent the night trudging round and round keeping his sheep to the middle of the field so none should be buried in the snow.

In 1905, the two brothers moved down to Dockwell, a farm on the moor's edge above South Brent still harsh enough to send solitary trees leaning away from the wind but where there was stronger soil and more chance of spring grass and autumn harvests of barley and oats. They ran the moor in the summer and took keep on the lower land around Kingsbridge for the winter, fattening wethers off roots for sale at Dodbrooke market, drafting strong six tooth ewes, 'lambed twice and sound in tooth and udder', for the bids of lowland breeders at South Brent and Ashburton in the autumn. They bought fresh blood in the way of rams from local flocks such as those of the Frenchs at Corringdon and, Michelcombe or John Woodley at Webland and pushed their numbers above a hundred for the first time.

In 1921 the two brothers parted, amicably it must be said, to farm in their own right. The flock was split in two and John brought his sixty ewes down to Sherrell on the southern edge of the moor, facing the sun and sloping gently to water meadows and marshes at it's foot. The Whitefaces did well here, lambing in March under the shelter of the high hedges. They were good mothers with plenty of milk for their lambs and strong mouths that cleared fields of Devon Champion swedes until nothing but the hollowed roots remained, lined across the land like defeated regiments of china plates.

By the first week of May, if the weather was right and there was no threat of thunder storms the ewe hoggs were sheared and put out to the moor. The ewes and lambs would follow in June, driven out across Hanger Down, where Dick Wyatt of Pithill and Sam Horton at Wilkie's Moor grazed their own Whitefaces, to Hall Cross and Greenwell lane over the wastes of Yadsworthy and Watercombe and away through the Moor gate. They spent the early part of the summer around Stall Moor, sometimes drifting out as far as Green Hill where the Plym and the Erme rise from their granite nursery. Where the mist can drop like a blanket and the only choice for a man out checking his stock was to leave go the reins and let his pony find the way back through the bogs and marshes, over Broad Rock and then down off the moor.

This was natural country for the Whitefaced Dartmoor as it had been around Combestone and Hexworthy, as it was around Poundsgate and Widecombe, evolving over countless years from the hardy mix of indigenous wild sheep that were strong enough to survive the harsh conditions, thriving through their own natural selection and shaping their surroundings as much as their surroundings had shaped them. It was right and proper to keep Whitefaces on the moor and John Norrish's were not alone around Stall Moor and Penn Moor. He marked them with 'a half take over the near ear' and a pitched N over the ribs to distinguish them from the others. Like those of Jim Northmore's at Hele or Richard Luscombe's next door at Uppaton, Jack Munford over at Watercombe and the Walkes of Yadsworthy, Jack Hext at Torr or the Luscombes of Hall and Wisdome. Most farmers in the parish of Cornwood it seemed kept Whitefaced Dartmoors and during the summer months they kept them on the moor. It was the way! The river Erme was a natural barrier to the east but if any strayed across it they would still find themselves in the company of other Whitefaces, Mrs Pearse's at Broomhill for instance whose flock grazed Harford Moor, or on odd occasions even as far away as John Savery's at Zeal or back out to Dockwell and Frank. There was a frienship that linked these people, that could draw them together at need, when gathering their sheep or at harvest, at dipping time or midnight calvings, a respect for each other, for Dartmoor and their livestock.

Time has a way of just plodding along and quietly changing things without anyone really noticing what it's up to. The world then was a weary place, preoccupied by other things. Men had returned slowly from the bitter harvest of the First World War and the bloodied soil of foreign fields, back to the mills and pastures of their homes. Many of course would never come back. But life, as they say, goes on. The sun never once failed to rise in the morning or to set in it's own time. Spring crept in behind the winter as it always had. Families blossomed with the birth of new generations, seed time and harvest never failed. Darker faces grew upon the moor.

George Woodley (son of Hermon) with sheep in Pithill Lane; from Wilkies Moor.

John had married Bertha, John Woodley's daughter, and together they raised their son Ronald. The routine necessity of farmlife continued at Sherrell as it did on every other farm, lambing, shearing, dipping, weaning, gathering the flock on the moor, driving them away to keep, picking out ewes for the sales and buying fresh rams. Young men became steeped in the ways of their fathers and their forefathers, as Ronald did with his cousin George Woodley who came to live and work in Sherrell. They learned the whys and wherefores of the land, they knew the needs and habits of their livestock and above all they knew their Whitefaced Dartmoors.

War, of course, returned and the need for good became paramount. Permanent pastures were ploughed under for potatoes and grain, even some of Combstone's black and rocky soil was turned for a crop of spuds, though they were never harvested. Efficiency became a game of numbers driven by subsidies and the view of quantity above all else. The Whiteface conceded it's ground to invaders from the north.

The Scotch Blackface was of course not unknown on Dartmoor before the war, but by the fifties it's numbers had grown beyond all expectation. It was a low maintenance sheep, unproductive when compared to the more traditional breeds like the Whiteface, but it could be left to fend for itself out on the moor for longer periods of time while the farmer concentrated on other things. Time had done it's stealthy work once more. The spread of these sheep did as much to change the face of Dartmoor in the latter half of the twentieth century as anything that had gone on there in hundreds of years previously. For starters there were many more sheep out on the moor than there used to be, and for greater lengths of time. Blackfaced sheep by and large are heather eaters and so the composition of the moor changed accordingly. The Whitefaced Dartmoor, though still popular, was gradually pushed into small pockets on the fringes of the moor.

In 1951, when Ronald was taking over Sherrell and George was establishing his own flock at Wilkies Moor, John Norrish and seven other good men and true formed the first committee of the Whitefaced Dartmoor Sheep Breeders Association. Their aims were not only to keep the breed going, but to push it forward into new areas and to improve it by the inspection of rams prior to registration. The Whitefaced ewe had always been sought after by the lowland flockmasters as a purebred to produce finished lambs when crossed with a downland breed such as the Suffolk or the Hampshire. If the way to the moor was now being barred by the Scotch then avenues would have to be opened up to the lower ground.

The shop windows for the breed were and still are the shows, like Cornwood, Yealmpton, Widecombe and in particular the Devon County. In the 1970s and early 80s the lines were strong, Ronald and his family took their sheep to Exeter and competed with the rest, stalwarts of the breed such as Miss Needham, Norman Stephens, Ken Soper, Edward Caunter, Adams and Howell, Mann Brothers and Archie Mortimore. These were times of fun and friendship, of strong horned rams and starched white coats, flighty hoggs that pulled to the halter and reared at the touch of the judges hand or the gaze of Royalty. Of characters like Ned Northmore, the peak of his cap permanently pulled above one eye and his ever present smile or Patrick Coaker, mischief never far from his fingertips.

By the end of the 1980s there were no longer Whitefaced Dartmoors on Sherrell Farm, the modern need for specialisation had condemned them to this small history. Crossed with John Tucker's Bluefaced Leicester ram they had made an impressive 'Whitefaced Mule', strong and prolific, but they never caught on. The Kerswell family down at Kingsbridge, even at the beginning of the twenty-first century, still buy them to cross with the Teeswater for a half bred ewe and there's not much they don't know about sheep. The potential is still there.

Whitefaced Dartmoors no longer graze the steep sided vale above Combestone or walk the roads from Dockwell down to Ringmore, they no longer drift across Watercombe waste and out to Stall Moor as they would have years ago or lamb under the high hedges at Sherrell. All these things are memories carefully wrapped in newspaper and put away for another time. Time, ah there's the rub! When all of us are but memories and the half forgotten stories of our times are brought out by the firesides of future years, when the barometer of change is tapped by fingers beyond this century, who is to say where it will stop, who is to say where time will have taken us? Will the memory of a man carrying an injured sheep through the woods one dark winters evening be forgotten? Will his kindness, his hard work and the ways of his children and grandchildren ever be remembered? Time has a strange way of creeping around in circles and making fools of those who say never. The gift of the three legged sheep may not yet be over.

A farmer of livestock needs to be able to cope with losses, for they are always coming along and Ronald Norrish was a realist about these things and Roger said, on the passing of his father, when an animal died, or the weather smacked of cruelty and uncompromising anger, 'Its just one of *them* things and you have to move forward' as his father would say.

Roger also spoke of the stories his father told of driving the sheep from Sherrell across Hanger Down, through Hall gates, across the Wastes and up onto the moor, him and Granfer Norrish and Uncle George, their dogs and their ponies. Of old Mr Wotton, sorting black bullocks with his pony and whip. Uncle Farge and his dog that could stop a Galloway cow by clinging to its nose.

The Norrish Family

TUNHILL AND NORTHWAY, WIDECOMBE-IN-THE-MOOR – NOW AT ADDISLADE, DEAN PRIOR, SOUTH BRENT

William Norrish was born on the 16th February 1891 and his wife Alice (nee Daw) was by coincidence born on the 14th April 1891. Their birth dates lie either side of the Great Blizzard of March 9th 1891, when the train at Princetown that journeyed to Tavistock was buried and chaos was caused everywhere on the moor.

William Norrish and his horse bringing sheep down Widecombe Hill (1930s).

William's first profession was 'Rabbit Trapper'. He was to rent Dockwell Farm, Widecombe, Tunhill and Northway before the family finally moved to Addislade Farm, Dean Prior around 1957–8. Whitefaces were kept and such were their importance everyone farming in Widecombe Parish had Whiteface Dartmoor Sheep. Mrs Reg Norrish (Marjorie, now in a bungalow at Addislade, with David her son, in the farm) said there was a steep decline after the war in Whiteface flocks.

William Norrish's son Reg (Reginald) was born at Tunhill in 1921. Marjorie said Alice (Reg's Mum) helped to keep the farm going. Marj' also recalled how Reg used to visit the local shop at Linchaford that was run by Tony Beard's grandfather in bygone days.

Whilst the family was still farming at Tunhill, Reg wrote this very interesting letter when still at school about their 'Dartmoor Farm'. This is as he wrote it around 1929. Reg actually titled it 'A Dartmoor Farm'.

'My home, "Tunhill" is situated in the valley of Widecombe in the Moor. It is very hilly around here and some farms are very rocky. The soil is light. There is some good pasture, some arable and some very rough. The chief things grown are oats, mangel (mangolds) and turnips. This is a stock-raising district. The sheep are mostly Whiteface Dartmoors with just a few Exmoor and Scotch. We have a fair once a year for sheep which is the well known Widecombe Fair. The farmers take their sheep to the Village Green and Auctioneers come out from Newton Abbot and sell them to the buyers. The sheep graze on the commons most of the summer. The shearing is done mostly by hand. They generally clip abut 12–14lbs of wool each and the lambs about 3lbs each. We sell the wool to blanket manufacturers of Buckfastleigh.

The bullocks are South Devon rather large in size. Some are light red and some dark red. The cows are fairly good milkers. We keep ponies which graze on the commons all the year round. We gather in the ponies once a year and sell most of the suckers (young colts) to the buyers who come around.

The homesteads are old fashioned with large open fireplaces. We burn 'fags' which is cut on the common (peat). It is cut and dried in the summer and stored for winter use. In some places we still use the old fashioned camp kettle for cooking.

In March we set fire to the gorse and heather so that the ponies and sheep can get at the grass. We burn heather in certain places to get fags. Our house is thatched. There is a cobbled yard on granite flags outside our door.

We have a big high kitchen with big oak beams across the top. We separate milk and the separated milk we give to the calves and pigs. My mother scalds the cream and turns it into butter which she (Alice) sells to a dealer in Torquay.'

Marjorie also told the story of a tame lamb reared at Tunhill that would go upstairs when Reg's Mum made the beds! As is often the case 'Mother' has the job of rearing the orphan lambs.

Mrs Alice Norrish (Alice) with her tame lamb at Tunhill in the wonderful old yard, that's enclosed here by the thatched Long-house. Lovely stone troughs; the Cider-come-pigs' trough and a large horse drinking trough, are in the cobbled yard, and in an old high wall in the courtyard, a stone dogs' kennel can be seen.

The Norrish family later farmed 'Northway Farm' Widecombe Hill for some twenty years after leaving Tunhill, probably around the late thirties and they rented Northway from Albert Norrish's wife, (no relation) on the death of her husband. In 1958 the family then moved to Addislade Farm, Dean Prior, Brent.

At this time they farmed abut 100 Whitefaces and they used to take winter keep of turnip before Christmas and swedes afterwards with grass-runs (runbacks).

Mrs Reg Norrish (Marjorie, known affectionately as Marj) recalls walking and riding bikes home from a Mr Bill Shilston's winter keep at Gulliver Farm, Staverton. She said in her wonderful Devon dialect that we always 'put 'em in swedes' in winter (the sheep). Marjorie also recalls walking sheep through Bovey Tracey to 'keep away' from their home farm. They had no car at the time.

The sheep would come home again in March to lamb. The Norrish's used Widecombe Hill (Bunhill) from Northway as their sheep lear in the summer (as seen on cover picture). Shearing and dipping took place and the lambs were weaned before the ewes were put on the moor. Ashburton Sheep Fair was used to sell sheep and buy rams.

Shearing at Northway by hand (Bill and Reg).

Mrs Norrish recalls Widecombe Fair in a field on the Woodah road and they showed Widecombes there in about 1943 (now called Wooder). At 'Two-Gates' it is recorded that Widecombe had a fair for a year or two.

She recalls vividly the 1947 winter 'when the sheep wire netting in the root field was laid down flat, thick with ice, and telegraph poles snapping off. Looking up to Woodah from Northway, trees were seen to be snapping off like carrots. Nothing moved up Widecombe Hill for six weeks. Bill Miners went to get meat via Buckland for the rest of the village with a tractor. Flatpoll cabbages had to be dug out by hand to provide a frozen feed.' Mangolds were cut up with a mangold (root) cutter.

The sheep bath (dip) at Northway was communal; Whitley's, Jack Daw (Fred Daw's father at Brownswell), Frank Nosworthy (Bonehill or 'Bunhill') all brought sheep to Northway.

Marjorie said 'sheep from Jack Daw's would be brought the night before to Northway for fasting and dipped the next day and also kept another night before returning to Brownswell.' Louis Hannaford of 'Blackslade' Widecombe is seen in a photo pulling sheep from the dip at Northway.

Dipping at Northway (Bill, Reg and Mr Hannaford).

Reg sold a hogg ram in 1965 at Ashburton for 80 gns and French's at Michelcombe bought the ram (refer to their story for photo). Patrick Coaker bought the ram a few years later, but had to pay the French's one shilling to ensure good luck.

The bungalow that Reg built at Addislade for his and Marjorie's retirement enjoys wonderful views towards Ashburton and Dartmoor; notably Rippon Tor and Buckland Beacon.

Whitefaces at Addislade. The ewe sniffs the bag expecting cake is in there! (Ken Norrish).

Richard Norrish explained that his father (a brother to William Norrish) kept Whitefaces at 'Riddon', Widecombe-in-the-Moor, another very old tenement and homestead for 'Widecombe sheep'.

Freda Wilkinson writes of a very old practice of 'laying up' enclosed sheep pastures on St Johns day (24th June) and leaving them to grow into 'foggage' for later winter feeding; such fields were known as winter lairs. Colpresse (1667) writes 'We commonlie reserve our dry land out of the North in the sun for winter feeding, if we can. Our highest ground is fittest for sheepe, the lower for cattle.'

The name appears on several Widecombe farms today, e.g. 'Winterlears' field and Mead on Northall and four 'Winter lears' at Bunhill. So keep was provided for winter at home. Such fields were usually sloping and dry and sheltered from the worst of the weather.

In the 19th Century this system could be supplemented or replaced by a catch crop of common turnips for early winter feeding, with swedes to follow after Christmas; but foggage was preferred, where the ratio of land to sheep allowed; as a diet mainly consisting of roots is not considered the ideal for ewes heavy in-lamb. Near to 1800, turnips were introduced into a crop rotation and as early as 1794 drilling seed rather than broadcasting had been tried. Up to the 1800's either two or four oxen were used for ploughing, generally with a pair of horses leading. The demand by the Navy for beef whether or not it was tender, reduced the use of oxen and increased the use of horses. By 1850 the use of oxen was rare.

Sir Francis Buller who purchased Prince Hall estate introduced Scottish black cattle (Galloway) to Dartmoor around 1790 later selling at £7–£8 a head. The Dartmoor sheep provided tasty mutton which was in great demand and Buller experimented by introducing some South Devon Sheep. Some of his Galloways went to Smithfield as meat.

Around the edge of the high bleak open moor in the 18th Century were unenclosed areas suitable for planting trees and rearing sheep or cattle.

In 1793 between 110,000 and 120,000 sheep summered on open land, but enclosures were probably responsible for a decline to 80,000 a little later and to 60,000 by 1810, although the less hardy breeds introduced might also have been responsible for the sheep's decline. Many thousands of acres were enclosed between 1790 and 1850 and helped to create much of the attractive countryside that fringes the moor, leaving 60,000 acres of central Dartmoor a picturesque but untamed place.

In the 19th as in the 20th Century many, perhaps most, Dartmoor farmers bought winter keep in-country for their sheep. At the turn of the 20th Century, Albert Norrish of 'Nor'o'way' (Northway) kept about a thousand Whiteface Dartmoors and bought fields of swedes, as well as grass and arrish 'run-backs' all the way from Daccombe to Kingsbridge. Freda Wilkinson said 'they used to say that by the time the last of Albert Norrish's flock had got through the gate of the first fields it was nigh on time for the leaders to move on to the next field of keep.

Formerly, it was generally reckoned that, with luck, the wool cheque should pay for the wintering away. In about 1910 turnips averaged £7–£8 per acre. In 1966 they were making from £35–£65 per acre.

Looking back to the early 1800's to see the cost of labour, we find that some labourers lived in cottages which were part of the holding or 'lived-in'. Part of their wages was normally provided as cider, something that by 1820 was beginning to be decried because of its effects on the labourers and their families. 'In 1800 a labourer could expect a shilling a day and a quart of cider'. Threshing, ploughing and cutting, setting and steeping hedges were paid on a piecework basis. Hedging and making up the wood into 'faggots' (bundles of smaller sticks) earned four to ten pence per yard and the building of walls on Dartmoor, six pence per yard.

Ned Northmore

KINGSHEAD AND STOANEN, WIDECOMBE-IN-THE-MOOR

Ned (Simon) Northmore who died in the year 2000 was another wonderful and knowledgeable character of his adopted Widecombe-in-the-Moor, where he was Uncle Tom Cobley at the famous fair for twenty-five years, but Whiteface Dartmoor sheep were also a real love of his. His grandfather lived at Yellowmead, Nr Sheepstor and, no doubt, gave him a strong link with the moor. Also his father farmed in 1915 at South Brent.

When Ned was only fifteen months old the family moved to Woodley farm, Kingsbridge. As a church farm (Glebe) it became sold in 1924 to a neighbour and the Northmore family were without a farm. Ned's father put his horses away to a Mr Baker, who helped them out at Malston Barton, where the horses were to work, and the Northmore's rented a house.

So, not wanting to part with his horses, the sheep and cattle were sold and the implements stored. The sheep at this time were South Devon and Greyface longwool.

Whilst at Mr Baker's, two farms came to let, and in 1925 Mr Northmore senior took Pollard's Coombe and Alston, Slapton.

A Whitefaced Dartmoor ram was used to cross with the South Devon sheep, the latter being the local breed of the South Hams.

The depression of the late 1920's and early 1930's was very serious for farming and a move to Mill Leat, Holne was made. Things were bad he emphasised; cattle were taken to market and no bid was given at all for the animals; there were no subsidies to fall back on and cattle returned home and were taken to market again in the hope of a sale.

In 1935 a move to Kingshead, Widecombe and renting from the Widecombe Manor estate. Ned later married a ladies maid, staying at the Old Inn, who came from Sussex. At this time Ned had just a few sheep.

Kingshead and Whiteface sheep painted by Ernest Knight.

He recalled buying ten broken mouths from Jim Smith's flock (Hexworthy) with few teeth for just £1 each. They had in all ten lambs. Five to six of these were ewe lambs. So from 'small acorns, great oaks may grow'! Miss Needham's flock also evolved from Jim Smith's lambs too.

In 1935 (and well before) Ned explained, all the farms of Widecombe Parish had Whiteface Dartmoor Sheep. Ned's own journey from South Brent to Kingsbridge and Slapton, back to Holne and then to Widecombe is also a journey in itself of the Whiteface Sheep from its birthplace's to its winter keep havens.

Ned remembered sheep sold and penning for them in old Ashburton Market against the high wall of the market (now only cattle and ponies sold there). There were, he said, two runs of iron pens and a board walk on top of the pens, for the Auctioneer to walk, from which to sell the sheep, which were penned either side underneath the walk (see photo of old Ashburton market).

When the Whiteface Breeder Association was formed in 1951, Ned said many sheep breeders were still Rendell's men and sold with them their unregistered sheep, but bought registered rams through Sawdye & Harris. A lot of Whiteface sheep went to Cornwall from these sales and were crossed for early fat lamb.

Also later, people like Bob Kerswell, Ned said, would buy 100–150 Whitefaces at Ashburton Sheep Fair because they were good mothers for crossing with other breeds like the Suffolk.

Ned joined the Association in 1953–4. Only 8–9 members when the Association was first started he recalled, and then other breeder's began to join.

Ned is the first exhibitor holding a sheep from the left of picture at the Devon County Show.

Ned is the first from the right holding a sheep at the Devon County Show.

During the 1950's the Devon County Show wanted to stop Whiteface Dartmoor Sheep being shown, so along with others Ned picked out some sheep to take and helped to keep the breed at the show for future years. He also had a lot of success showing the Whiteface wool. He also won the under 50's flock competitions in 1980, 1982 and 1985 and showed me a 'door full of rosettes' from local and Devon County showing successes and was winner of the breed champion at Devon County Show in 1975 and 1976. In 1984 for example, he won the John Harris Trophy for the best Whiteface Sheep shown at Yealmpton Show.

Neds showing achievements remembered by a 'door full of rosettes'.

Ned also judged and tattooed sheep for the Association with Terry Phipps for many years.

An old photo shows him judging show sheep at South Brent when the show was held at the old station bridge end of Brent. Greyfaces and Whitefaces were seen here together, being shown in their separate classes.

Ned was affectionately known as the 'tooth (teeth) and ears' judge, for his insistence on seeing in the Whiteface sheep a small thick ear (denoting hardiness) and good short strong teeth (helping longevity); two strong breed points. He felt the growing of more ear today was due to sheep being kept better. Also his definition of a true Whiteface was for it to be 'clean-legged and bold-headed'! (devoid of wool in these places).

As seen in the 1979 flock book records for Kingshead, he consistently kept no more than 41 ewes in the flock. Also he always purchased two new rams every two years. Some of the flock masters whose rams Ned bought and that sired his own flock, were from Cecil Caunter, Norman Stephens, John Savery and Miss Needham.

He felt sheep were kept much thicker and grazed much tighter in numbers in the past and behaved more like scavengers.

He said using the moor for him was a problem. Ewes and lambs were turned out sometimes before shearing and would come back prickles and 'vuz' (gorse) all over. Also out in the vane or fen (vene) as he called it, they would come back black all over from rubbing in the 'turf-ties' or pits, supposedly it is required that the turf be replaced after the peat has been removed from below, to preserve the cover of herbage. The commoners also had the right of cutting 'vags' where the peat may be very thin; slabs of the turf were removed, overturned to dry and used as fuel on open hearths and burnt. These 'vags' were also piled up in order to dry on the moor before collection, along with the peat from the 'turf-ties', during summer.

Ned referred to the different products used over the years for dipping sheep and dieldrin was mentioned and before that he referred to 'Arsenic' being used and how it turned the dip water blue and he said jokingly 'at least one sheep died through inhaling the arsenic dip, but it killed everything else and there certainly were not any parasites left!' It had to be used in a dilution with water.

All Ned's sheep went to Stoke Gabriel in the winter. Ned and Frank Nosworthy would get

At Brent Show. The standard of the Whiteface sheep was very high with an excellent class of rams (Ned judging).

out 5.00 a.m. of a morning and drive sheep from 'Woodah' (and 'Wooder', old spelling) (Widecombe) via the Rising Sun, Fishacre, Red Post and Berry Pomeroy to Stoke Gabriel.

When these same sheep were driven home, heavy in lamb, in late winter on reaching 'the hills', they would squat down in the road. Whilst waiting for these to recover the hoggs would continue on ahead and go into another farmer's field before the exhausted sheep caught up.

Ned took some keep at Hennock once but a mineral deficiency caused black rings around the eyes of his 'Widecombes'. Frank Nosworthy was a Widecombe neighbour at Bonehill.

The winter root and grass keep sales in the 1930's Ned recalls, would take the auctioneers at Newton, Totnes and Kingsbridge a full afternoon to sell; another tradition slowly dying out today, and sheep certainly are not walked anymore to their winter keep.

The story of dogs driving away Scotch sheep surfaces again and Ned's dogs were no exception; Ned said they drove them away because the sheep smelt like goats!

Ned remembers a ram he sold to Horace Nosworthy (Chittleford, Widecombe) turned out to be a 'gate crasher' and also knocked Horace over in the field one day, so a Jack Brown of Dunstone Cottage told Ned.

On another occasion it seems Horace bought an expensive ram at Ashburton some years ago, for 40 gns. (when 10 gns was the normal price) and Horace's father was deaf and couldn't hear what the price was the ram made, and Ned remarked that Horace's father kept saying 'what was the price, what was the price of the ram', but no one would tell him (thinking no doubt his son had paid too much)!

In 1986 Ned retired from farming to 'Stoanen' in Widecombe. He made £40 each of ewe lambs and Miss Needham, had a black ewe lamb from Ned. Ned felt black sheep resulted from breeding being too close with sheep! and perhaps freaks and mutations were more likely to occur!

On one occasion at lambing time Ned's wife came rushing in to get Ned at the farm because there was a sheep lambing. She told Ned that she thought the lambs were already dead and rotten. When Ned investigated he found the feet of a living *black* lamb!

Ned spoke at length of the bad snow winters. In 1927 when he was at Slapton, many people hadn't seen snow before. The Slapton to Kingsbridge roads were full of snow. The workers were shovelling snow away from hedges and no sheep were to be seen. So Ned cut a long pole to find the sheep and some that had been buried for 14 days came out alive. Ned said in the bad winters there were sheep everywhere, even in the back kitchen, to give them a safe haven.

Eventually roads were cleared to leave just a foot of snow for the horses to 'scuff' it up and achieve some grip with their feet. In 1947 at Kingshead, Ned had 4 acres of turnips that looked like they were in 'glass cupboards'; each turnip frozen all round in the ground. Hay ricks were used but with sledges behind the horses taking away the loose hay.

Ned remembers taking off a Machintosh in the kitchen and it stood up on its own, frozen stiff with ice. Also icicles hanging down from the horses mouth bits and nose extended to the ground; freezing their breath. Doors had to be hammered open.

The horses had to be driven around the field edges using the harrows, even into March of 1947, to try and shift the snow before drilling. Ned said 'when it snowed he always got blocked in at Kingshead'.

In 1963 it was weeks before he eventually got his sheep away to their so-called winter keep. He went via Haytor and there was a tunnel of snow, a by-pass made, and snow some 20 feet high either side of the road.

When cutting out the hay from the ricks (with a hay-knife) there were big slabs of frozen ice before reaching the good hay underneath. In 1978 a roof collapsed at Kingshead and killed 11 out of 14 bullocks belonging to Ned, due to a heavy snowfall.

On recalling the snow-winters like 1947, Geoff Hill at Lamerton said he was told that the animal food situation was so desperate that even thatch was taken off the roofs of barns and houses to feed to the horses!

Interestingly too, he knew of Ned Northmore here at Widecombe because Geoff was a bell ringer for Lamerton Parish Church, the same time as Ned rang for Widecombe and was in competition with him too, at their respectful churches.

For 'the best of breed at Widecombe Fair 2000 in the open Whiteface Dartmoor classes, the Ned Northmore Perpetual Memorial Trophy and Champion Rosette have been presented in Ned's name.

There are also the Messrs Mann Bros. Challenge Cup for the best Whiteface Dartmoor Ram and the Abel Perpetual Challenge Cup donated by C.W. Abel for the best exhibit of W.F.D. Sheep confined to Exhibitors who own a flock of 80 or under.

The Nosworthy Family

FORMERLY OF WEST SHALLOWFORD, WIDECOMBE-IN-THE-MOOR

Before moving to Southway, Tom Nosworthy and his family were at West Shallowford, Widecombe-in-the-Moor. The Nosworthy family were farming beside Joe Mortimore who as another Whiteface breeder, farmed East Shallowford. Tom Nosworthy was born at West Shallowford.

The Nosworthy family and their connection with Dartmoor sheep can be traced back to the 1880's and no doubt before because Tom Nosworthy's father's mother was a Caunter at Sweaton where Whitefaces were kept. It is said that at one point there were as many as one thousand Whitefaces at Sweaton in the past.

In 1951 registered as one of the first Association Members of the Whiteface Dartmoor Sheep Breeders a Mr H.A. Axford farmed at Sweaton (Poundsgate), having married Bill Caunter's daughter of Sweaton Farm. Tom Nosworthy's grandfather was John (Jack) Nosworthy and Tom's father, Henry Nosworthy. Tom now lives at 'Southway', Widecombe-in-the-Moor. It is interesting to find that a Frank Nosworthy was at Bonehill (Bunhill), George Nosworthy at Wooder(ah) and Horace Nosworthy farmed at Chittleford, (different families).

We find Horace (H.W.) Nosworthy in 1951 registered with the Whiteface Dartmoor Sheep Breeders Association when he farmed Chittleford.

Under the Parish of Widecombe in a history of Devonshire dated 1857, it is fascinating to find that another family named that of Smerdon, farmed Bunhill, Wooder and Chittleford (a Robert Smerdon farming Bunhill). Tom Nosworthy remarked that 'Everybody (i.e. farmers) kept 'Widecombes'.

Their hardiness enabled them to live in their harsh surroundings and was one of the reasons for their survival up until modern times. Tom commented 'That they must have a hell of a

The 'Widecombe' rams await the shearer.

constitution of breeding because they have become inbred more now, and yet as a breed remain very much the same today'.

Tom also said 'That the winter keep expenses was paid for by the cheque for the wool clip', confirming again how lucrative the wool price could be in the past.

The winter keep involved a journey on horse-back from Shallowford with Tom and his father driving the sheep for one to two days to Yalberton near Paignton (the other side of Marldon) and to a Mr Bill Hunt who looked after the sheep. They would stay the nights at Broadhempston.

Spring grass keep was also taken at a Mr Stoneman's at Broadhempston. The moor rights with Shallowford were on Spitchwick Manor. Tom said 'The keep also carried a lot of cattle back when he used the grazing; there were Scotch sheep and ponies and around two hundred bullocks from Corndonford and Cator (Turners and Irish). Some of Tom's Whitefaces found a lear in Big Stannon, and were dipped along with others such as the Mann's in Little Stannon Newtake dip. Settling back into their lear, was also part of the shepherding, after they were dipped.

Tom Nosworthy won the W.F.D.S.B.A. Cup in 1964 for the best flock of ewe lambs. In 1959 at the Ninth Annual Show and Sale of Whiteface Dartmoors on September 3rd in the old ram class judged by Reg Hill and Peter Hannaford, second prize was awarded to Frank Nosworthy and in the same year Frank won third prize for the best coated ram, (a differnt family of Nosworthy's).

Tom remembers the old market at Ashburton in 1951 being used for sheep and seeing Bill Langdon's (Bittleford) Whiteface Sheep penned beside one of the market walls. Also he recalled the Turner brothers, Corndonford having Whiteface Sheep before they had Closewools.

However, Tom spoke of the pressure on the Whitefaces and the reason for their decline. His father, Henry Nosworthy, 'bred off his Whiteface ewes using a Greyface ram and eventually bred the Whiteface influence out'. Also crossing with the Suffolk became popular because breeders were looking for more lambs. Together with these changes the wool price dropped and during the early days of sheep subsidy (hill) the Scotch was favoured, before the Whiteface became recognised as a hill breed for subsidy payments in its own right.

However, as a foot note to all this, Tom said 'That the young wether's meat of the Whiteface Dartmoor hoggs used to be referred to as 'angel meat' because it was so sweet when cooked and eaten'.

Remembering the bad snow winters, Tom recalled the story of his uncle Ned (Caunter) who in 1891 rode a horse and walked the snow-high hedges from Sweaton to Chillington, Kingsbridge, to check sheep there in the bad blizzard of March 9th. Apparently it took him two or three days to get there and back, Cecil Caunter's Grandfather Albert had sent Ned.

In the 1947 and 1962–3 snow winters, George Smith (Moorman at Hexworthy) said the Scotch sheep buried along the reaves and in the gulleys on the moor were harder than the rabbits because the former came out alive but the rabbits died.

Robert Nosworthy recalled that Joe Mortimore caught as many as 2000 rabbits at East Shallowford when he and May moved to the farm in their first winter. Robert explained that turnip fields had to be fenced all around to try and protect the turnips, and keep rabbits out!

Written in a History of Devonshire published in 1857, a Richard Hannaford (farmer) farmed at Shallowford and because it also records a John Hamlyn farming both Corndonford and West Shallowford we are to assume Richard Hannaford was at the now East Shallowford once farmed by the Mortimore family. As recorded too, the Nosworthy family later farmed West Shallowford.

Hazel and Douglas Nosworthy

ILSINGTON

Another family of Nosworthy's once farmed Middle and Lower Bonehill Farms, Widecombe. A great-uncle Frank (big Frank) to Douglas Nosworthy now at Ilsington farmed 'Bunhill' Farm (Lower Bonehill). Middle Bonehill was farmed by John Nosworthy (Jack) whose family brought up Douglas's father 'Little Frank'. Higher Bonehill is also named as a separate farm.

The named Bonehill Farms and Bonehill rocks to the north cannot be more descriptive and accurate of this remote terrain.

It is hard to believe that so many of these, so tough to farm, farms and inherently poor, and born on rock, existed on the slopes of Widecombe Hill. Here farmers carved out an existence on just thirty or forty acres in this unforgiving landscape. Whiteface Dartmoors would have been very much a mainstay animal and just six or seven cows were classed as a herd.

In Kelly's Directory of Devonshire 1914 it says the soil is light sandy and the subsoil granite. The crops are cereals and roots of all kinds, mangolds, cabbages, kale etc, and about four thousand acres of the parish is moorland! (Widecombe).

However, despite the crops suggested, sheep spent a lot of time away to keep. Little Frank Nosworthy's sheep went away to keep at 'Wrigwall' Bickington and are seen coming back to 'Bunhill' along 'a Dartmoor road' towards Bonehill rocks in a dated photo. Frank and Dennis Nosworthy were cousins, as Dennis's father was big Frank Nosworthy at Bunhill, a brother to Bill Nosworthy little Frank's father. It is assumed that the sheep returning from keep were sharing the grazing away, and so some also belonged to Dennis's father.

'A Moorland Road'. Frank and Dennis Nosworthy and their flock of Whitefaces near Bonehill. (Courtesy of Caroline Belam).

Douglas was born at Hatchwell where his parents got married and went to farm in 1935. Then there was a move to Pitton Farm, Widecombe, before the Second World War.

The Daws on his mother's side farmed at nearby 'Natsworthy'. On one particular day at 'Pitton', Douglas took it into his own hands, when not very old, to set alight Hameldon. Douglas explained he thought it wanted burning badly, but there are woods on all sides too.

Swaling under Kings Tor, Hameldown.

His father found Douglas was responsible and gave him a good hiding and sent him to bed. Then in a different mood the next morning his father said, 'you didn't do a bad job after all'!

Hazel also recounts they went on Swaling parties from Holwell and matches were dropped everywhere.

Recalling the 1962–3 winter at Buckland and farming Beara Farm, Douglas said, 'that was a hell of a job', cus they were lambing 'out-doors'. He used to rotate seeing the sheep during the day and night with his father, under blizzard conditions.

Again recorded in Kelly's Directory of Devonshire of 1914 it says a Fair is held on the second Tuesday in September, yearly, for cattle; when Dartmoor sheep and ponies too are bought at Widecombe.

The Pearse Family

RATTERY AND NORTH BOVEY

When the Second World War ended and my father returned to Devon he worked for a while on his brother Lionel's farm at Walreddon, Tavistock. Two years on from this he took his first farm at Rattery. Glebe Farm was forty-seven acres and a Devon County Council holding and tenancy.

In 1954 Leonard attended St John's Fair at Tavistock and bought twenty Whiteface Dartmoor ewes for £6 a piece (£120). This amount of money would have purchased two newly calved cows at the time. It seems the sheep were a bit thin and Tom Brown, the Auctioneer at the time, said on knocking the sheep down, 'Look after them boy, they might do you a bit of good'. Lewis Walke, lorry haulier at South Brent, brought them back to Glebe Farm.

These sheep were put to a Greyface Dartmoor ram bred by Garland Rogers, which had been purchased a week or two earlier at Ashburton Sheep Sale for 18 gns. These sheep reared 17 doubles and 3 singles (37 lambs). One of the lambs was stricken with joint ill, but my mother nursed it for three weeks and it eventually stood and started to play. It was decided to put the lamb back in the field with the other sheep and continue to bottle feed it with them. However, on dropping it inside the gate, the lamb gave a bleat and its mother recognised her lamb and she then went on with her two lambs again. (The poorly lamb never looked back!).

Twenty ewe lambs were retained for breeding. Like their mothers, their eyes were as 'bright as buttons', typical of the character of Dartmoor sheep Leonard remembers.

The seventeen wether lambs were sold to Buckfastleigh Co-op for £5.10s.–£6 (approx. £100). The sheep's wool returned £60. One ewe was lost when she was tailed out on a full stomach. The remaining nineteen ewes were re-sold at Totnes Sheep Sale in early August of 1955 and made £11.50–£12 each. The gross return, which included a valuation for the 20 ewe lambs came to £400.

Leonard's first 'Fergie' tractor purchased that year cost £530 (new).

The Greyface ram sheared 32lbs of wool for its first clip and was worked two seasons before being sold at Brent Sheep Sale for 32 gns.

When farming at Barnecourt, Lustleigh with my father and brother Jim and with a large number of sheep kept, Perce' and Wynne' Rice and their son Brian would shear my father's sheep. I distinctly remember them shearing some Whiteface x Greyface ewes that were very alert sheep, whose wool reflected in the quality of these sheep.

Wynne Rice was equally as capable as the men at shearing sheep. Perce Rice is no longer here, but his tradition and high standard of sheep shearing and hedge laying lives on, and many young people today still practice these skills.

Over a Devon hedge you might have once peeped,
And seen Perce and Wynne shearing some sheep,
With a rolled fag (Woodbine) seeming pierced between Perce's lips,
He had one of those contrary 'old Dartmoors' draped around his hips.
So, Wynne too would help shear the sheep and always bring the lunch,
And together at noon they would sit on the wool and munch.
Also in winter, hedge after hedge, Perce would turf and steep.

Arriving at dawn, when others were asleep.
With Devon shovel and bill hook,
He soon gave a hedge a fresh look;
With an old hessian (corn) bag tied with string,
There was no need for mack or leggings to bring.

Perce Rice's father Bill did this same hard manual work.

Whitefaces came to Barramoor in the mid-eighties to start a new pure breeding flock for Hazel and Colin Pearse. The foundation sheep were bred by John Savery and purchased at Ashburton Sheep Fair. The first ram used was purchased from Terry Phipps at Poundsgate, but was bred by Miss Needham.

The flocks overall conformation was much improved by a ram I purchased at Ashburton Sheep Sale that was bred by Terry Phipps. The type of breeding ewe that resulted gave our flock a more modern look and the better conformation helped to improve the saleability of their pure lambs. We keep all our male lambs entire.

There is nearly always a leader sheep!
Walking along 'Long Lane' away from the Long House.
(Photo: Chris Chapman).

A Patrick Coaker ram sired by an Arnold Cole ram continued to give our flock an even breed-type resulting from good ewe lambs.

This was borne out in the fact that the flock in 1995 won the Association Brian Harris Memorial Cup for the best flock of ewe lambs, repeated in 1997 and the year 2000. These lambs were sired by the Coaker ram.

The influence of all the different breeders rams on the flock was now becoming apparent. In particular the progression of the ewe lambs bred off Terry Phipps and Patrick Coaker rams up through the flock, helped us to win the 1997 over 50's flock competition, to gain second in 1999 and then to win over 50's again in the years 2000 and 2003.

The judging in 2000 was done by Audrey Stock of Tunhill and Terry Phipps (winner 1999 of the over 50's).

I purchased the last ram bred by Miss Needham in the Autumn of 2000 that was judged 'best-coated' ram at the Association Sale, he has now sired three generations of our Whiteface flock.

The flock seem to find our free-draining granite area to their liking. We achieved considerable success with a ram I bred myself out of a Terry Phipps bred ewe and sired by Patrick Coakers bred ram.

In 1998 we showed the above ram at Okehampton and in August it won the Whiteface

Four rams used on the flock over time. (Photo: Chris Chapman).

Championship. Okehampton Show has provided classes for the Whitefaces in recent years and it is well supported. A return to Okehampton in the year 2000 gave us a 2nd prize for our ram. The 1998 Okehampton Show saw Francis Maddock judging the Whiteface sheep classes.

At Widecombe Fair in 1998 our ram was awarded the Championship.

Also in his final outing in 1999 to Ashburton Show and Sale in October, the above ram was placed first, having been placed first at Widecombe the previous month. He was not beaten, therefore, over four shows previous to the year 2000.

On taking the same ram to the Devon County Show in the year 2000 it won the woolled exhibit of the White Face Dartmoor breed judged on the hoof. (Wool on the hoof).

Moving on to Yealmpton Show in August of 2000, the ram continued his winning ways and was judged the best Whiteface Dartmoor Sheep by Archie Mortimore and was awarded the John Harris Trophy.

Three times champion; Okehampton, Yealmpton and Widecombe. Held by Hazel Pearse.

Then in the 'sheep fleece wool' judged by Mike Voisey from the Liskeard Devon & Cornwall Wool Depot, at Yealmpton Show, the ram again won first prize in the any Long Wool Breed class.

So very unusually for any breed, this particular ram was first for his wool both on the hoof and with his fleece in the same year. We presented our ram for the last time in the 2000 showing year at Widecombe, where he was first in the old ram class judged by Archie.

Hazel Pearse also explained that Whiteface Sheep were also walked from Widecombe Fair after they were purchased there by her father, William White, and her uncle Harold Wonnacott and driven eventually to Thornworthy, Harold's own farm, in the 1940's. (The sheep were kept 'half-crease').

Strangely, before William White later moved to Barramoor, the said sheep stayed a few days at Barramoor when the Wills family farmed there, in order to rest before they finally got to Thornworthy (Chagford Parish).

Colin and son, Paul, holding their home-bred ram.
(Photo: Chris Chapman).

Here at the northern (N.E.) limit of their existence (apart from the moor itself) near to Fernworthy reservoir, life seemed to suit the Whitefaces.

When Sylvester Mann and Archie Mortimore inspected our sheep just after joining the Association, we had several ewe lambs with brown patches in the ears, head, tail and legs like a 'rust' colour. However, Archie and Sylvester always accepted what was referred to as 'rust' on Whitefaces, as an indication of purity!

Interesting then to read in an article in the U.S. Department of Agriculture's, Bureau of Animal Industry, the years 1889–1890, mention of the Southham Notts (one of 4 Devonshire breeds noted by Vancouver (1808) the other being the Exmoor (Notts) the Dartmoor and the North Devon Nott (a closewool sheep). The Southham Notts also called by Vancouver the South Devon Nott; a long-wooled sheep, having the feature of brown faces and legs.

These sheep it seems inhabited the Southern part of Dartmoor from Axminster or the Vale of Honitor westwards to the borders of Dartmoor it is reported; such is the strength of breeding traits, could the rust gene have originated back here with this extraordinary native breed?

In 2002, The Sylvester Mann Memorial Cup was awarded for the 'best ram' running with the flock at time of Inspection (right in photo). The W.F.D.S.B. Association Annual Flock Competition. Won in 2002 by T.A. Phipps and 2003 by C. Pearse. Left in photo, the W.F.D.S.B.A. Challenge Cup presented by S. Needham for 'Best Flock of over 50 ewes'. (Both cups at Barramoor).

Freda Wilkinson thinks the Greyface Dartmoor with its mottled face and legs, very long wool and hornlessness could have come from the South Devon (Ham) Notts.

More than just a Whiteface! South Devon cows seen feeding in the middle of the picture. (Photo: Colin Pearse).

It was interesting to see at Christmas 2000 when it snowed how our Whiteface ewe hoggs in the snow, whilst searching for grass, rolled up large snowballs on their chests as they moved forward with their heads down in the snow. (picture). The snow clung on because of the freezing temperatures, and they were scavenging for grass.

In very severe long cold winters the whole fleece of longwools can become snow-laden and frosted snow can hang down on the flanks of the sheep and weigh them down; as a

At Princetown there would have been 20 feet of snow. Here probably at least 12 feet of snow. 1962/3 – Long Lane, Barramoor, an awesome amount of snow, emphasised by the small Terrier! 'It's a long way down'! (Photo: Hazel Pearse).

consequence sheep buried in snow drifts, especially our Whitefaces would have this additional problem of immobilising them and jeopardising their escape.

Barramoor. The experience of snowfall in April (here a mini-blizzard, April 3rd, 2000), serves to remind the Dartmoor farmer that winter is not over yet! A warm 'milk-bottle' for the lamb!

To my embarrassment a few years ago when my ewe lambs were being tattooed for the flock book record it was noticed that one of the lambs was a ram lamb. It was remarked jokingly, 'are you lambing earlier this year Colin, because we have found a ram lamb.' Of course, the oversight is probably because I keep all my ram lambs entire and fattened them as ram lambs! I needed an excuse!

However, despite having to cover up my tracks sometimes, I still feel that sheep breeding is very much in my blood. If sheep interest is a genetic thing then this following event might confirm some of my thinking.

My mother's father, W.J. Tuckett (my grandfather) kept South Devon Sheep at Warm Hill Farm, Hennock, Bovey Tracey. In 1939 some of his South Devon wool together with the wool of the other South Devon flock association members was sent to the Golden Gate International Exposition Wool Show, California (between September 23rd and December 2nd). His display of wool (market class) won Jim Tuckett first prize in the Wool Shop Awards (and specials trophies) for England.

Other countries competing in their own right were New Zealand, Scotland, South Africa, South America, Canada and Australia.

In the breed class, W.J. Tuckett was second to A. Darke, S. Herish Farm, Kingsbridge who achieved first and fifth with his South Devon's wool. Fairweather Bros. were third and fourth from Home Farm, East Charleton, Kingsbridge. A.H. Phillips, Pencorse (or Pencourse) Summercourt, Cornwall was sixth place.

Paul married Vicky (née Rabey) in August 2003. As a vet's assistant from Cornwall, her keen interest in animals has transferred to the farm and the showing of sheep.

Three generations of Pearses (Len, Colin and Paul).

Edwin Pearse (Uncle Edwin's story)

NOW AT ST. COLUMB-MAJOR, CORNWALL

Whitefaces, moor grass and stone walls seem to go together (evidence of a sheep creep at the place of the water trough).

From a family of six boys and four girls Edwin Pearse (an uncle to Colin Pearse was the eldest of the lads and Leonard Pearse (Colin Pearse's father) was the youngest, the whole family living at Bowden Farm, Buckfastleigh. Edwin is now in his 95th year (sadly now passed on).

Edwin Pearse travelled to many farms away from Bowden and into the South Hams to shear sheep. He used to shear 50–60 sheep a day using just hand shears, starting at Kingsbridge and finishing up at Bere Alston. In one season he would shear around 3000 sheep.

He explained that the hand shears were made of solid steel; very strong and firm and when sharpening them it was as much as Edwin could do to press the shears down on to the grinding stone, turned by someone else, to help put an 'edge' on the sheep shears. Sheep shears as part of a stand and turned by hand by someone other than the shearer, came before electric shears; Edwin apparently used one of these to cut the rest of the family's hair! They took in turns to turn the handle!

When shearing at Reg Hill's Farm at Grimstone, Blackawton (Edwin used to live in) he said, the sheep were wonderful big 'Dartmoors' (Whitefaces) like donkeys and sheared very good fleeces of wool; coming off as one fleece in many cases using the hand shears.

Shepherds say when shearing lambs late in the year you must keep their 'waist-coat' on and not shear all their wool off, to allow for better wintering.

There were four or five hundred Whitefaces at Mr Hills and Edwin said: 'They would come in day after day as a very even flock of sheep'.

This happened over sixty years ago and must be one of the oldest individual stories of working with Whitefaces. Edwin said 'Reg Hill also had big Whiteface rams he sold, but remarked that it was difficult finding different lines of sheep even back then to help mix the breeding'. However, Reg Hill used to breed dozens of rams for sale at Ashburton Fair and sold rams privately too.

Reg Hill's wife said to her husband on one occasion that it would be worth keeping a ram from a particularly good sheep. However, Edwin explained at that time several hundred of Reg's Whitefaces were worthy of breeding a good ram.

The sheep were actually summered at Hexworthy where the Smith Bros (Jim and George) as 'moormen' agisted the stock and money changed hands for keep and attention.

Edwin said when it was near the time to putting the sheep on the moor from Blackawton, they became restless and would, no doubt, even travel from Blackawton to Hexworthy unattended, remembering their way to the moor.

Edwin farming in his own right from 'Down Lane' Tavistock took Whiteface ewes to Dousland Sheep Sale near Yelverton and gained first prize for his pen of sheep and top price, on one occasion.

Whiteface Breeders Exhibition of Old Photographs

The focal point of an exhibition at Widecombe Fair in 2003 were a large collection of photographs showing the history of Whitefaced Dartmoor sheep in Widecombe and around the moor.

The exhibition would not have been possible without the generosity of the members of the Whitefaced Dartmoor Sheep Breeders Association in making their photo's available, and Chris Chapman's help in scanning the photo's.

Hazel Pearse and Clyde Coaker.
(Photo: Colin Pearse).

The night and previous afternoon of the fair the heavens opened and it meant we had little time to assemble all the photos and accompanying shepherd and paintings!

A splendid painting of Green Hill and sheep drifted by Edward Caunter was painted by Charlotte Angus! (nee Kingsmill).

Devon Life magazine wrote of the exhibition (Vol. 8 issue No. 3) as celebrating the history and 'survival' (a compliment to the breeds resilience) of the traditional Dartmoor Whiteface sheep which, although not officially listed as an endangered species, was in decline until the formation of the Whitefaced Dartmoor Sheep Breeders Association in 1951.

The letter also says the sheep would have been a familiar sight to generations of

Painting by Charlotte Kingsmill.
Edward Caunter; Whitefaces, pony and dog Shepherding Whitefaced Dartmoors across from Nakers Hill and Green Hill near Hexworthy.

'Tom Cobleys', since a stage in their history was as descendants of the 'native heath sheep' that grazed Dartmoor in the 17th and 18th centuries.

Devon Life record also that Beatrice Chase (Olive Katherine Parr) a local author, buried now in Widecombe, was instrumental in bringing to life an ailing Fair in the 1930's. Sometime around here it moved out of the village to 'Two Gates'.

Her love for Widecombe and Dartmoor reflected in her novels like, 'The Heart of the Moor', and 'Through a Dartmoor Window', and very fascinating too, a book she wrote called, 'A Book of Answered Prayers'. One of the answered prayers in this book seems to be the finding of 'Widecombe-in-the-Moor, Venton' etc. for Beatrice Chase!

In 'The Dartmoor Window Again', in the first script, her feelings for Dartmoor are set in granite for she writes:- 'To all who whether in the flesh or spirit have looked through "The Dartmoor Window"!'

'Wool collection day'. Hazel Pearse and haulier Anthony Barrow. (Photo: Chris Chapman).

Thomas and George Pearse

KINGSETT AND HERNSPITT, WALKHAMPTON AND MEAVY

As a result of finding Thomas and George Pearse of Hernspitt farm as registerd on the Association's first members list, another captivating Dartmoor and Whiteface story is revealed.

Entering the W.F.D.S.B.A. Annual Flock Competition in 1952 as Messrs Pearse Brothers, they achieved second prize in the best flock of under 50 ewes. However, on the loss of his brother Thomas in 1953, George Pearse gained first prize on his own in the above competition in 1954. The President of the Association in 1952 and 1954 was Cecil Caunter and the respective Chairman's were John Savery and W.A.F. Webber.

Thomas Pearse was born in 1887 and died in 1953 at the age of 66, having worked the farm at Kingsett, Walkhampton, and George Pearse born 1890, died in 1960 and also worked the farm.

Miss Needham recalled that the Pearse's had a good type of old-fashioned Dartmoor and lovely wool-type Whiteface sheep.

Kingsett and Hernspitt are good examples of wonderfully powerful and evocative Dartmoor moorland farm names depicting struggle, remoteness and hardship in an era of attempted self-sufficiency.

Kingsett is down the valley from Peek Hill Farm.

In the valley is the Newleycombe Lake, a stream that joins the Mew immediately below Nosworthy Bridge and very near to the upper end of the Burrator Lake.

Elizabeth Stanbrook in her book, 'Dartmoor Forest Farms,' writes of a John Hooper, farming Nuns Cross Farm. However, John Hooper also found spare time employment working for Mr Pearse, the farmer at Kingsett Farm (presumably George, Thomas and Sam Pearse's father!).

At Kingsett, John Hooper would collect hayseed from the bottom of the cart and take it back to Nuns Cross Farm to improve the pasture there. His lunch, it seems, regularly comprised a pig's ear which he would bring with him to Kingsett, so writes Elizabeth Stanbrook.

Crossing explained of two mining houses near Black Tor Fall and how in August 1907, a colt belonging to Mrs Gill of Stanlake fell into the chimney hearth of one of the houses and was imprisoned for three days before Mr Pearse of Kingsett rescued it after seeing the mare grazing nearby.

The Pearse's sheep, whilst at Kingsett, would have run the moor around Crazy Well Pool right through to Princetown.

John Colton explained that the Pearse's really kept their Whiteface flock for their wool. They did not sell many sheep and they kept around 60 Whiteface ewes and made up to 100 with the wethers. Some of the wethers were kept until they were broken mouth just for their wool.

When these wethers came in off the moor to 'common turnip keep' their fleeces would be tied (matted and tight to their skin) due to the harsh environment of the moor.

Also agile sheep like these used to the wide open spaces afforded them on the moor, were difficult to keep from straying in the 'inbye-fields' (close at hand). Small-holed sheep netting, John Colton explained, was unrolled and laid along the top of the stone walls by the Pearse's, lapping out over either side of the walls. Therefore, being wider than the walls it helped to discourage sheep climbing up and over and thus escaping back to their moorland lear. As much as 12lbs of wool was sheared off each of these sheep. Wool stored here worth 2/6d a lb at one point dropped to 4d a lb in 1937. (Wool sold in 2001 made as little as 16 pence a pound in old money!).

John said bringing the wethers in from the poorer keep off the moor a while before shearing, gave their wool fleeces, due to the influence of better feeding ground, time to 'heave off' as the 'grease and yoak' content increased. So they were easier for shearing as the wool lifted from their skin.

John explained, 'that the turnips were often shooting out and flowering yellow, whilst the sheep were still kept fenced in the roots. They were kept there, no doubt, to find a feed amongst the 'bolting' turnips to help eke out the winter's keep as spring slowly turned to summer!

However, things were set to change for the Pearse's of Kingsett as Burrator Reservoir had been completed in 1898. Plymouth bought some of the Burrator Watershed in 1916–17 and some of the farms in this valley were shut down and taken in hand at this time. However, it seems that Thomas and George Pearse moved to 'Hernspitt' in Meavy Parish. Kingsett, however, was still being farmed by another brother, Sam Pearse, indicating that Kingsett must have been outside the first shut down of the valley farms. Burrator being in the Meavy Valley, has an impressive circle of tors around.

The sunset reflects Sheeps Tor on to the low water of Burrator Reservoir (Autumn 2003).
(Photo: Colin Pearse).

Sheeps Tor overlooks Burrator reservoir. After which the Sheepstor Village and Brook were named; also among other tors, Lether Tor is very impressive on the northside of the reservoir. It is said the present seclusion of the village denies its busy past as a terminus on the 'Jobbers Raod', an ancient trackway used by the 'wool-jobbers' who travelled across the moor collecting home-spun yarn and fleeces. Then Sheepstor it seems provided rest and shelter for man and packhorse and a lucrative source of trade from the large sheep-farming community in the surrounding valleys.

Sheeps Tor and Sheeps Tor village church tower, seen to the right.

Sheepstor Parish is still in 'Venville' giving the farmers there the right to pasture their stock on Duchy land during the summer months.

Travelling from Dousland to Burrator Dam it is found that the road is carried over the dam to Sheepstor Village.

The sheet of water, (now during 2003 is just like a pond, due to drought) which the Mew, the Hart Tor brook (the Newleycombe Lake and Narrator brook) contribute to form 116 acres, acting as a storage reservoir for Plymouths water supply.

On driving towards the dam, the view of the lake and the hills grouped around it, is a memorable sight.

Samuel Pearse (and no doubt Tom and George from Hernspitt) continued to farm Kingsett until the mid to late Twenties as recorded in a Parish occupations book of Meavy; staying there just before the reservoir was extended at this time, ready for flooding. So farming ceased

Mr Sam Pearse digging out Whitefaced Dartmoor sheep from the drifts at Harford, three weeks after the blizzard of Christmas 1927.

in the valleys of the River Meavy, the Narrator Brook and Newleycombe Lake, which supply the reservoir, in order to preserve the purity of the water.

Sam Pearse also rented Nosworthy Farm at the other end of Burrator near Nosworthy Bridge. In 1927 he moved to Broomhill Farm, Harford and in his first winter had to rescue his Whiteface Dartmoor sheep from huge drifts (15 feet high) trapped in the blizzard snows of Christmas 1927. During this same winter, my father Leonard Pearse was only seven years old and he recalls his brothers and sisters using a wheelbarrow to carry sheep down a makeshift plank, having dugged them out of the snowdrift; the family were 'crying with the cold' my father remarked, at Bowden Farm, Buckfastleigh. Sam Pearse later moved from Broomhill in around 1934/5 to Mead Farm, Harford.

When the Pearse's left Kingsett, there was no compensation given to the tenants (of the Maristow Estate) by the Plymouth Water Company; so because it was on the watershed, it was just taken. Also a grazing right application on the Forest of Dartmoor was also refused to the Pearse's on moving, that had always been attached to their farm!

The re-settlement of farming families because of the siting of new reservoirs has been a difficult issue over many years. Notably at Fernworthy and Roadford and of couse, at Burrator, many families were traumatised. Fernworthy Farm was an old homestead built in 1690 on the edge of the moor near Chagford. A bridge near to the farm (packhorse and slab-clapper) under which the Teign could be seen to flow can still be seen during times of drought; used originally as a crossing to the farm.

Old Packhorse Bridge. Flooded by Fernworthy Reservoir, shows up in the dought of Autumn 2003.

The Peek Family

HAZELWOOD, LODDISWELL AND WALLOVER BARTON, BRATTON FLEMING, BARNSTAPLE

Richard Peek moved from 'Hazelwood' Gara Bridge in 1987 to Exmoor. Farming here in the South Hams area his father, Captain Peek (W.G.), kept the Greyface Dartmoor sheep but then in 1951 changed to 'Widecombes'.

Whiteface sheep were taken up to Exmoor and to Wallover Barton, Bratton Fleming, Barnstaple, by Richard Peek farming at one time over 1000 ewes of which 250 were Whitefaced Dartmoor, but Richard felt the breeding of Whitefaces had become very narrow and the blood lines too close. He thought the Blueface Leicester would be a good cross on the Widecombe improving its prolificacy and producing the right sort of carcase.

It has been quite common over the years to find the Exmoor Horn breed of sheep on Dartmoor farms and on the commons of Dartmoor. This close-wool (horned) type of sheep, well suited to survive under hard conditions on its native Exmoor and may have even found life on Dartmoor a measure kinder.

However, to find the Whiteface Dartmoor Sheep on Exmoor seems to be unique to the Peek family, for very rarely are they seen outside Dartmoor or South Devon as a breeding flock.

Our native breeds of sheep especially the Whiteface seem to do better within fairly strict boundaries, where soil-type in particular dictates its success, and liking the black peaty soils of Dartmoor. Their excellent pony-like feet, hardiness and moderate wool cover adhere them to survive and breed successfully on Dartmoor.

Taking the Whitefaces to Exmoor, Mr Peek jnr. said, did reduce their size and they were inhibited by mineral deficiencies like copper and selenium, but the Peek's liked the sheep because, unlike some hill breeds (e.g. Cheviot), they kept their wool on and thereby helped

Snow on the far horizon on Exmoor as seen from Dartmoor in early April 2000. Whitefaces find a little grass between thawing snow.

them through the winters. They achieved a lambing percentage around 100–130% and found them a good crossing sheep along with the Suffolk. This, in turn, also produced an excellent first cross ewe that would take any down-type ram or continental terminal sires.

The flock prefix changed in 1987 from C.P. (Capt Peek) to R.P. (Richard Peek) and Mr Peek jnr. took on the Whitefaces and joined the Association at this time.

Captain Peek enjoyed notable successes in the over 50's Flock Competition and won the W.F.D.S.B.A. Challenge Cup presented by Miss S.C. Needham in 1975. In tandem with this competition, the best flock of ewe lambs is also judged and Captain Peek (W.G.) won the Brian and Julie Harris Memorial Challenge Cup presented for this competition in 1968, 1969 and 1972.

Sires used since 1980 on the flock were bred by Ron Norrish, G. French (Geoff), Edward Caunter, W. Doidge, Archie Mortimore and the Bonds at Pullabrook. George Wakeham bred ram hoggs to sell at Ashburton. Consistently 50 ewes were kept in the flock.

George Wakeham was very much involved with the Whitefaces at Higher Hazelwood as the farm bailiff and shepherd. Captain Peek was told when he went to Hazelwood around 1950 by the neighbours, that if he was to keep sheep they would die. There hadn't been sheep before at Hazelwood!

Captain Peek farmed both Higher Hazelwood on the high side of the valley and Crannacombe in the valley. South Devon cattle were always kept and showed at Dartmouth and Kingsbridge Fatstock Shows.

However, Greyface Dartmoor sheep were introduced and didn't die, but were not financially viable. George Wakeham explained they had a lot of big lambs and were a lot of trouble to lamb. George told Captain Peek that this wasn't good enough and a change to Whitefaces took place.

George Wakeham already knew of Whitefaces and was only thirteen years old when he sheared his first sheep using hand shears at John Dameral's, Crabdon. George said these were John's own Whitefaces and he was a 'Brent man.' Also George's father, Arthur Wakeham, used to grow 'swede-turnips' at Wagland Farm, Diptford and he let them out to 'Farge' Norrish. Farge Norrish used to take the swedes and bring in one hundred and twenty Whiteface ewes from Dockwell Brent. George remembered Farge used to ride on horseback and drive sheep into Wagland; it was three acres of swedes with a six acre runback.

On one occasion at home when George was only fifteen years old, Farge Norrish offered George one shilling a sheep if he would lamb his Whitefaces; this was at the beginning of the 1930's at Wagland.

George, who is now eighty-four years old, recalls 'it was one of the best flocks of sheep that you could see on four legs'; clean-faced and clean-legged. George said that 'what he saw of the Whitefaces at that time there wasn't a better sheep around'.

The first Whitefaces at Hazelwood came from Brent Sheep Sale in 1951 and were bought from the French Bros at Corringdon. Thirty six-tooth sheep were purchased. A ram bred by John Savery was purchased there for eight gns. at the Association Sale. George said he went to Zeal Farm before the sale and picked out the ram he liked from four all in together.

Fluke disease was a problem on the wetter parts of Hazelwood, however, George managed eventually over two hundred ewes at Hazelwood, of which, sixty five were pure Whitefaces. He stayed with the Peek family for thirty four years and the farm increased to around six hundred and fifty acres. George recalled that the Whitefaces got a lot bigger down here on a farm that would grow plenty of grass.

During the dry year of 1976 the sheep spent a lot of time on 'Blackdown', a moorland-type piece of the farm of eighty acres. The seventy six Whitefaces increased as a flock, and produced eighty six lambs that fatted well and when Jack Cann of F.M.C. came to pick out the fat lambs he commented, 'You've got 'em here today George'!

John Savery encouraged George to join the Association and went with him to the meetings. George said Norman Stephens did a lot of good for the Association. George tattooed with George Woodley and Norman in the fifties and up to the 1970's, and went all around Runnage, Peter Tavy etc. etc. He said Norman Warne of Heathfield was next door to him at Hazelwood. Registered as a first association member (1951) was a T.E. Stephens at 'Zeaston'.

However, there were no Whitefaces this side (the Loddiswell side) of Hazelwood. Seemingly the Peek's flock was as far south into the South Hams as you might find a breeding flock of Whitefaces and now, with Richard, are as far north as you might venture in Devon and near to Exmoor with Whitefaces.

The difficulty George highlighted, with breeding Whitefaces today, is that 'one can't go far enough away with the breeding and it becomes too close'.

John Symons' name comes up again, farming at Helston Churchstow; he bought Whitefaces from Hazelwood.

The first ram George purchased for 37 gns he sold for 45 gns as a full mouth to Bill Major at Ipplepen to cross on a flock of South Devon ewes. There was, however, breeder competition to buy the ram, because George said Sylvester and Arthur Mann liked the ram.

George explained crossing a Whiteface ram on South Devon ewes is the right way to cross the two breeds. But others did cross the South Devon rams on Whiteface ewes; however, George felt the resulting cross from the latter mating is not quite right, or the same as using the Whiteface ram, (a genetic anomaly!) The aim is to plus the milk and keep down the fat of the first cross.

George Wakeham became interested in using the Clun rams on some Whitefaces producing he said a very lively (easy lambing) and FIT EWE. He went on occasions to 'Craven Arms' in Shropshire to buy rams. There at the sheep sales he said thirty or forty sheep would enter the ring and were still being sold as they quickly left it, (driven around an auction ring as a group). The choice of the South Down as a cross didn't appeal to him as they are too short in the leg. These can be seen, however, in the very old Ashburton Market Sheep Sale photo being offered for sale, and as Greyfaced crosses, and impressive sheep too!

He explained that sheep numbers were once very high at Kingsbridge Fair (five to six

A 'wool-fleece bed' seems a little warmer on Mum's back!

thousand) and at Brent in any one sale in the past. George said he attended 'Brent Show', on the right hand side of the Avonwick Road coming into Brent and Geoffrey French was the judge.

George recalled with dismay how, on one occasion, a ram he bought only made four lambs! When he realised no other ewes were lambing he had a closer look at the ewes and saw them 'jumpin (ing) to play' across on the hill; a sure sign that a sheep is not in lamb!

However, one of his ewes at Hazelwood lambed twelve times and still had her old teeth!

Reliving the snow winter of 1962–3 George said he rode his horse over gates unseen because of the high snow and he had two ewe hoggs buried for three weeks. He went to feed a few bullocks at an off barn (riding his horse) with his dog, and when he came outside the barn he noticed his dog was up by the hedge wagging his tail. George tied his horse up to a 'hedge stick' and saw a breathe hole in the snow. He took hold of a wire netting stake nearby and began to break the snow away and he eventually found his sheep.

Whether with the cattle or with the sheep George said he always had his dogs with him and one of his favourites went blind at seven years old and he had to have him 'put down'.

George finally spoke of Reg Hill who farmed at Grimstone, Blackawton who drove his Whitefaces 'riding behind 'em' to Hexworthy, for the moormen to look after them in the summer (George Smith). George Wakeham explained how there is always a leader sheep in the flock and the leading sheep of Reg Hill's flock would go on in front and the rest would follow. He said 'they were lovely clean faced and legged sheep'. During the latter years of this drift from the South Hams he explained how there would be cars beside the sheep, but on the sheep would still go towards Dartmoor, through Diptford, Moreleigh, Marley Head and through Rattery down to Buckfastleigh below Dean Prior and across the A38, up over Dartmoor via Hembury and to the top of Staddicombe and, finally, on to Hexworthy leaving Holne to their left side and Holne Chase to their right side.

Terry and Margaret Phipps

NEW COTT FARM, POUNDSGATE

Terry and Margaret moved to what was Lower Tor Farm, Poundsgate in 1977. Having bought 'Tor' they then added a bungalow and called the farm 'Newcott'. There have been Whiteface sheep here for nearly 25 years with Terry and Margaret. There is a long history of them here too. Terry started his flock with some of George Woodley's sheep and also Norman Stephens and Ken Soper sold Whitefaces to Terry.

Widecombe 1985. The Trant Family Cup presented to Terry by Ned and Sissie Northmore (Kingshead).

Initially Mann's breeding was used, buying a ram that cost 22 gns. Then a Trants ram followed in 1981 bred by John Savery. The Trants ram showed at Devon County Show in 1983 was winner of the breed championship as a six-full mouth sheep. Also, incidentally, the Sid Trant Cup presented at Widecombe Fair was also won with the Trant bred ram; the Cup presented by Ned and Sissie Northmore. Interestingly too, in the year 2000–2001, Terry has bought and been using 2 four-tooth Whiteface rams bred by Fred Trant junior of Sunnymead Farm, Bridestowe; the last rams of his flock. Sadly, the remaining Whiteface sheep on Fred's farm were affected by the foot and mouth cull. Such was the attachment that Fred had to his animals it quite sickened him to see the threat of foot and mouth. This is not the 2001 celebration the Association ever dreamt of!

So success for Terry at Devon County Show with breed champions in 1985 and 1988. The Totnes Show Cup was won in 1980 and 1986 i.e. the Whiteface Dartmoor Challenge Cup and also the John Harris Trophy for the best Whiteface Dartmoor Sheep in Yealmpton Show was won in 1983. So, when we look on cups Terry's name comes up.

On the farm too the over 50's Flock Competition has been won on five occasions. In 1982,

Margaret, Michael and Terry. Devon County Show 1988 – Championship Two Tooths, judged by Jack Roskilly.

Terry winning the Old Ram Class at Yealmpton.

1986, 1991, 1993 and 1999. He judged the flocks in the year 2000, following his 1999 success and he was also the Whiteface breeder's judge at Devon County Show in the year 2000. Also he had some 12–15 years tattooing flocks with Ned Northmore and Archie Mortimore, also judging many times at local shows all over the Dartmoor and South Hams region.

Over this time Terry's wife, Margaret, has been keeping the flock book records for some 15 years for the Association, relevant to the tattooing on the farms each year and also acted as Social Secretary. She also kept the points assessments through the year for Cups at Shows and on-farm competition. At Widecombe Fair as well, rosette presentation and cups and order of animal presentation for judging is assisted by Terry and Margaret.

A unique experience occurred for Terry in 1985 in meeting Princess Anne at the Devon County Show, with his Whitefaced Dartmoor Breed Champion.

The unique situation of winning the interbreed at Cornwood Show with a Whiteface ram beating the Scotch into reserve place was achieved by Terry.

His flock now number over 200 ewes. Securing the last of old lines of Whiteface breeding with the last rams of many flocks, has enabled Terry to avoid too close his breeding of Whitefaces. Notably French at Corringdon, Irish's at Grendon, Warne, Stephens and Trants.

Last year (2001) Terry has kept his sheep all winter (since October) at Parkfield, Staverton (all his ewe hoggs) and this in-country keep has enabled them to grow into big sheep.

Reflecting on the difference in the vegetation on Dartmoor, Margaret remarked that Leusdon Green near to the Tavistock Inn and Newcott, used to be very bare of growth during the late 1970's, but today it's grown-in and one can't walk through it. Swaling practices were different in the past and on the open moor the flowering heather might take several years to re-establish after burning, but recovery was assured. Whereas today the ferns can take over along with the native grass species, such as molinia. Whortle berries (Werts) too are less common, strangled by other wild plants on the moor also referred to as 'urts' and 'hurts'!

Recalling amusing and unusual events, Terry joked about his tattooing journeys. Archie

(Mortimore) he said 'gets lost outside of Widecombe, especially down the lanes to Cornworthy and Dittisham'!

Margaret explained an unusual lambing experience. She was unable to sort out two lambs at birth and so it was decided to have a caesarean birth by the vet on a particular ewe. What was revealed was Siamese twins joined at the breast obviously impossible to lamb by natural birth and they could not survive. I think initially, two heads were felt, with the caesar ewe! They also still have a ewe that has survived total blindness through birds removing her eyes, no doubt having been on her back. She was only then a hogg but somehow she runs with the flock and gets around and has two lambs most years and mother and offspring seem to find each other.

Remembering the snow of 1978 Terry said that 18 big timbers were split in their farm building, but miraculously the roof caved-in with animals safe either side of the timbers.

Terry was the first to supply Whiteface Dartmoor Sheep to the Prison farms at Princetown a few years ago. They do have a habit of taking on 'lesser Breeds'; also Greyface Dartmoor and North Devon Cattle and Highland cattle. The Greyface sheep are still kept and have been over the years, along with Cheviot and Scotch Blackface Sheep, at 1600–1700 feet above sea level. Apparently, a Governor of H.M. Prison Dartmoor in the 1800's bred a flock of 'Improved Dartmoors' that were black, from Greyfaced Dartmoors.

George Cole who worked for the Prison Service on their farm for 43 years (as shepherd) explained 'that sheep were freezing to the ground when they were lied down in the very cold snow of the 1947 winter'. He said 'there were 15 horses working on the farm when he joined'. In 1947 they also used a wheel sledge and tractor to go around the farm. When returning to the stables the big fire helped them to 'thaw-out', but it was still very cold and you stood over it. Coats removed would stand up frozen stiff on their own in the stable. George recalled having to climb out of the back bedroom window with snow up to the sill, in order to try and get to the front of the house.

In the past January and February was always bad, but with better springs. Now things have turned around with mild wet winters and late poorer springs.

Back where George lived at Yellow-Meade they decided to feed some sheep in the quarry in the 1947 winter; fairly free of snow, and it seemed to provide shelter. However, the problem was the wind changed direction, as it seems to when blizzards are on, and the whipped-up fallen snow filled the quarry and buried and killed around 40 sheep, just from snow blown in, that was lying around outside the quarry.

The Rae Family

LOWER LANGDON, NORTH BOVEY

A ewe and her two lambs at Langdon.

Quentin's wife Lindy (nee Allerfeldt) said her father was fed up with chasing Scotties and so Carl Allerfeldt (her brother) and Lindy bought 12 ewes (W.F.D.) at Ashburton Sheep Fair in the mid 1970's from Mr Norman Stephens (Barleycombe) and these sheep were kept at Yarner, the home of the Allerfeldt family until Quentin and Lindy Rae took over Lower Langdon in 1981. At this time Quentin purchased two more pens of sheep at Ashburton Sheep Sale from W. Barons (Bill).

This ram was known to the Rae's as 'The Heavy Fleece Sheep' and was used as a logo for the Association tie.

Originally, the only ram lamb produced from the first ewes of Norman Stephens by a Patrick Coaker ram, was kept and at seventeen years old it still had pencil thin teeth albeit some were snapped off, before it died. A Norman Stephens bred ram was added when the influence of the Coaker ram began to recede. This ram was out of a ewe that had no teeth when she was twelve years old. The mother of these two rams lived until she was 21 years old, when she was taken to market as a cull by Bill Barons for Mr Stephens.

There have always been people that want to acquire Whiteface sheep because of their easy manageability and the constitution that their breeding seems to hold.

A heavy fleece ram with its wool touching the ground on its flanks, and from the breast, was the model for the launching of the Whiteface Dartmoor Sheep Breeders Association tie, and was bred by Quentin. This sheep logo is now shown on the Association's tie.

Quentin was showing somewhere on one occasion, Phil Abel was judging and Phil remarked, 'Is this the ram you bred yourself', and Quentin proudly remarked that it was a grandson of the sheep represented on the tie.

Flock judging at Langdon (under 50's).

The Rae's had many showing successes at all the local shows and at the Devon County Show and, also, in the under 50's on the farm flock competition. Notably too, his flock wool quality brought him much success at the shows. The under 50's Flock Competition was won by Q.S. and L.J. Rae in 1988 and 1995.

Quentin gave me a book printed in 1891 that had a chapter on the sheep of Great Britain. However, it was printed in Washington for the U.S. Department of Agriculture and it was the sixth and seventh annual reports of the Bureau of Animal Industry for the years 1889 and 1900. A section on the sheep of Great Britain is quite revealing.

It says 'The sheep is the mainstay of English Agriculture, the foundation of English prosperity and a potent factor in British commercial supremacy'.

The wool trade was a monopoly of England from the earliest records till at least the middle of the 17th Century and the woollen manufacture is today one of their leading industries. English history is woven with wars entered into to protect her woollen trade or to strike down those who came in competition with it, and her statute books are full of enactments restricting both importation and exportation of wool.

When the sheep was introduced into Great Britain is not known, but after its conquest by Caesar the Romans established a woollen factory at Wincester from which it is naturally inferred that sheep were cultivated at that time. The cultivation seemed to be of fine-woolled sheep, for when some of the Wincester fabrics reached Rome they were highly appreciated and a Roman writer records the fact that 'the wool of Great Britain is often spun so fine that it is in a manner comparable to the spiders' thread'.

What sheep furnished this wool it is idle to inquire, for history is silent on the subject and we are left to conjecture, knowing only that when history did take note of the existence of various breeds, many breeds were, 'found suitable to the localities in which they were raised,' and we doubt not that for many centuries after the Roman conquest, certain distinct breeds were perpetuated, with little improvement and little change.

At the present day, i.e. 1890, the breds of sheep exhibit extraordinary diversities of size, form and other characteristics caused, it may be believed in part, by a difference of descent, by the long continued influence of climate, food and other agencies and, in part, by the effects of breeding and artificial treatment. And this process is a continuous and continuing one. Old breeds have given way to new ones and new breeds have been formed by judicious crossing (but many remain with their old characters).

Thus, the varieties of British Sheep are so numerous that upon first sight it appears impossible to classify them. But they can be divided by the length of their wool – long-woolled, short-woolled and middle-woolled.

Secondly, as to the presence or absence of horns; termed the scientific or physical classifications. A third classification may be adopted having a reference to, 'the place or district in which such breeds are supposed to abound, to have originated or gained their greatest perfection'; termed 'geographical system.'

Referring to 'Dartmoor Sheep' as a 'forest breed', it says they preserve more decidedly their identity inhabiting the heathy tract of granite forming the Forest of Dartmoor.

So of the 'Forest Breeds' two remain which keep their sameness. They exist, the Bureau of Animal Industry says, 'in the elevated country between the Bristol and British Channels', (now the English Channel).

The 'Exmoor', inhabiting the district of 'Greywacke' of the 'Forest of Exmoor', at the sources of the River Exe on the confines of Somerset and Devon. The 'Dartmoor Sheep' inhabiting the 'Forest of Dartmoor'.

The 'Old Forest Breeds'; England before the Norman Conquest was covered with forest and much of it was in the same condition in the reign of Elizabeth.

Vast tracks were in later times in a state of commonage, upon which the inhabitants of neighbouring towns had right of pasturage for cattle and sheep.

The native sheep, as discussed, of these ancient forests and commons presented distinctive characteristics and formed well defined breeds.

Writing here at the end of the nineteenth century it is said that several of these 'forest breeds' yet remain and until late in the last century (1780–1790's) were quite numerous in Windsor Forest, Sherburne Forest, Mendip and Dartmore Forest etc. However, it says many are now no longer recognised as separate varieties, and few remain without intermixture with the sheep of the adjoining country.

Small hardy forest breeds started to decline and heralded larger breeds with more prolificacy and earlier maturing lamb.

Yet a few still remain relatively unchanged through their isolation over time. The Whitefaced Dartmoor is still a part of this 'old history'.

It says 'along with the Exmoor sheep (of the Forest of Exmoor) they have long attracted attention from their having supplied the well-known Okehampton (spelt Oakhampton) mutton, also named from the sheep having been killed at that town, whence the carcasses are sent to London'. But the Oakhampton mutton now (1890) not only included that of the forest sheep, but that of the crosses between them and other breeds. But Youatt described the sheep that provide the Dartmoor mutton as diminutive horned sheep kept in the neighbourhood of 'Oakhampton'; it would be difficult to dismiss some of these sheep as not being the ancestors of today's Whiteface Dartmoor Sheep.

The report says, also, that they are everywhere of nearly the same character and betray on a smaller scale a great affinity with the Dorsets, but their hardiness would not compare with our native breeds.

The 'Dartmoor Sheep' (Whitefaced) the report continues, are very small and have long, soft wool in which respects they differ from the other 'forest breeds'.

They have white faces and legs and generally have horns (a fact borne out by Heather Bond). They are small in the head and neck and small in the bone everywhere; the carcass is narrow and flat-sided and they weigh when fat from 9–12 pounds per quarter. They produce delicate mutton, which finds a ready sale at high prices in the metropolitan market and the flesh of the old wethers, when it has been hung a sufficient length of time, has considerable resemblance to venison.

These sheep are exceedingly *wild* and *restless* (as reported in Ken Sopers reference of 1867–9) and are apt to break their pastures when removed to a more enclosed country. (This 'yark' [lively] characteristic is still evident in the breed.

They are well adapted to the barren district to which nature assigned them, but on the whole are not profitable because of their small size, defective form and above all (again emphasised) their wild and restless temper.

They are it says in danger of becoming extinct because they are being crossed so persistently with the Leicester and Southdown! (and the Suffolk in more recent times).

In referring to the Exmoor sheep, the report says they are another mountain race, yet smaller, wilder and more intractable than the 'Dartmoor' yet in ranging heaths so near the 'Dartmoors' they differ in some respects, and so may be termed a breed (close-set fleece with wool well up to the cheeks).

The Roskilly Family

PETER TAVY, TAVISTOCK

Tom Roskilly's father (Jack) introduced Whitefaces to Nutley Farm in 1964. Prior to this time Greyfaced Dartmoors had been kept for a long period in the Roskilly family. Whiteface Dartmoor rams were used, as Tom explained, to help modernise the Greyface to the needs of the time. The introduction of the Whiteface brought about cleaner heads and legs in the first cross sheep. So the Roskilly's left the Greyfaces behind around 1980.

Tom also indicated that there was, from the mid-seventies onwards, a lot of pressure put on all our native breeds through the introduction of the Blue-faced Leicester and crossing it with the Swaledale sheep to produce the prolific 'mule-type' sheep.

However, the 'hey-day' of the Whitefaces, during the 1960's and early 1970's, was the use of their sires fairly widely to replace and improve the Greyfaced Dartmoors and mapped a period during which the former increased for a while.

Tom said the heartland of the Whitefaces is Widecombe, but as farming became more of a business and sheep and people travelled further, more prolific sheep started to be kept from the mid-seventies onwards.

Local native breeds don't suit, he said, the modern management especially the housing of longwools. Also there is the serious problem of the 'gene-pool' contracting, as the right of our local breeds is challenged by outside forces and other breeds, and in-breeding producing breed faults and subsequent wastage, and through simply a lack of availability and choice of sires.

The Whiteface Dartmoor flock at Nutley rose from 100 to 150 sheep during its peak years. In 1987 there were 100 ewes recorded and the ewe lambs that year were bred by a Cyril Abel ram. Other sires used were bred by Edward Caunter, Mann Bros., John Savery and Henry Bond.

During 1981 and in 1988 there were 90 ewes in the flock. In 1981, 55 ewe lambs were tattooed and their sires were bred by Edward Caunter, Mann Bros. and John Savery.

Jack Roskilly judging at Devon County (1988). Tom's father is still to be seen judging sheep at local shows from Tavistock to Widecombe and beyond.

The Rowse Family

CUDLIPPTOWN, PETER TAVY

During 1951 Harry Rowse registered his Whiteface Dartmoor flock with the Breeders and Flock Book Association when farming at Cudlipptown, and is on the first members list, abbreviated as HR.

Bryan Rowse recalled how his father used to go across Dartmoor to Ashburton, presumably to the Association Meetings and Sheep Sales. They had no car and taxis were used, and Leonard Ball used to lorry neighbours' sheep to the Fair. Bryan said, 'the lorry belonged to Mr Bert Cole, the village garage owner, and the Bedford made a terrific din grinding up and down Dartmeet Hills!'

Also Bryan explained to win a cup at Ashburton was, for the Tavistock breeder-farmers, very much a 'feather in their cap'.

The soil type and climate of Widecombe and around produced naturally showing sheep, and Bryan remembers the competition from people like Richard Coaker at Runnage was of a high standard, and at Tavistock side it was more difficult to achieve winning ways with the Whitefaces! Bryan recalls helping his father leading their sale rams around the ring at Ashburton Fair. However, success did come Harry Rowse's way for in 1953 he was awarded first prize for the Best Flock of Under 50 Ewes in the Annual Flock Competition of the W.F.D.S.B.A.

Sheep inspection time at Cudlipptown.

The President at this time was Cecil Caunter, the Chairman, Geoffrey French and, of course, Cecil Harris was the Secretary.

Harry Rowse like so many of the old traditional breeders, studied the wool very closely, for at that time it was a product in demand. Also for showing purposes, Bryan said his father liked to see a strong curl in the wool. The curl seemed to be seen more in the flocks of the earlier breed with their sheep foraging amongst the prickly gorse-heather Moors. The tight curl was seen as an advantage under 'moorish' conditions, and also as a true Widecombe wool trait. Horns of the rams were very prevalent too, tending to curl sharply.

Again the 'Widecombes' were used to improve the Greyfaces' wool in terms of quality and also add hardiness to the Greyface breed.

'The lovely photo of founder members and sheep under the scrutiny of the inspection committee can be seen at Harry Rowse's farm at Cudlipptown'. This was taken during the early days of the Association beside the high trees and walls around the farmyard. Bryan explained that the only difference in the photo of the inspection committee if taken today, would be the loss of four of the trees on the background 'hedge-wall'.

Something that somehow sticks in Bryan's mind at Ashburton was seeing the large rock area to the west of the old Ashburton Market. Then when the A38 carriageway was formed it was chiselled out and carved through to build the road, and the rock in its previous form, no longer to be recognised.

In an account rendered by the foresters of the four quarters of the Forest in 1502 Venville rent is accounted for from places that included 'Chodlype' (Cudlipp) and also written as 'Codelep' and from 'Petarstavie' (now Peter Tavy) in the West Quarter of the Forest. Further back in time the word 'town' in Saxon Britain meant a settlement.

Crossing says Cudlipptown was a collection of several farms. When lands and property of England were recorded under Domesday, Cudlipptown is documented as 'Culitone' and as a tiny hamlet.

Later in 1832 history tells us it was severed from the parish of Tavistock, being one of the possessions of Tavistock Abbey. Bryan explains that Cudlipptown was actually part of 'Hurwick Manor' (Hurdwick Manor) and it was here the Monks came for recovery of their illnesses!

The farm's attachment to grazing rights on the Moor over time is confirmed by the fact that Bryan's Grandfather kept 150 Scotch sheep and 50 Whitefaces on Cudlipp (Town) Down, under White Tor, in the area of Walkham Head and Blackabrook Head.

The diligence for, and value of keeping a diary is revealed by the detail in Bryan's Grandfather's diary in the early part of the 1900s, with the detail of personal experience and observation. Bryan said his Grandfather in his diary sometimes called the sheep the 'Dartmoor English' (the English Breed); a lovely definition that perhaps gave them distinction from the Scotch sheep that were imported to the Moor, that could be referred to as 'Dartmoor Scotch', but without the long history of the former on Dartmoor.

Further information comes from the diaries. Bryan said, with tongue in cheek, that his Grandfather either had a lot of time to spare in 1903 or was a true 'diarist' for he notes the number of the individual wool packs and their contents, which varied between 298 to 480lbs each. It seems Bryan said, that his Grandfather sold almost exactly the same amount of wool weight as he does himself today!

The Savery Family

ZEAL AND LINCOMBE, SOUTH BRENT, DIPTFORD, TOTNES

John Savery senior had his own unique style with the Whiteface Dartmoor sheep and his contribution to furthering their breeding was immense. The obsession he had for the breed points and characters, like a small ear, good horn and bearded chin character of the rams, neat, tidy feet and short sound wearing teeth, were all very evident in his own close-breeding flock; scared of losing these almost sacred points. Still evident with sheep bred by John Savery, are all these highly prized traits, in flocks throughout the Association today; sheep with very clean heads and legs etc and at Lincombe today (Robert Savery).

John Savery, in with his sheep where he loved to be!

John had a very deep love for his sheep and showed and managed them to the end of his life; and John's family of Robert, Dorothy and John at some point in the family's evolution became involved in the Whiteface sheep. John (jnr) said 'his father lived and breathed his sheep.'

John Savery's (snr) grandfather was a founder member of the South Devon Cattle Herd Book Society (a bull called 'Admiral' of Savery origin is in the first book) and at this point 'South Devon Sheep' were also farmed. There were cups for showing mangolds too. The 1860's would have recorded John's grandfather in farming.

John's father was born in 1888 at Great Lincombe and also farmed Holne Court as well. However, he didn't like the moor, as John became to love it, and was more of an in-country farmer.

John Savery was born at Lower Lincombe in 1911. His interest in sheep was obviously a genetic one because there weren't Whitefaces around to start him off and his interest started very young with the sheep around the 1930's.

Robert thought his father bought his first sheep from Ashburton Sheep Market, but John's own father was not at all in favour. This occurred in the early 1940's when Zeal Farm was purchased. With some hesitation it was vaguely recalled that some sheep came from a Mr Shepherd!

John (snr) was not given much encouragement to take on Zeal Farm when he viewed it with his father because it was felt to be an isolated hill farm. When viewing the farm, the farmer's son showing them around was asked by John Savery if they had the newspaper daily at Zeal, and the reply came as 'once a week if you're lucky' and even the wireless arrives a day late'!!! 'Really' replied the Savery's.

Dartmoor on John's doorstep! His dog is just visiable, 'shepherd and dog keep eye to eye'.

Cattle and sheep were used to graze Brent Moor and the rights were attached to Lower Lincombe, before even Zeal Farm was taken. The moorland rights on the open moor and Brent Moor included the area around the Avon Dam. John remarked that if it wasn't for his Galloways on the moor in the dry year of 1976 (little rain fell between February and September) the Dam would have gone dry! Robert commented that this was typical of the witty humour of his father. Sheep insisted on returning to their 'Avon lear' after flooding!

Whiteface sheep were put on the moor for summer grazing once sheared. This helped to keep their feet sound, the sheep fitter and helped 'natural flushing' when they came in country in the Autumn. The importance of never missing winter dipping related to wool quality and fleece conditioning and keeping scab-free. In 1935 John stockpiled some wool worth only 3d a pound and kept it for two years when it went up to 4½d a pound. Robert recalled that for his father's pleasure, wool collection day was his best day of the year. John's profound comment was 'that his Whitefaces never owed him a living'.

Their wool had a strong curl in the hoggs and, no doubt, would become weaker and smaller in their curl as they became older.

John Savery jnr commented how important an animals head was to his father. He said if his father could see the head of an animal he could tell what the 'backend' was like; Whiteface sheep and South Devon cattle both have wonderful heads and this relates to the whole animals constitution!

In 1951 John became one of the founder members of the W.F.D.S.B.A. In 1950 the Royal Show was at Stover, nr Newton Abbot. A foot and mouth ban prevented livestock showing. The big shows especially moved around. The Bath and West was held at Exeter and Launceston and in place of a cup a bronze medal was won by John.

The new cups John presented where he won cups outright, were always solid silver. Displayed at John Savery jnr's are a whole host of cups and trophies that his father won over

Painted at Yealmpton Show: 'The Showground'. The unmistakable John Savery! (Courtesy Gluvian Galleries – Andrew Miller).

the years. At least six cups were won outright through three consecutive year winnings or three out of any four years (see attached).

In 1958 at the Bath and West Show held at Plymouth, John had the Championship with his ewe and lambs. There were cups and awards for his sheep all over.

Widecombe Fair was the highlight and climax of his year because everybody would be there competing; all the top breeders and sheep.

From 1967–70 John Savery Snr was President of the W.F.D.S.B.A.

Robert and John continued the tradition of showing and judging in their own right.

Robert used to go with his father around the shows and judged at the Devon County in his own right in 1999 and before.

Robert Savery awarding Champion ram and Breed Champion to Phil Abel at the Devon County Show 1999. An interesting story relates to these two breeders families, for this ram came from John Savery's flock. John Savery sadly died before he could show it. Cyril Abel saw this sheep as a lamb and thought it had potential then, but John too, liked it, and wouldn't sell it!

Robert Savery remembers walking sheep as a boy from Lincombe to Strete, Dartmouth to their winter keep and a bottled fed lamb Robert recalls rearing, followed him and in turn the rest of the sheep followed. At least some twenty miles on foot. Sometimes the sheep were lambed at the away keep, and farmers, or their sons, would go and lamb them on the away farms. However, the Savery's sheep came home.

John Savery (snr) liked the style of the Mann's sheep and had a lot to do with Cecil Caunter for which between them there was a lot of friendly rivalry in the competitions. The neat small ear character of Hearn's hardy sheep appealed to him, as did their milkiness; its importance not to be forgotten in the Whitefaces for helping prolificacy in lamb survival.

Sires used by John include; Fred Trants, John Irish, Ron Norrish and John Hearn in a flock ranging from 50–110 sheep.

The Whiteface sheep Dorothy and her husband Dennis kept were given them by John.

A 'Group' of Whitefaces at Cornwood Show.
Left to right: John Savery Jnr, Dennis Robins and John Savery Snr.

Philip Coaker judging, 1991.
Ashburton, Whistley Hill.

Then in the 1990's John attempted a come back with Whiteface sheep and because the price was so poor he bought back his own sheep from Dorothy at Holsome Farm, Diptford and refounded his own flock and the Association inspected them and registered them at Wheeldon (John jnr's farm). He also took on at this point, some of Robert's Whitefaces.

The late John Savery told me that it was not uncommon to see as many as 60 rams at Ashburton Sheep Sale and even more through the 1950's; all Whiteface Dartmoor sheep.

He kept just the best ram lambs himself and wouldn't hesitate to castrate them if he didn't like them.

The close proximity of Brent Sheep Sale to Zeal meant he sold two-teeth and a few draft sheep at the Fair. It was convenient to walk the sheep into the Sale. He remembers prices from £12–£28 in the 50's and 60's. This helped him to establish his breeder's name.

Sheep and collie sheep dogs always go together and at Ilsington, not so far away, the West of England and Devon Championship Dog Trials are held. John always had dogs around him, and he won with his dogs both the West of England and Devon Championship Trials (each championship) three times.

On one occasion John Savery jnr went out to see his father and, of course, he was taken to see the sheep out in the field and John put 'Roy-boy's' foot in its own neck collar and sent it after the rams. This was to slow the dog up so the rams would not be frightened and the dog later returned to have his foot taken out and, obviously, it wasn't the first time this had happened. (Other dog's names were Speed and Nell).

When John's sheep were tattoed, he would ask the members to 'come up stairs' and, in fact, up the 'Grannary Steps', obviously the jobs been done and the sheep are on their way down! (at Zeal Farm). (Courtesy Margaret Phipps).

Included in the skills of sheep management, shearing sheep rates very high. The Savery's were not without this talent. 610 sheep wre sheared in eight hours at Zeal Farm, South Brent in 1970 by John Savery (30) and Roger Poyntz-Roberts (27). John Savery cut himself early on during the record attempt, but still managed to shear 345 sheep in eight hours. The previous area record was 439 sheep in a day set up by Bill Hill and John Andrews at Halsanger Farm a month previous.

The highest recorded speed record was in 1964 by a New Zealander shearing 565 ewes in eight hours 53 minutes (Colin Bosher).

Hand shearing in the past could record 60+ sheep a day. This technique is still favoured to prepare sheep's wool for showing. Hand shearing down both sides, the wool recovers better than clipping by machine. There are combs for different degrees of shearing on modern machines.

John Savery jnr not only sheared with great competence but also judged, in particular, Young Farmer's Competition at the Devon County Show, Royal Welsh, Bath & West and Royal Cornwall shows. Also, he came a good second in the 'golden shears' all comers' competition which included foreign competition in the past. There is certainly a passion here for the job and the sheep, for it is very hard work!

The Whiteface Dartmoor fleeces can, on occasion, be very tied to their skin and have to be teased away with great care when shorn. Very often the whole fleece can be taken off like a piece of hard carpet and become a ready made 'waist-coat! albeit a bit discoloured.

The on farm judging of John's Whiteface flock. Appreciated by Arnold Cole.

The faces of clean heads and spritely Widecombes at 'their Dartmoor Best'. John is remarking on 'the improvement to his flock!'

CUPS

Ashburton Sale
Best Coated Ram – Presented by Miss Bodington 1956, 1958, 1960, 1961, Outright
Best Ram – Presented by C.E. Caunter 1953, 1954, 1955, Outright
Best Old Ram – Presented by Mann Bros 1967, 1968, 1969, Outright
Best Old Ram – Presented by John Savery 1971, 1973, 1976, 1980 Outright

Widecombe Fair
Best Ram in Show – Presented by W.F.D.S.B.A. 1954, 1955, 1957, 1958? Outright
Flock Over 50's – Presented by W.F.D.S.B.A. 1952, 1954, 1963, 1965 Outright
Challenge Cup – Presented by Miss Needham in 1973 1974, 1976, 1978, 1988 & 1990
2nd Pen Ewes Association Sale
1st Pen of 2 Tooth Ewes Association Sale

SHOWS

Bath & West Show – Plymouth 1958
Championship with Ewe & Lambs 1st Ewe & Lambs
1st Ram Hog 2nd Ewe Hoggs

Cornwood Show
Champion x 2 Reserve Champion x 2 First x 4 Second x 2 Third x 2

Yealmpton Show
Res Champion x 1 First x 2 Second x 1 Third x 1 Fourth x 1

Widecombe Fair
Champion x 2 Res Champion x 1 First x 8 Second x 5 Third x 3 Fourth x 3

Totnes Show
Res Champion x 1 First x 2 Third x 3 Fourth x 1 Also Champion in 1990's

Now in 1999 a Memorial Cup presented by John Savery Jnr as a Perpetual Challenge Cup for the Champion Whiteface Ram at Association Sale at Ashburton.

At Widecombe Fair on Tuesday 12th September 1989 John Savery Snr was the judge for the Whiteface Dartmoor sheep.

This all speaks for itself.

The Soper Family

MORELEIGH AND BLACKAWTON

Here the Soper (Ken) and Trant family came together, because Doreen Soper was before marriage a Trant and her father was Sid Trant. Also Fred Trant (snr) another Whiteface enthusiast was a son of Sid Trant, and a Whiteface breeder. Also Fred Trant (jnr) (now at Bridestowe) kept Whitefaces, and was Fred Trant (snr's) son, (Sid's grandson).

Sadly the foot and mouth of 2001 was to involve young Fred Trant's Whiteface flock, as on a contiguous farm, something he was unable to accept at the time!

Mrs Soper was born at Leigh Farm, Bickington. She used to drive her dad (Sid) in a horse and trap from Slapton, to catch a bus to Newton markets on Wednesdays.

In 1943 the war time evacuation resulted in the Trants moving from Dittiscombe near Slapton to Rowden and Bittleford, Widecombe-in-the-Moor. Exercises and preparations for the 'D-Day' landings across the Channel in Normandy were made at Slapton.

Whiteface sheep were increased through the buying out of the Langdon flock as a result of the untimely death of Bill Langdon, at Bittleford. However, this is where Pat (Bill Langdon's daughter) and Patrick Coaker and their family now farm.

Ken Soper's father also kept Whitefaces and some other breeds of sheep.

Ken recalled the 'Devon County Agricultural Association', as it was then called, when it came to Newton Abbot in 1924.

May Pearse (nee Tuckett) still has a first prize rosette, dated 1924 won for sheep by her father W.J. Tuckett (Jim) at that show.

Doreen and Ken Soper were married in 1952 and rented land from Ken's father (John) at 'Morley Parks' Moreleigh. They remained here until 1965 when they bought a smaller place in Blackawton.

A very significant photograph of the 2nd Association Sale in September 1952. Sid Trant is holding the winning cup and card for this 'close-curly-coated' ram, both he and John Norrish behind are proudly dressed, waistcoats and watch chains etc.

Ken was very much a Sawdye and Harris person, and he bought with the help of Cecil Harris, his first Whitefaces at Ashburton Sheep Sale; just 20 sheep in 1952.

His first sheep were not registered and came from a breeder he named as Wilkie! It is possible this is 'Wilkeys' Moor, where a Sam Horton farmed and kept Whitefaces near Cornwood. Ken's first ram was bred by John Savery.

In 1965 the Sopers moved to West Drayton, Blackawton.

Ken holding a Competition Cup at 'Morley Parks', 1958. (Probably 'Moreleigh' means – lee of the moor!)

Ken's Whitefaces won both the Association's under 50's flock competition and the over 50's flock competition in the 50's and 60's and in 1963 and in 1965 the W.F.D.S.B.A. Brian and Julie Harris Memorial Challenge Cup, presented for best flock of ewe lambs.

Cecil Caunter and Joe Mortimore when the latter still farmed at Shallowford, sold rams to Ken.

Ken and Doreen were proud to judge the Whiteface Dartmoor sheep classes at Yealmpton Show, when the show celebrated its centenary (100 years) as an agricultural show in 1986.

Ken's son, Graham, with Devon County Show winning Whiteface Dartmoor ewes, May 1959. Complete with rosette placed on the ewes head!

In 1977 Doreen judged at Widecombe Fair with Mr Roskilly (Snr) from Tavistock and Henry Perranton (Liz Savey's father) from Diptford in the interbreed sheep competition. Ken also judged at Widecombe Fair in 1968, at Ashburton twice, once in 1973, and at Cornwood in 1978.

This story has produced a wonderful range of photo's depicting the family's passion for the sheep and their place on the farm, and on the moor, and by the 'moor's gate'. This strong enthusiasm shared by all the family, and with showing too!

In 1964 Ken won his only ever *first for wool* at the Devon County Show; his previously best achievement, a female breed Championship in all competitions at the show. This he did on the 27-05-77 (1977). A wonderful achievement for Ken.

When Ron Norrish was the Chairman and Ken Soper was President of the W.F.D.S.B.A. in 1972, the Association celebrated 21 years of its inception since 1951. Also Ken Soper was President of the W.F.D.S.B.A., 1970–1973.

Ken spent ten years tattooing Whiteface Sheep (recorded in the lambs ear; the year of birth and owners prefix letters).

As a result of their services, Doreen and Ken received a glass trophy from the Association in 1979, proudly displayed at Doreen's home in Ashburton.

Doreen remembers showing the flock in the Flock Competition herself, when Ken was having an operation on his knees.

Doreen Soper is a wonderful positive lady, full of grit and her bubbly character must have been a massive inspiration to Ken during his struggle with arthritis.

Ken's father was a very traditional stock farmer and liked his South Devon Cattle and Whiteface Sheep and told Ken that when he took on the farming, 'there were to be no "blackbirds" imported to the farm!' (no other breeds of animals).

Although there were no 'blackbirds', there were certainly black sheep, and two ewe lambs by a Joe Mortimore ram came black.

The photograph shows 'turnips' eaten down to a shell, and kale stripped of its leaves in the background. Without this food, winter would be even harder. The ewes wool is 'spiky' and discoloured, but the lambs for a genetic reason are, 'throw-backs', and jet-black.

John Sawdye too from 1973 was the Association President.

One black lamb is rare, two is special! They are ewe lambs born in 1957 and were bought by John Sawdye as a nucleus of his 'black Whiteface Dartmoor Flock!'

Also Doreen's father, Sid Trant, helped to found John Sawdye's black sheep flock in 1959 with a black ram lamb, born at Leigh Farm. John's flock would breed alternate years black and then white.

A black ram with John Sawdye's flock (1959) in John's 'Garage Field'.

The forest rights were used extensively at Bittleford from 1943 onwards which were on Winney's Down, where the Coaker family's sheep run now and leared. Sheep would have been walked after shearing via Postbridge from Rowden and Bittleford, through 'big Stannon' up by the fold and on to the open moor at Winney's Down.

Fred Trant, Doreen's relation said he dreaded the job of walking up over the high moor. Some sheep would be lost in the Forest and some die during the summer.

Rhona Parker, Doreen's daughter, recalled with fascination how little the sheep would deviate from the road, despite other animals alongside grazing and that they were just instinctively heading for their grazing lear on the moor, not requiring much help to reach their destination in summer.

Doreen also said that some sheep put out on the moor at Stannon hunting gate could travel as far afield as Okehampton.

However, Ken said the flock also had a regular habit of returning night-times to their lear and the gate at the Stannon side of the moor.

Rhona also explained that their family's sheep were driven from Rowden to the dip at Little Stannon. 'Dipping was a big day', and the sheep driven by dogs never wavered on their way from the road.

Fred Trant also remembered Bill Miners was the main haulier that took his father's sheep away to 'turnips' in winter and so another trip for the sheep to help complete their year's feeding cycle.

One of Ken's dogs, Bruno, would drive the flock on the farm and then separate the young sheep, all in the same field, taking them to the other side of the same field; collies just have a great instinct to work sheep.

So Ken shows great affection for Whitefaced Dartmoor sheep and their shepherding and history.

To this end he was insistent he read to me 'a reference he has dated 1849'.

Stannon hunting gate and a 'proper' record of the Whitefaces place on the moor.
Left to right: Rhona (nee Soper), Roy Trant, Fred Trant and Hetty, 'collecting the last lot of sheep'. Whitefaces in their true home, farmed with warm affection.

I think it confirmed the interest and passion he has for Whiteface sheep, and the detail in their long history on Dartmoor, and Dartmoor farms, and into the South Hams, that excited Ken.

Ken (on left) at the Devon County Show 1971.
With Edward and June Caunter.
Here Ken is seen judging.

With Edward Caunter and Patrick Coaker.
Edward has won!

The reference is from the 'Rural Cyclopaedia or General Dictionary of Agriculture', and of the Farmer, Stock Farmer, Gardener, Forester, Land Steward, Farrier . . . Edited by the Rev. John M. Wilson – Vol. IV Q-Z (sheep).

This wonderful reference pin points just one stage of the Whitefaces long journey through history from very early times, and their original breed attributes and characters confirms why they have survived up to modern times (2001).

The article says, 'the "Dartmoor sheep" are hardy and well adapted to the district from which they take their name. They are small, wild and restless and difficult to be confined, but though bred on the heath, are commonly fattened on the plains. They grow slowly and attain an average weight of about 10lbs a quarter. Their face and legs are white; their wool is soft, and their flesh is much in demand, not only in near, but distant markets.'

The Exmoor Sheep are rather smaller it says, than the Dartmoor, but greatly resemble them in general appearances, in disposition, in habits and in value.

Their head, neck and bones are small and delicately formed, their body is comparatively narrow and flat sided and the males have a beard under the chin, somewhat like that of goats.

This bearded 'vestige' can still be seen on the chin and part way down the neck and on the chest of modern Whiteface rams, and even on older ewes on the lower neck.

So over the years Ken Soper was highly successful with his pedigree Whiteface Sheep and won trophies and scores of rosettes in local shows and the Devon County Show.

However, worsening arthritis forced him to retire and in 1971 they moved to their present home in Ashburton.

Ken was born in Cornworthy and actually moved to Moreleigh in 1917. Sadly Ken passed away in 2001.

So this story becomes a tribute to him, and this book to many other breeders who loved their Whitefaces and are no longer with us.

The Steer Family

SOUTH BRENT

Wensleigh Steer, Norman's father, moved from Modbury to Dockwell Farm, South Brent (not to be confused with Dockwell, Widecombe) in 1952. He started his Whiteface flock in 1954 from Woodley, Norrish and Brown bloodlines and his flock soon grew to 120–150 ewes.

Wensleigh maintained the good pure breeding through the purchase of a John Savery ram. He paid 53 gns for the ram, which was the highest price paid up to that time for a registered Whiteface Dartmoor sheep, from the Ashburton Association Sale; and he later bred good rams from him. Wensleigh was a flock book member and enjoyed the Whiteface sheep. The Savery ram, Norman remarked, was unusually strong coated and handled very hard in his wool.

In 1963 the flock was dispersed on the farm. As a neighbour, Norman later purchased some of Robert Savery's sheep and also from Bill Doidge at Tavistock. Norman said local showing has been practised over the years and again recently.

As a young boy Norman has always been very keen about the breed and just loved Whiteface sheep, especially their alert and lively nature and good mothering instincts. Norman recalls lambs sired by a Terry Phipps ram and one particular lambing year, when he had four doubles and one single, and there were eight ewe lambs and just the one ram lamb from the five sheep.

Ned Northmore judging at Brent Show, a strong class of Whiteface rams. Looking very closely at the ram's ears, for thickness and size.

He can recall Brent Show (as distinct from Brent Sheep Fair). Ned Northmore also judged and showed at the old show (Whitefaces). There was an attempt to revive it in the 80's–90's but it didn't succeed, Norman recalls.

Norman Steer's memories of South Brent Sale are vivid. He remembers that the Whitefaces were sold there in quite large numbers (700–800 sheep) in a mixed breed (especially in the past with the Greyface Dartmoors) sale. There were he recalls, as many as five lines (rows) of Whiteface Dartmoors and many rams too for sale.

Norman Stephens, John Savery, George Woodley, Ronald Norrish, French's (Corringdon), Warne's Greendown, Pearse's Meavy, were all present at the sale with their ewes and rams and together with Norman's father and, no doubt, many others too.

John Wakeham and Messrs R.H. Luscombe and Sons were the main auctioneers for the Greyface Dartmoor sheep.

However, Messrs John Maye & Co (later to become Luscombe & Maye), Messrs Rendells and Messrs John Pearse & Sons would, no doubt, have had a share of the breeding ewes, wethers, lambs and rams of the Whiteface breed.

During the Seventh Annual Show and Sale on September 5th 1957 at Ashburton, W.S. Steer gained a third prize in the 'Ram any age', with a Sid Trant ram placed first by the judges; George Woodley and Harry Norrish (W.H.).

In the 'Best Coated Ram' class, Wensleigh Steer achieved first prize, with C.E. Caunter second and French Bros., Corringdon third with John Savery in reserve place.

At the 10th Annual Show and Sale of Registered Whiteface Dartmoor sheep on September 1st 1960 judged by Leonard Ball and J.K. Soper in the 'Ram any age' first and second prize went to W.S. Steer, Dockwell Brent and J.W. Mead third also of South Brent, and reserve R. Norrish, Sherwell Ivybridge, so a cluster of breeders in this area won the prizes away from the Widecombe breeders.

In 1953 W.S. Steer's flock of under 50 ewes was awarded Third Prize, signed by the President C.E. Caunter and the Chairman G.H. French and Secretary C.H. Harris, in the Annual Flock Competition of the Whiteface Dartmoor Sheep Breeders' Association, for the best flock of under 50 ewes.

Also in 1955 W.S. Steer was awarded second prize in the same competition.

The Norman Stephens Family

BARLEYCOMBE, SOUTH BRENT

Norman Stephens married Joan Woodley and the two families' interest in Whiteface Dartmoor Sheep has been very important over many years.

A big hug for a Whiteface Dartmoor ram from its owner, Mrs Joan Stephens of South Brent, after it won the Whiteface ram any age class (Ashburton 1979).

Robert Woodley, said he had a lot of respect and love for his uncle who he said, put a lot of time to his Whiteface Dartmoors and almost had an obsession (its not difficult!) for the breed as a traditionalist, but also with visionary ideas.

Robert regards himself as a more commercial person. Flock competition winning was an achievement of Robert's with his own under 50's flock of Whitefaces in 1994 and he also did the rounds with judging at the local shows and on breeder's farms.

Norman Stephens worked for the French's at Corringdon before becoming a farmer in his own right and keeping Whitefaces at Barleycombe. Norman sold sheep often at Ashburton. In 1982 he won the W.F.D.S.B.A. Challenge Cup for the best pen of ten ewes.

In 1973, 1974, 1977 and 1982 he won the best flock of ewe lambs, judged on the farm during the flock competitions, and in 1975, 1978 and 1983 the best flock of under fifty ewes.

If a bloodline was on offer at the sales and near to the last of a particular Whiteface Breeder's sheep, Norman would try and buy it before it disappeared and keep it specific and study its strong points.

However, Robert needed to intensify his farming with around 500 sheep and this meant the Whiteface didn't suit and it became the weak link for him in his modern system.

Norman tried to find a blend of wool with Whitefaces that might produce the perfect carpet for Axminster. The Drysdale sheep was crossed that has a very fine type of wool. Norman thought he might make a name nationally as well as locally for their Whitefaces and spread the bloodlines. He realised that the original Whiteface ewe crosses well with a lot of our breeds like the Closewool, Suffolk and Border Leicester etc.

To show this to the breeders the W.F.D.S.B.A. had an informal open day at Barleycombe

Norman Stephens and Doreen Soper at Barleycombe 1975.

Farm, South Brent by kind permission of Mr N.D.J. Stephens on the 4th May 1978. The Hon. Sec. at the time was J.E. Harris Esq. Light Refreshments and Licensed Bar applied for; so the invitation read. There was carcase assessment by Lloyd Maunders. There were Whiteface ewe hoggs by an Archie Mortimore, 6 tooth ram on show. Lots of other breed crossing examples could be seen. There were Suffolk x W.F.D. ewes (greyfaced) crossed again with the Dorset Down (with lambs).

North Country Cheviot x Whiteface Dartmoor Hoggs with lambs by a Whiteface Dartmoor ram; exhibited by A.H. Cole the flock owner, (whose flock numbered 50) were shown at Barleycombe.

The lamb percentage reared was 120% (good for 'first lambers') and they were born on the

The Stephens Flock. Mrs Stephens and 'lovely clean legged and clean headed sheep' in sweeping countryside of hedge and field.

20th April 1978. There were Dorset Horn x W.F.D. x Suffolk; the lambs reared were 181% with this cross. Also Drysdale Whiteface cross ewes were impressive. Also the Fin' x Whiteface x Dorset lambs were on show and the Suffolk crossed again with a Suffolk x Whiteface Dartmoor, could be assessed. A host of mixed breed bloodlines carefully chosen were put on display.

However, perhaps confirming one of the reasons for the success of this crossing was the fact that Norman also had a fourteen year old Whiteface Dartmoor with her Whiteface lambs at the open day. The longevity and constitution of the breed shining through and contributing to the hybrid vigour of the many crosses.

Norman Stephens had a ewe flock of forty sheep in 1981, and sires used after 1979 included a number of breeders; e.g. Archie Mortimore, Brown Brothers, Patrick Coaker, W. Irish, Dr Dadge and Geoff French.

Mrs A.E. Stock

TUNHILL, WIDECOMBE-IN-THE-MOOR

Mrs Audrey Stock originally kept Whitefaces in 1952 when living at Higher Hisley, Lustleigh. She bought ten sheep from a Mr Cole at Lower Torr, Leusdon (Spitchwick). At this time she used to borrow Miss Needham's rams.

In 1959 she moved to Barons Hill, Avonwick. Audrey felt the Whitefaces, when they were in the South Hams, lost some of their hardiness and certainly didn't like wet feet; they don't like it that well all the time off the granite. These sheep are as history tells us, well suited to Dartmoor and thrive quite well on its meagre vegetation and harsh climate, and the granite derived soil-type suits them.

After moving to Tunhill, Widecombe in June 1994 and, eventually, purchasing some of the original land that once belonged to Tunhill, she was able to buy some Whitefaces once again. In 1997 she bought thirty-four of the late John Savery's ewe lambs.

Audrey worked a Mann's and Phipps ram (originating from Geoffrey French). She eventually gained 16 ewe lambs from the flock mating. She sold ten of these Whitefaces as two-tooth breeding ewes at the Ashburton Association sale after they were awarded first prize by Harry Kerswell who judged in the year 2000. Also, in 1999 she won the under 50's flock competition. Then together with Terry Phipps the over fifties competition winner for 1999, she helped judge the year 2000 entrants of the Association's flock competition.

In the year 2000 Audrey won prizes at Widecombe Fair in the open classes. Also in the local classes for Whiteface Dartmoor sheep she won the Patrick Coaker Challenge Cup for the best pen of local Whiteface Dartmoor Sheep.

So Tunhill, where the Norrish's and others once kept Whitefaces has, through the roundabout of ownership change, Whitefaces again now with Audrey Stock. Audrey said 'there was no question in her mind which breed of sheep she preferred and instinct drew her to the Whiteface Sheep that seem happier at Widecombe'.

The moorland area of Blackslade and Venton mire (moor) adjoin Tunhill and Shilstone Rocks also joins Tunhill. Interesting too, that Audrey now walks across Venton to see Miss Needham at Dipleigh.

The Tunhill road is described in Crossing's guide to Dartmoor. About midway between Newhouse under Rippon Tor and Cold East Cross a track leaves the road and runs down in a northwesterly direction to the Ruddy Cleave Water which it crosses not far below its source. Here is a gateway, formed by the old walls of the Newhouse enclosures on the right and those of the Blackslade enclosures on the left. Passing through this the track ascends the hill and runs down on the further side to 'Tunhill Farm', leaving the gate leading to Blackslade on the left.

In a book written in 1857 on the history of Devonshire a certain John Smerdon farmed Tunhill and also Bunhill was farmed by a John Smerdon, one assumes the same person! Whilst Elijah Smerdon farmed Dockwell also in the Parish recordings of Widecombe-in-the-Moor, also Wm Smerdon farmed Higher and Lower Wooder, and to complete the farming Smerdons, Robert Smerdon farmed Chittleford.

Page wrote of 'Widdecombe' (100 years ago); not withstanding its situation in a deep valley between the spurs of Dartmoor, this moorland village is bleak enough in winter. 'Widdecombe in the cold country good Lord!' is a local expression and a true one (although other northern towns and villages on the moor have a similar label), particularly when the northern blast comes roaring down between Hameldon and the opposite tors. 'Widdicombe folk be plucking geese today', is a phrase frequently heard along the southern slopes of Dartmoor when a snowstorm is raging and woe then the traveller who is wandering out on the trackless waste!

Terry R. Stockman

EAST PEEKE, SOUTH BRENT

Leaving school at the age of 15 years Terry said that all he wanted to do was to go farming. His interest in farming and Whiteface Sheep came from his visits to Albert Andrews at Owley where John French later also kept Whitefaces trading as the French Brothers with Geoffrey farming Corringdon with Whiteface Dartmoors too. Terry's father helped with the farming to enable Terry to get the start he wanted.

Terry R. Stockman of East Peeke is found as one of the first registered flock owners listed in 1951 and only one of a handful still living today to celebrate the Association's half centenary.

Only a few Whitefaces were kept at this time by Terry. However, with ill health and retirement prospects he still hopes to keep around 60 of his Whitefaces on some of his own land. East Peeke is rented privately from the naturalist, H.G. Hurrell.

Terry emphasised that this did mean that lambing time was a problem with foxes due to the opposite views of his landlord with regard to wildlife protection and conservation.

Farming up against the moor as Terry does, meant that during the Spring as vixens (she-fox) were cubbing, the foxes were hungry. It meant sheep had to be housed at night and it caused a lot of extra work to protect the newborn lambs from the foxes.

Terry's grazing rights on Ugborough Moor adjoined Peeke Farm. Ewes with their ewe lambs were put out on the common after the weaning of the wether lambs during Summer. This ment the ewe lambs became leared for the following year to their particular area.

Terry said his father started with Whitefaces. Yet again the faith attached to the Whiteface Dartmoor Sheep is confirmed when Terry explained to me 'that they always had a good name'. He said they had plenty of milk and were very hardy.

Talking of Ashburton, Terry remembered sheep being offered for sale in the market where cattle are sold now. Also he recalled ponies, some tied to rails, on sale day near to the station. The railway playing its role in transporting animals away from Ashburton's market. At Chuley Road, Ashburton, the trains final destination at the market place, a 'goods house' and 'engine house' still remain near to the garage, where holding pens once contained animals, later loaded onto trucks.

The name of Pat Spiller came up as the wool packer at Churchwards and how Terry was awarded one year a 'best fleece prize'. Wool used to be profitable and I explained how two tons of wool, when sent to Liskeard (to the Devon and Cornwall Wools Depot) this year only yielded eight hundred and eighty pounds in payment. Terry succinctly remarked 'you won't go on holiday this year!'

Terry's wife has had to keep the farm going since Terry sadly has suffered a stroke.

The Stone Family

RUDDY-CLEAVE, BUCKLAND-IN-THE-MOOR

The Stone Family moved from Slapton to Buckland-in-the-Moor in 1947 and to Bowden Farm.

Whitefaces at Bowden, shepherded through the yard by Wilfred and a young Fernley. This dated homestead of thatch and stone and 'drip stones' (thatching lips) stacked on the chimneys, some redundant where slate replaced thatch.

Wilfred became interested in Whitefaces and when he first kept them he had some half-crease from L.G. Warne and Sons of Greendown, Buckfastleigh. This form of partnership involved sharing the cost value of the sheep and their output in terms of the wool clip and number of lambs sold between two farmers.

Wilfred Stone went on to win prizes for his flock, notably a second at Widecombe Fair in 1961. Also rosettes included a first for ewe lambs. He also achieved a first prize for his Whiteface flock in the under 50's competition, when the sheep were shown on the farm in 1984. Also at Ashburton Sheep Fair and the Association's sale, he was awarded second prize for the best pen of 10 ewes.

His moorland rights with only a small flock (30–50 ewes recorded after 1979) were only used limitedly. These rights were on Buckland Common and Pudsham Down.

Wilfred Stone with his First Prize rosettes and cups.

Sires used on the flock were bred by N. Warne, Patrick Coaker, John Irish and Terry Phipps from 1979 onwards.

Henry Bond is recorded as buying a Wilfred Stone ram in 1983 and lambs registered by this ram are accounted in the 1984 and 1985 register.

Wilfred's son Fernley, who farms at Ruddy Cleve, Buckland-in-the-Moor, also won, as an Association member, first prize for two-tooth Whitefaces at the Annual Association Sale at Ashburton some six to seven years ago. Ruddy Cleave is said to date back eight hundred years as one of the earliest settlements in Buckland-in-the-Moor.

Patrick Coaker tells the story of a ram he bought from Wilfred Stone at Ashburton Fair, and how he took it back to his farm at Bittleford and then the ram somehow made its way back to Wilfred's farm at 'Bowden', Buckland within a matter of a few hours! Patrick said it must have jumped cattle grids, hedges and gone through Lizwell, swam down one river and used its extraordinary 'homing' instinct and determination to arrive home again.

Freda Wilkinson, from her agricultural history of Widecombe and East Dartmoor, records how Vancouver in 1808 writes, 'On the importance of common grazing on the commons belonging to the Parish of Widecombe in the month of October last, that there were estimated to be no less than 14,000 sheep, besides the usual proportion of horned cattle.

'The number of sheep thus summered and kept the year round on Dartmoor, the depasturable parts of which, in a dry summer, is one of the best sheep walks in the Kingdom, is not easy to ascertain; but if any inference can be drawn from the returns made from 'Widdecombe' and interestingly Buckland-in-the-Moor; their numbers must necessarily be very considerable indeed. A dry summer, as just observed, is always the most favourable for these sheep-walks. These afforded in the months of August and September last (1807), flocks more numerous and in much higher condition, than has ever been observed by the surveyor in any part of England, when such have not been aided by access to the enclosures or artificial food'.

(Tonkin {Canden's Britannia – 1789} reckoned that 'Dertmore' {Dartmoor} yielded 'pasture every summer to near 100,000 sheep').

Moving away from the real story somewhat J.L.W. Page in his book (1892) and Exploration of Dartmoor and its Antiquities, explains that one or two ancient superstitions linger still in these Devonshire wilds, relics of Celtic or Saxon 'heathendom'.

Not long since in the village of Buckland-in-the-Moor, Midsummer (1890) Day was marked by a ceremony almost as barbaric as any rite of our pagan ancestors. A sheep captured, apparently, without much reference to the law of 'meum and tuum' was placed on a block of granite lying in the middle of a field, where the youth of the village literally sacrificed it, sprinkling each other with the blood.

Elias Tozer, writing Devonshire and Other Poems, with some Account of Ancient Customs, Superstitions and Traditions, was unable to discover the significance of the ceremony, but states that it was reputed to be a superstitious sacrifice of Celtic origin.

It is no coincidence perhaps that the 24th June is St John's Day. This is a day that many sheep and cattle were traditionally put out on the moor (went to moor). Was this ritual to ensure the animals stayed young and out of trouble by having a sheep sacrifice involving the villages youth?

During the snow blizzard of February 1978 (about the 18th February) some of Fernley's sheep at Ruddy Cleave were trying to keep up with the snow near to a blackthorn hedge; the latter was some ten feet high in a little plot nearby the farm. The sheep kept going round and round on a circle of snow and flattening it hard as it froze; but they were gradually getting higher and higher as the snow built up. However, some of the sheep must have slipped off and became covered in snow between the drifts and the thorn, but somehow they were OK.

However, at Bowden Farm in 1962/3, Fernley recalled some of his father's sheep being put in a lane for shelter, but unfortunately there was a big trunk of an oak tree in the lane some 3ft square and big rings had been cut off the trunk some 3ft x 3ft (like big round bales). The snow drifted into the lane and eventually, when digging out the sheep, they were found huddled behind the oak rings some weeks after, but they were dead and obviously the tree in the lane did the sheep no favours. Sheep burrowed into ricks, just their tail visible! (The animals in severe winters were starving, hay ricks did collapse on sheep as they undermined the ricks, desparate to eat the hay!).

'Shearing excellence is rewarded at show' was the W.M. News headline of September 4th 2002. The Devon County Show held its competitive shearing classes at the unusual venue of Ashtree Farm near Newton Poppleford. The competition was unable to be held back in May as part of the Devon County Show, due to Defra Foot and Mouth restrictions. The competition was won by a New Zealander, called David Fagan.

Craig Stone, brother to Lloyd, and both Fernleys sons, won the Young Farmers Championship open to competitors under 26:- 1st C. Stone Buckland-in-the-Moor, Ashburton, 2nd S. Rogers Barnstaple, 3rd S. Pullin Weymouth, Dorset.

Taking this a stage further on the day, Craig was a credible third in the Devon County Show *senior* championship.

In the summer of 2003 the 'Golden Shears World Shearing Championships' were held at the Royal Highland Show in June.

Shear Talent

IT TAKES STRENGTH, STAMINA AND SKILL TO BE A CHAMPION

You can see every muscle move as, beaded in perspiration, the young men complete their finely rehearsed sequences. Each one of them has performed every action thousands of times and knows that the finesse of his performance is as important as the timing.

These highly-toned hunks have come from all over the world to impress the crowds and the judges: some by road, some by rail, others even by air.

And while their performance at the show is important to them in their own right, they also have bigger goals in their sights. Devon precedes the Royal Highland Show, in Edinburgh, in June, where the Golden Shears World Championships will take place.

And as shearing is an international occupation – one that shifts all around the globe depending on the changing seasons – the shearers' international reputations are something that remain close to their hearts and their bank balances!

Alan Derryman, from Sidbury, competed for 20 years as a shearer and represented England six times in the world championships.

He confirmed that the shearers would come from all over the world to compete at the show.

'They'll be from all over the UK but there will also be quite a lot from New Zealand, Australia, a lot of European countries like Poland and Hungary and even America,' he said.

Alan said it was a fiercely competitive sport at its top level.

'The real serious guys will go to the gym to prepare, not so much for these competitions but more when they're going for a world record. If you consider that the world record for ewes is 720 in a day, well that's 80 an hour and it takes some strength, and stamina. Hand shearers did well to shear 60 in a day!

'They are very fit men,' Alan said.

Craig at work, 'a sheep under the shearer's spell'! (Devon County Show guide, Saturday, May 10, 2003).

(Courtesy of the *Western Morning News* and Stone family).

Richard and Jill Tregear

CORNWORTHY

Originally Richard and Jill Tregear worked with sheep at Cornworthy where a Mr Langer kept Whitefaces along with other breeds. It soon became apparent that the Whitefaces were good sheep to work with.

So when starting to keep animals themselves they decided to put together some 'Widecombes' and bought seven sheep from Mr Bill Doidge at Ashburton Sheep Sale. Also a pure ram bred by Philip Coaker was used to help establish their own flock.

Richard and Jill became interested in showing their sheep as Association Members. They thought it necessary to wash their sheep, but soon realised that no one else did and so their early showing success was affected by this as the judges thought the sheep didn't look like Whitefaces in their 'glossy-white' fleeces.

However, regularly over 9–10 years they have shown sheep at the Royal Cornwall Show and done especially well in the 'Any Other Pure Breed' classes. In 1999 Richard and Jill won the 'Best Longwool' in the above class with a 4-tooth ewe (Laura) at the Royal Cornwall. Also in August of 1998 they won the Champion Male Whiteface (Lawrence) at the Cornwood Show. This ram was just a shearling and had excellent breed characters in respect of horn and teeth and was sired by a Bond Family ram.

Richard Tregar and Champion Ram at Cornwood Show.

The Cornwood Show was bigger and better than the previous year with a record breaking 1700 people enjoying the new Blatchford Estate site.

For several years Richard and Jill have enjoyed the Stithians Show and here too they achieved success in the 'Any Other Pure Breed' classes, gaining recently third out of a class of ten in one particular sheep class.

In 1998 their two-tooth ewes made £65 each which was top price at the Ashburton Association Sale.

Jill also has Whiteface Dartmoor sheep skins cured at Buckfastleigh and then uses some herself or sends them on for hearthside rugs for other people.

Jill tells the amusing story of a ram Paul Vincent bought from them and how Paul lent it to a friend of his. Their friend was having difficulty on one occaion in pulling out an old wooden stake from the ground. The ram was nearby and, jokingly, he invited it to have a go which, to his surprise, it ran forward and head-butted the stake and broke it off!

Shepherding and looking after sheep is a responsible job. In a Devon countryside looking very different from that of today, with large areas of heath as on Dartmoor, the shepherd's task was a formidable one. Looking after ewes and new-born lambs without modern veterinary drugs, washing and shearing the sheep (and greasing moorland wethers and sheep for over-wintering to help shed winter rains and keep away 'scab') attending the sick and injured and always being ready to lead the sheep to fresh grazing, gave the medieval shepherd plenty of work.

As a 13th Century book on animal husbandry stated, 'it profiteth the Lord to have good shepherds, watchful and kindly, so that the sheep be not tormented by their wrath, but crop their pasture in peace and joyfulness, for it is a token of the shepherd's kindness, if the sheep be not scattered abroad, but browse around him in company. Let him provide himself with a good barkable dog and lie nightly with his sheep!'

Below is an example of expenses for looking after sheep in the 14th century:-

Expenses

One permanent shepherd and one permanent shearer – joint wages	18/- per year
Red stuff marking sheep and lard mixed with tar to grease sheep	8 pence
Hurdles of wood	14 for 2/-
Boy at Lambing	1/6
Pound of Candles	2 pence
Shearing Sheep	5 for 1d
Free food and drink for Shearers	

Receipts

12 sheep injured at night by dogs unknown	Sold £1.1s.2d.
Fleeces	6½ pence
Lamb Skins	7½ pence
Fresh Wool	£9.13.4d. per sack
Refuse or broken wool	3 pence per pound

A weight measurement used was called a Clove which equalled 7lbs in weight. 52 cloves to the sack. =314lbs in a sack. £9.13.4d. per sack paid = 1/6d–1/7d per lbs.

Reference:- Cotswold to Calais by Marian Woodman, Sabra Publications, Gloucester and Gloster Graphics.

The Vincent Family

BRAMBLE TORRE, DITTISHAM, DARTMOUTH

We, the Vincent family, Sally and Paul, Tom and Katy moved to Bramble Torre Dittisham in 1982. At that time the house had been separated from the farm by the Webber Family who had farmed there since 1923, but had broken up the property when the parents died and left the house to their daughter Dorothy, and the farm to their son Desmond. At first we had only the house and three acres, but in 1991 I was made redundant from Thames Television in London and at the same time the farm came on to the market. The original holding was approximately 60 acres but some was sold to a relative farming next door and so only 25 acres were available. Subsequently a further 25 acres have been rented on a yearly basis. Two Jacob ewes were the first sheep bought, and with me working from childhood memory of farming in Ireland and Cornwall and Sally with no experience at all, being a Londoner, much of the first months were a combination of holding a book in one hand and a drench gun, hyperdermic, dagging shears or what have you in the other. We thought it funny, our neighbours thought it hilarious and the sheep were extraordinarily tolerant. So after the next spring we had seven Jacob's and we realised that we liked sheep.

Paul looking for Whitefaces at the Ashburton Show and Sale, 1999.

What breed? We wanted a native breed, local and were told that the most important thing to look for was that it was a breed we liked. After going to the shows that year the outstanding breed was the White Faced Dartmoor, local to Devon, hardy, thrifty, not too large for a couple starting in sheep in middle years, good meat and wonderful wool.

Under the guidance of Jill and Richard Tregear, with their small flock only a mile or so away we approached Mrs Bond on the moor and bought 6 four-tooth ewes that had all successfully lambed before. 'No use both of you being amateurs'. This small flock was the

For a minority breed this was an excellent draft of sheep at Whistley Hill (notice the ear notching). (Photo: Sally Vincent).

nucleus of a 50 ewe strong flock now. The first ram was bred by Jill Tregear from one by Savery's, and subsequently a new ram was bought in from Quentin . . . In 1998 we introduced some slightly larger animals at the Ashburton sale, from Colin Pearse because we were a bit concerned that our flock was generally a bit small. This has proved successful. In 1998 we came third with our ewe flock and our lamb flock in the associations flock competition, and in 1999 the lamb flock again came third.

Paul's sheep sourced at Barramoor, shading under the large granite stones – home from home. (Photo: Colin Pearse).

This flock tends to throw doubles most years, lambs fairly easily, and because we lamb in April when the weather is kinder the ewe and lamb/s are put out within 24 hours unless there is some problem. All our original reasons for choosing WFDs have been proved correct. Quiet, manageable sheep, good mothers with plenty of milk, producing a fine carcass and superlative wool. By using a WFD ram on Jacob ewes the meat is really good, although the resulting black wool, however fine, at 1p a kilo is depressing to send to Liskeard.

We have only few reservations about WFD on rich South Devon land. 1) They tend to suffer from footrot or scald unless treated and watched at least every 6 weeks. 2) It is very important to shear wethers being kept over winter in August/September to avoid spending every day in January/February pulling them out of hedges or where ever there are brambles! 3) Early shearing and spraying/dipping is important, as the thick strong wool is paradise for flies.

Whitefaces entering the spray/dipper; they like going uphill!

If you like sheep, it would be impossible not to be impressed by this brave, solid and dependable breed.

'. . . hey Sep, where's that bloke with the stop-watch gone?'

In the past it was not uncommon for a farmer or farmworker to fall into the old-fashioned 'sheep baths' used for dipping many sheep. Before 1991 and the Ministry's compulsory dipping, 'the timing of sheep' in the bath was pioneered.
(Courtesy *Farming News*).

As an aside, Tom Vincent, now working in Tokyo Japan as the creative director of an Internet advertising company, used a photograph of a WFD to illustrate an advertising technique to a large American Corporation which subsequently employed his company to work for them in the Far East!

A bustling sheep fair in the field, that continued as the Association Show and Sale born in the old Ashburton Market.

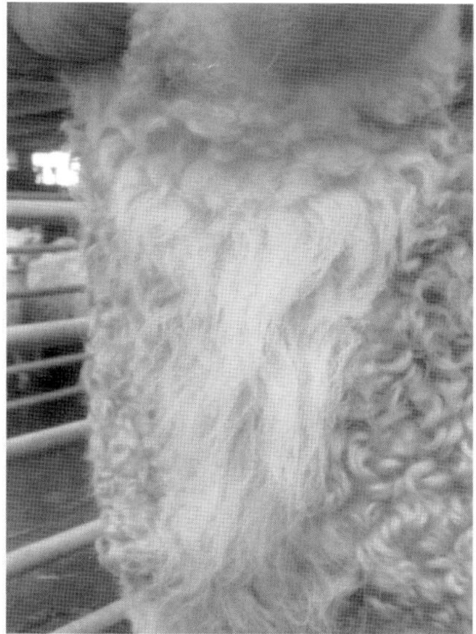

A distinctly bearded-wiry chin and breast.

The beard in evidence again, and a 'straight-hairy' area covering the lower thigh of this Savery-bred ram (hind leg). (Courtesy of Sally Vincent).

Richard Mann made this observation, and Sally Vincent photographed the sheep with a digital camera. This is a *very* old trait in the wool, still seen today!

The Warne Family

GREENDOWN, HEATHFIELD, AND QUARRY FARM

The Warne Brothers took Whitefaces to Greendown, Buckfastleigh in 1948. Norman Warne moved to Heathfield, Modbury (Ivybridge) in 1953 when the brothers split their farming ways.

Messers L.G. Warne and Sons when farming at Greendown in 1951 joined the W.F.D.S.B.A. and flockbook as seen on the first members list.

Whiteface sheep were favoured by Norman's father when he moved to Greendown, as this farm with moorland rights, was more suited to the breed. Previously he had kept South Devon sheep. A few foundation sheep came from Frank Nosworthy, Widecombe.

The Whiteface Dartmoor Sheep Breeders Association judges book of Rams recorded between 1954 and 1960 that on Sept 2nd 1954 L.G. Warne purchased W.H. Thomas's First prize Ram Hogg for 14½ gns at the annual show & sale – Judged by H.G. Woodley

Norman commented that Whiteface sheep were certainly smaller in the past and more suited to adjisting on the open moor.

Norman judging at Widecombe Fair 1996. Phil Abel's ram was also Champion at the Devon County Show and Totnes in 1996 (Okehampton and Yealmpton 1995).

Throughout Norman's interest in, and membership of, the Whiteface Association he has shown, judged, sold and bought Whiteface sheep and rams. He has won prizes at Yealmpton Show and Widecombe Fair and also at the Ashburton Autumn Produce Show & Sale held in early October.

Norman consistently kept 90–100 Whiteface ewes as recorded in the flock book from 1979 onwards and 40–70 ewe lambs and still has a sizeable flock today.

A comprehensive mix of breeders rams have been used over the years, i.e. J. Hearn, R. Norrish, H.G. Woodley, C. Abel, Miss Needham, Edward Caunter, P.W. Coaker, J. Irish, Henry Bond and F.A. Mortimore.

Norman Warne at Yealmpton Show in 1997, awarding Cyril Abel the Championship for his ram.

E.A. Warne at Greendown kept around 50–60 ewes and used Norman Warne's rams and H.G. Woodley and Edward Caunter's; producing 20–30 ewe lambs a year from 1979 onwards.

C. Warne, quarry Farm, bred from 20–35 ewes and used John Hearn and Brown Brothers rams from 1979 onwards and in 1987 and 1988 an Adams and Howell ram sired their flock. In 1986 O.E.C. Warne won the Association Cup for the best flock of ewe lambs.

Mrs Norman Warne recalls how their granddaughter became interested in a black female sheep that turned up in the flock (not uncommon as already mentioned in Whitefaces and Greyfaces and thought of as being lucky), and when it became in-lamb itself the grand-daughter kept asking 'when is it going to lamb'? However, to everyone's surprise it eventually produced two white lambs; apparently the black offspring come in alternate years as a rule from the black ewe! (as a recessive gene).

Dave Webber

HAWSON, (SCORITON) HOLNE

David's father and grandfather had Whiteface Dartmoor Sheep and the breed David said 'have been associated with the family for as long as he can remember.' So yet another corner of Dartmoor around Scoriton and Holne where the popularity of the sheep has been recorded for hundred's of years; in Domesday records too.

David's father (and himself) have won trophies and competitions with Whitefaces since 1920 at Hawson. His father had a part to play in helping to found the W.F.D.S.B.A. in 1951 when farming Hawson Farm. He also was a regular at the Association Sheep sales at Ashburton selling and successfully showing sheep at the annual event. W.A.F. Webber is recorded amongst the first twenty seven breeders to join the Whiteface Dartmoor sheep breeders association in 1951, with Prefix, owner and identification letters given.

In reference to the Judges book for Rams from 1954–1960, W.A.F. Webber is found on September 2, 1954, to have won class 6 for the Best-coated Ram Hogg, it went on to make 24 gns in the Ram Hogg class in 1954, 3rd prize was awarded to W.A.F. Webber, and Len Hill of Uppacott purchased the ram, also for 24 gns. In 1952 W.A.F. Webber won the W.F.D.S.B.A. Challenge Cup presented by Sawdye & Harris for the best pen of ten ewes.

In 1954 W.A.F. Webber was the Associations chairman.

Also in the 1950's when the Devon County Show was held at South Molton, David himself received a first prize for two-tooths and he was twice a winner at the Devon County Show.

First prize two-tooths at South Molton.

He recalls Miss Needham and Miss Bodington also travelling up to South Molton, among others like Cecil Caunter. Also he rode his motorbike home from the Show. During the early mid-eighties his flock rose to 140 ewes.

In 1980 the Whiteface Dartmoor Sheep Breeder Association Flock Book recorded one ram hogg sire bred by W. Irish (Walter, Cator) 38 ewe lambs, sire bred by P.W. Coaker and 100 ewes in the flock of David Webber. Other sires used were French Bros., J Savery, T. Phipps and Brown Bros.

Comparing sheep prices with rent, David recalls that in 1942, rent was just one pound per acre and old ewes were making £7 and he said catching rabbits could pay the rent. Twenty five years ago lambs would be making £5 and Scotch ewes £17 each.

David recalls Billy Lane of 'Churchwards' would come and grade wool on the farm. Sometimes the wool would be stored for months and even a year on the farm before grading. 1946–7 he remembers being paid £300 for his wool from a flock of 100 sheep.

Today's prices are not much different, as the excuse is made that the World is 'awash' with wool, due to the increase in synthetic fibre availability, creating unfair competition for natural fibres.

Moorland grazing has been used by David on Holne Moor and he also recalled with fascination how on one occasion his Whiteface Sheep were took out to 'Brimpts' to summer graze and to stay supposedly for a few months (having been dipped at Hexworthy nearby). However, within a matter of a few weeks they all found their way home to Hawson and Scoriton unaided!

It was interesting to read in a February 14th edition of the 1947 Farmers Weekly of the effects of the snow-blizzard on Dartmoor and this whole area. From the village of 'Ponscombe', (which I think must be 'Ponsworthy') last week a telegram was sent to Princetown; it read no bread since January 27th when the blizzard commenced; please send bread and cake by post. It seems a van got to within 2½ miles of the village the same day. A farm worker and tractor took supplies to the village.

The Widdicombe Family

CUTWELLCOMBE, AVONWICK

John's grandfather farmed Cutwellwalls in the 1920's. He had Whiteface Dartmoor sheep. John's father, Maurice, moved to Cutwellcombe with one South Devon and had Whitefaces in 1960. 1980 was the time of John's father's (Maurice) death and just after this the Whitefaces on the farm came to an end. John said the economics of keeping just a small flock of Whitefaces were not at all good.

Maurice Widdicombe ushering up his rams (August 1976).

'Back to the wall', but proudly showing off his Whiteface ram (August 1971).

In 1978 at the Association sale, M.K. & J. Widdicombe won the W.F.D.S.B.A. Challenge Cup for the best pen of 10 ewes. Ashburton Sheep Sale was a regular occurrence in the seventies for the family.

At about this time the flock book recorded a 35 ewe flock for the Widdicombe family. In 1980 and 1981 the sire used was bred by Edward Caunter. Then by 1982 the ewes in the flock were sold. Some remaining ewe lambs in 1982 were sired by a John Savery ram.

John's brother Alan and his father Maurice, showed at the Devon County Show, especially rams (but also ewes) several times in the mid-late seventies, around the high period of their Whiteface breeding.

The proudest moment John recalled for his father Maurice, was to be asked to judge at Widecombe Fair. Maurice felt it was the top Whiteface Show because it was a gathering of all the moormen and true Whiteface breeders. With his father Maurice, John used to take their sheep to Widecombe Fair in a car trailer.

John told the story of a prize-winning ram that was showed at Ashburton and how the

John and Alan Widdecombe at the Devon County.

owner thought if he were to take it to Widecombe Fair it must surely win there too! However, the ram won nothing! On walking the ram home, the farmer met the Vicar; 'Fine weather (wether),' said the Vicar. 'He isn't yet, but he will be when he gets home,' replied the farmer! (He was going to castrate it because it didn't win at Widecombe.)

Champion females at the Devon County Show 1979.

A story about the weather in real circumstances comes up again and anything to do with a bad cold snow winter always puts sheep, in particular, at risk.

Snow in the lane at Cutwellcombe, January 1979.

John Widdicombe explained that snow well above his five-bar gates and filling the lanes around about Brent and also his farm near Avonwick, came in 1962/3. Their sheep at Christmas 1962 were 6 weeks away from lambing and because the drifts were so high the sheep were not found for some weeks, but when they did finally reach them some of the Whitefaces had given birth to their lambs under the snow. However, the effects of milk and mineral deficiency, and the length of time spent under the snow meant the lambs came out blind, but amazingly they were still alive. Their survival was also due no doubt to the fact that 'Cutwellcombe' situated at around 400–450 feet above sea level, has an advantage over Dartmoor, at a high average of 1,000–1,500 where stock might be. But this still says so much for the whole character of the breed, its durability, its breeding stamina and the hardiness transferred into its long term breeding.

The name 'snow-blindness' is often given to a condition we today call 'twin-lamb disease' or 'pregnancy toxaemia' in ewes. Although often related to a lack of exercise to mobilise the body's 'fat-ketones', it is more to do with stress, like a sudden, and extreme change in the weather, as in a bad blizzard, hence 'snow-blindness'. Also the sudden shutting off of a much needed highly concentrated supply of energy feed, as the sheeps pregnancy reaches its latter stages, and where twins are involved; (as when *sheep* may be buried for some time in snow-drifts).

The weather on Dartmoor can certainly spring a surprise or two. One of the most bizarre Septembers of the last century occurred in 1919, when extremes of summer and winter occurred within ten days of each other. After mid-month, night-time temperatures sank below freezing in many parts of the country. The cold snap culminated in a day of widespread sleet and snow showers on the 20th; the earliest date in autumn for significant snowfall in lowland Britain during the last 100 years.

The morning of the snow the ground at low levels in Scotland was covered, with a substantial covering over higher ground throughout Wales and the West Country.

The official weather observer at Sheepstor on Dartmoor reported two inches of snow fell on Exmoor and (above 1,600ft) on Dartmoor. All around Princetown on the moor there was enough snow to 'track rabbits'!

On the flanks of Snowdon, snow lay six inches deep down to 1,200ft contour and above about 2,500 feet the mountain-side remained snow-covered for about a week.

Nothing remotely like it has happened here since, although an exceptionally early snowfall was reported from the higher parts of the Scottish Highlands (above 2,000 feet) on September 4th 1925.

John Widdicombe has been helping the Young Farmers' Club members over the years, from all over the area, which have been competing in organised stock-judging days and evenings in the South Dartmoor area. They have been judging sheep, beef, pigs and Dairy animals. Cutwellcombe Farm hosted one of the events. The South Dartmoor Y.F.C. Group comprises Dartmouth, Ivybridge, Kingsbridge, Newton Abbot, Roborough, Tavistock, and Totnes.

The family entered the flock competitions and won the under 50's ewe flock in 1981 and the best ewe lamb flock was won in 1980 by Mr J. Widdicombe. On winning the flock competition, any member is then expected to judge the flocks entered the following year on members' farms.

John judged on occasions with Edward Caunter as a co-judge. John explained that when judging the Whitefaces himself, he was keen on breed points such as clean legs, clean heads and general breed characteristics. However, Edward, because he was a good stockman John said, who fed all stock very well, was keen to see a flock looking well and, therefore, tended to give points on the management of the flock shown.

The first sheep John was given was a black sheep when he was only 14 years old. It was a ewe lamb and a twin to a white lamb and he always knew the white one because it had a black naval patch. The black lamb never bred any black lambs. Its father was a John Irish ram.

The use of the moor actually ended in the 1920's, also the farm is now the wrong side of the carriageway to claim L.F.A. subsidies.

However, John said of the Whitefaces that they are a wonderful sheep in the home situation they love; i.e. where they have access to the moor through opening a gate from the farm, thereby keeping them fit and not fat at the right time. Then bringing them in to the better farmland for tupping and lambing.

Speaking of some of the older Whiteface breeders, he recalled Wif (Wilfred) Irish always used to wear a piece of white heather in the lapel of his coat when he visited Widecombe Fair. John also said Norman Stephens was a man to be remembered and who did a lot for the Whitefaces. It has been said of Wif Irish, that he used to cover up an area of heather with an hessian bag to make sure the purple flowering heather turned to white! Yet natural white heather can be found!

When only 12 years old John recalled buying a pen of old ewes from the French's of Michelcombe at South Brent sheep sale in about 1968. They cost £9–£10 each. His father said what teeth have they got and looking in their mouth he discovered they were nearly toothless (averaged two-teeth)! However, through feeding extra corn they nearly all carried their twins and this gave John a good starting flock.

Tom and Sarah Widdicombe

WOODLANDS, HAYTOR VALE, NEWTON ABBOT & LANGDON, NORTH BOVEY

When Tom and Sarah first decided to keep some sheep, primarily to keep the grass healthy for the horses, they were naturally drawn towards the Whiteface Dartmoors. The land at Langdon previously was owned by Quentin Rae and lies between Chagford and Ashburton. It came complete with an old ewe and her lamb plus the last remaining unsold ewe belonging to Quentin. A further twenty ewes and a Woodley ram wer purchased from Patrick and Pat Coaker. This ram was used for two years. For the year 2000–01 a new ram was needed and Tom paid over three hundred guineas for a Savery bred ram at the association sale. Although this ram left some lovely ewe lambs and a young ram lamb, Tom found the Savery ram dead in the field just less than twelve months after it's purchase.

Provided Tom could find a suitably bred ram this year the ewe lambs retained will help form a nucleus of breeding stock for the future.

Tom explained that as novices in the world of sheep breeding he has found the Whitefaces an excellent beginner's breed. No ewes have been lost during lambing over a period of four years! 'On getting a bit anxious and twitchy at lambing time', Tom was convinced his assistance in lambing ewes was probably not always absolutely necessary, even premature at times.

Whitefaces at their best against a granite wall, with two young lambs in Springtime.

Tom said one of his main problems has been finishing off lambs as fat in the autumn. Slow, late maturing breeds like the Whiteface ideally require to go down to easier land in the South Hams for finishing later in the year. Tom explained that a mark of how good these sheep are is their vigour and longevity, despite such a limited gene pool.

The Widdicombe family is fascinated by the breeding of these sheep.

Tom said 'that even working in a small way with Whitefaces it's good to feel that he is helping preserve an important part of the heritage of the area.'

Tom has selected his stock on the basis of good milking ewes, resistance to worms, good feet and breed character faces and wool curl. Tom said he expects to gain experience from other breeders.

The Widdicombe family's enthusiasm and the breed's adaptability are reflected in lambing results over four years.

1998 to 99 22 ewes – 32 lambs . . .	1.5
1999 to 2000 28 ewes . . . 43 lambs (1 set triplets) . . .	1.53
2000 to 2001 32 ewes . . . 40 lambs . . .	1.25
2001 to 2002 28 ewes . . . (4 barren) . . . 31 lambs (1 triplet) . . .	
(excluding barren sheep) . . .	1.29

The average lambs per ewe for the first two years is higher because in 1999 there were only two young two-tooth sheep in the flock.

So, the average lambs per ewe according to age taken over four years;
21 x 2T had 21 lambs . . . av. 1.00
30 x 4T had 43 lambs . . . av. 1.43
23 x 6T had 34 lambs . . . av. 1.47
32 x FM had 48 lambs . . . av. 1.50

Despite the nature of their extensive moorland homeland (outside this barn) at North Bovey, the Whiteface can be prolific and rear triplets. So for this ewe its 'Triple Vision'!

The Wilkinson Family

BABENY, LYDFORD (FOREST OF DARTMOOR)

The parish of Lydford is the largest in England extending over nearly 60,000 acres. It includes the whole of the ancient area known as Dartmoor Forest, the boundaries of which were first fixed in a perambulation of 1240, and have remained practically unaltered to the present day.

With the passage of time the spelling of Babeny has changed from Babbeneye (1260) through Babene(a)y (1481) and Bewbeney (1588). Known as 'Babb's well-watered land' e.g. the farm lies by the Walla Brook.

In 1939 Arthur Edward Wilkinson came up from Daccombe, Torquay to Babeny; what Clarry his son called 'a bit of a rabbit warren'. In other words the farm had become run-down by rabbits and poor farming.

However, Freda explained that the most profitable crop before the war was the sale of rabbits. The farmers 'hired trappers', who caught the rabbits (ferrets and traps were used). These were bought by the 'trappers', who sold them on again.

Babeny is immediately above the confluence of the East Dart and Walla Brook; it is an ancient tenement (seventeen named by 1563, and later thirty five in number).

Babeny along with Pizwell is one of the oldest and are mentioned by 1260.

The holders or tenants, as they are called, have a right of turbary and pasturage and until 1796 also had a right of enclosing 8 acres of land if the father and grandfather of the tenant had held the farm successfully. This enclosure was termed a 'Newtake'. It was said 'these Forest tenants were bound to do "suit and service" at the Duchy Courts and to assist at the drifts'. During the 19th century the Duchy started 'buying in' ancient tenements and properties.

Enclosure on a vast scale occurred during the 1800's; from 1820–1898 it was estimated that 15,000 acres had been walled off either side of the main road through the Forest.

Whiteface Dartmoor sheep were introduced at Babeny during the Second World War by Arthur Wilkinson. (The pony and cattle drifts were helped by the 'Venville tenants').

Clarry commented that with few breeders even at this time it was difficult to secure an unrelated ram and there appeared to be the wrong inbreeding programme!

Riddon Ridge summered the sheep. Riddon itself on the Walla Brook, not far from Babeny is another ancient tenement, and has part of its boundary with Babeny.

In 1945 Freda and Clarry were farming 'Laughter Hole Farm,' in the parish of Lydford, and this was a forestry smallholding and Clarry paid five shillings rent, and worked on the forestry too.

Clarry used to go to Babeny to help his father the rest of the time.

Sheep used to be taken to the Torbay area in winter. Owner and sheep left Ponsworthy on foot via Lizwell Woods and across the Webburn (river) to later cross the A38 to reach Torquay and the sheep stayed and survived on a diet of roots and grass through winter.

In 1951 Arthur Edward Wilkinson became a member of the Whitefaced Dartmoor Sheep Breeders Association (and flock book) joining the unique first list of members.

At the 5th Annual Show and Sale on Thursday September 1st, 1955 he purchased a ram hogg that gained second prize in its class and shown by George Woodley, 'Wilkesmoor', Ivybridge, paying 18½ gns. In 1957 a sale of all the Whitefaces took place at Babeny.

Clarry and Freda themselves moved to Babeny in 1958. Their son Jez now farms at Babeny.

Freda Wilkinson has written extensively on Dartmoor; its farming and sheep etc. She is succinct in her vision of a farmer's needs and jokingly quoted this saying; 'a whistling woman and a flock of sheep', went the old saying, 'are the two best things a man can keep', (Why? because they'll keep him!)

In 'Dartmoor the Country magazine', Freda wrote of 'The beasts of Dartmoor' (issue No. 5 Summer 1999) the South Devon Cattle and the Whiteface Dartmoor sheep were filmed at Barramoor North Bovey.

She wrote not of the wild beasts of Forest, Chase, and Warren, who when Dartmoor was under Forest Law were privileged 'to rest and abide there in the safe protection of the King for his delight and pleasure.' No, she chronicled the domestic livestock which she said have lived in a degree of symbiosis with Dartmoor man for several thousand years. It is these grazing animals and the folk that tend them that have made the Dartmoor we know and love. Without them most of it would be impenetrable scrub.

The South Devons are still seen on the moor, the largest breed of cattle native to Britain, kept as suckler cows. When oxen were used for work on the land their steers were 'broken to the yoke' at three years old; strong and docile, ploughing over the moors ground into 'ridge and furrow'.

The native and traditional sheep on the moor is the Whitefaced Dartmoor which has its origins in the medieval West British Sheep, and predominantly kept for wool in previous centuries.

In 1789 Freda says it was reckoned that around 100,000 sheep grazed on Dartmoor every summer. In 1804 it was reported 14,000 sheep were grazing the Widecombe parish commons alone, the greater part of which being wethers, and kept on for their wool (up to four or five years old), were left on the moor all the year round. The Dartmoor sheep have been largely replaced by the Scotch Blackfaced and the Swaledale. The Scotch Blackfaced sheep first appeared on Dartmoor in the first half of the nineteenth century. Lady Lamb of Princehall having imported several shiploads from Scotland. A Mr Hogg assisted her (lamb and hogg!)

Freda said, they were 'heather-croppers', able to get their minerals and trace elements from the deep roots of heather, but not so the Whiteface that preferred to graze grass of the rested newtakes. The Scotties too, were better able to shed the rain than the Whitefaces.

In 1969 Freda Wilkinson wrote an unpublished account of the 'Agricultural History of Widecombe and East Dartmoor.'

She said the sheep on these farms 'the moorlings' were Whitefaced Dartmoors. She said, there are now two breeds of Dartmoor sheep. One we call the Greyfaced or 'improved' Dartmoor which is an altogether larger, heavier, long wool sheep than the original Dartmoor of Widecombe. It is popular in the districts bordering Dartmoor, but is almost never seen on the Moor proper even in the summer months. It was probably developed, Freda feels, during the 19th century by crossing the Whitefaced Dartmoor with the South Devon Nott.

Reflecting on how arduous the moor can be, Freda spoke of how snow was said to be seen on the moor in June in the hollows at Tavy Cleave after the blizzard of March 9th, 1891.

In 1947 she said, 'it was ice on ice' with trees and telegraph poles breaking and snapping to the ground.

There was no telephone, no electricity, no cars or water. The water was pulled up from the wells by hand.

Freda spoke affectionately of Peter Hannaford who she said 'had local history at his finger tips, and his great memories would go back one hundred and fifty years and encompass a big circle of moorland life.'

Jez Wilkinson explained that Peter Hannaford was a great Whiteface advocate and was a neighbour at Sherwell (Sherril). Jez talked of Peter coming to castrate their lambs. Jez said, 'he would be telling a tale whilst castrating with the "burdizzo" (a two-handled oversize pair of pincers) firmly clamped on the lambs purse. The lamb would sit there on the ground patiently thinking, no doubt, "when is this all going to end", with by this time, its eyes watering.'

Peter Hannaford would also be seen judging sheep at the Ashburton Sheep Sales in the fifties.

Freda told another story that Peter Hannaford recalled of how a sheep shearer was taking a long time to shear a particular sheep. The boss said, to the shearer that he thought he should go and get a turnip to give the sheep, because he felt by now the sheep must be getting hungry.

The shearer remarked that if the sheep had been given more turnips in the winter its fleece would have been better to shear now in high summer!

Freda spoke of a sheepfold at Sherril where she thought, as sheep became more domesticated were led, (from the fold) to graze by day over a ford onto the moor.

Finally she said the burnt gorse produced 'black sticks' from gorse-stems burnt to charcoal when swaled in March, that were collected to light fires in the homes, also referred to as 'light-sticks'.

Salving (Freda Wilkinson)

At the onset of winter the old sheep men used to protect their sheep particularly the wethers, that wintered on the moor, by 'smearing' them with tar mixed with grease. Besides giving some protection against cold rains and snow, it discouraged scab, a troublesome skin disease caused by mites which cause the affected animal to rub off it's fleece and was life threatening.

The Tavistock Abbey farmers used much tar and 'tallowns' (tallow) against scab in the Middle Ages.

The Rural Cyclopedia of 1849 describes the process of smearing. 'The salve should be thick enough to be capable of being taken up by one finger . . . and thin enough to be easily rubbed off when drawn along the skin . . . most readily applied while the sheep lies upon a stool, of such suitable breadth and length to contain its outstretched body, while the operator sits astride . . . the end of the stool'.

The wool is parted longitudinally into rows without a pile being allowed to lie across them. The salve is applied directly to the skin along each bared row and the rows should be perfectly parallel to one another and such distance that the deposition of salve along each may reach through the bottom of the piles to the deposition along the next row so that the whole skin may be equally salved. No portion of the salve ought anywhere to touch the wool except at the roots. An experienced operator can salve 20–28 sheep a day. Sometimes rancid butter or poor quality butter was used.

Robert and Paula Wolton

LOCKS PARK FARM, NORTHLEW, HATHERLEIGH

The Whiteface in Hatherleigh

I have farmed in and around this area of North Devon for the last 28 years and during that time I have had various breeds of sheep, depending on type of land, circumstance and requirments. Devon and Cornish Longwools, Mules, Suffolk crosses, Herdwicks and a brief (though never again) flirt with Shetlands as someone mentioned to Robert, my husband, that they ate rushes – they don't!

Whitefaced Dartmoor sheep (Path Field) in amongest the said rushes and the snow, home from home!

We took on our present farm, Locks Park, Hatherleigh, in 1990. Its pastures are really best suited to cattle, but even here it is a struggle. Wet, cold, rush infested clay pasture, north facing with a short grazing season – the cattle are in for about seven months of the year. Great for snipe, and beautiful, but difficult land to make a living from! We look enviously on the relatively well-drained and firm grasslands of Dartmoor which we can easily see a few miles to the south. The high, rugged tors of North Dartmoor however, serve to remind me that we are just one of two flocks being shepherded on the North Devon side of the said moor.

I felt that the land would improve from being grazed with sheep as well as cattle – but which breed could survive and thrive on this type of land? Continental breeds were never an option for me: I am a firm believer in our traditional, native ones, preferably those that come from the area where you farm, though I did contemplate the Romney Marsh – as it may have known how to use the scuba diving equipment issued in winter! Having looked at most of the Devon/Cornish breeds I eventually settled on the Whiteface – though not bred to our very wet conditions underfoot they are, nevertheless, used to rain. I had heard that they were long-lived and hardy, also medium-sized with clean legs, so likely to be easy to handle and light enough not to poach the land, or become too clagged. Good fleeces with superb wool provide insulation against the wet. Last but not least, I believed they would have the ability to 'do' on our diverse, but difficult, pastures, and produce tasty lamb in the bargain.

Decision made, I went about getting rid of the various miscellaneous sheep on our farm and purchased my foundation ewes from Arnold Cole. That was in the summer of 2000. They looked superb and settled in easily. Having come straight off the high moor, they probably thought the lush field we put them in was heaven. I could see from Arnold's face that he too thought they were in for the good life, little did he or they know that in a few short months the land would once again be totally waterlogged and as soft as a sponge pudding.

That first autumn Matthew Cole very kindly lent me a splendid shearling ram (bred by Philip Abel) bought at the *last* Whiteface Dartmoor Show and Sale to be held on the sheep fields, Ashburton. Everything was hunky-dory as they say and I was looking forward to my first lambing . . .

Robert and I had been away. It was 2 a.m. on Saturday 24 February 2001, and I was driving home down the motorway with Robert fast asleep beside me. I turned on the radio and caught the back end of the news stating something about – foot and mouth? . . . up north? . . . little did I know then that this was the start of the most frightening, horrendous and extraordinary period of my farming life.

Twelve hours later we were to learn FMD, as we came to know it, was not just 'up north' but on our doorstep not a mile away. Chaos ensued. Within the next 72 hours the future of farming and rural communities was to change forever. I was alone, frightened and scared – pyres burning at each compass point. The stench of rotting bodies overwhelming.

Neighbours being taken out one by one. I, surely, must be the next to go . . . Contact only by phone, email, endless news flashes and number watching – as one infected farm became ten, ten fifty, fifty a hundred, two hundred, three, four . . . one by one, friends, acquaintances, strangers, all gone. Calving and lambing imminent – and rain, incessant rain, day after day, night after night – when would it stop; this epidemic, this horror, this nightmare.

We survived. Two days before they brought in the 'contiguous' rule the last of our neighbours' stock were taken out. How or why we stayed clear no one will ever really know. It could be the extensive nature of the farm or the breeds of cattle and sheep. Both traditional, native breeds – the Whiteface and the Devon Red Ruby. Is it possible that these breeds have a better immune system? Are they better equipped to resist diseases such as FMD, TB and the like? Or was it just luck?

There was a positive side to this tragedy. The incredible support, comfort and prayers from folk far and wide. I will *never* forget them and the courage they gave me to soldier on. Also, thousands of people across the country saw Whitefaces and their lambs for the first time, on the video diary I made for BBC's Countryfile programme!

Life moves on. The flock has now established itself and through culling and selective breeding we have some excellent sheep that cope and thrive with all this farm throws at them. We have to keep a close eye on their feet, the land being wet, soft and free of the tors and rocks of Dartmoor, so I run the ewes through footbaths every so often, and that together with regular trimming does the trick. I lamb indoors in March, and have fat lambs ready to sell by July.

The farm is organic, registered with the Soil Association. This could have caused difficulties for us, because the land is prime fluke country and deficient in certain minerals and vitamins. However, the Association has given us the necessary derogations to cope with this, and we provide licks and drenches as required.

I market under 'Traditional Devonshire Meats', under a positive label – 'Buy a steak in the countryside'.

I sell the lamb and beef raised on the farm direct to people throughout the country. The lamb is proving very popular and many of my customers tell me that it's the best they have ever had. Some rave about it. Mutton is also becoming more popular – I have a few very enthusiastic customers. I am also looking at producing smoked lamb and mutton. The knowledge that this was carried out in the Lake District as a way of preserving meat in the past was told to me by the breeder of my Herdwicks, who's family have farmed there for many, many generations. The fleeces, which I have tanned up at Bridgewater, are beautiful, and sell well: this is a side of the busines I am keen to expand, making the most of their exceptional wool.

And have the sheep improved the ground? Yes, the winter grazing helps to keep the rushes in check, the wild flowers in the meadows get better each year, and the grasses seem sweeter.

The sculpture at Hatherleigh Market reinforces the passion of the farmers here and all over, for their sheep, assessing their attributes, with an intention perhaps to buy!

I made the right choice! The Whiteface.

An Appendix: 'Let the Whiteface Sheep continue to deliver'!

The susceptibility of animals to disease has always confronted good stockmanship and husbandry and Scrapie is one disease in the news at the moment.

Yet down the centuries, natural selection playing its part to suppress a lesser disease.

Now a voluntary programme of testing challenges our minority breed towards being 'scrapie free' with its flocks. It is too small a breed to risk any removal of its sheep that is anything but unavoidable.

Paula suggested to the Farmers Guardian, that any culling could be of the 'best Whiteface-type' and this could endanger the breeds overall future. The Whitefaced Dartmoor is unique geographically to Dartmoor and the South Hams area of Devon and has become acclimatised over a long period of time.

Paula suggests a softly, softly approach to breeding out the VRQs, i.e. genes which are thought to be susceptible to the scrapie disease (virus).

Breed characteristics that have sustained our sheep over generations like small thick ears denoting hardiness, good teeth and feet, strong 'yark' sheep, wool staple and quality etc, should, Paula thinks, be 'scored' and come before any culling for scrapie.

Those animals with a high score she says can be crossed to a ram tested with the correct genes, so that, hopefully that line is saved, (provided genetical inheritance works in its favour). Paula says we need time to think this through, and I think too, there needs to be special dispensation to protect a minority breed for the future, to allow our very special sheep, whatever time they need, as no doubt a compulsory scheme will be planned to replace a voluntary one!

Sheep and dog and an enthusiastic owner. One of Britains oldest domesticated breeds. (Courtesy *Farmers' Guardian*).

Arthur and Rosemary Wrayford

HIGHER WOTTON FARM, DENBURY, NEWTON ABBOT

A dual interest in sheep; Arthur and Rosemary wrote down their individual stories; the instinct and love of sheep was refreshing. Alfred Wrayford ('Uncle Alf') has one of those perennial faces you remember seeing on sheep sale say! geneial, knowledgeable and respected with quality stock. Alfred's father (Arthur's grandfather) was called Daniel Wrayford. He kept Whitefaces at Higher Wotton around 1901. These sheep were bought at 'Haytor Vale' when a sale took place there, before a move to Ashburton (already recorded) at a later date.

These sheep were crossed with a Hampshire Down. Alfred said during the war, bigger carcasses were required and then the 'Devon Longwool' was used. Perhaps this is where the 'top-knot' gained prevalance (wool on head!) with the Whitefaces.

Arthur's own early memories of sheep were in the early fifties, when his father, another Daniel Wrayford, kept about 100 mostly Whiteface ewes. The flock was maintained by purchasing 20 or 30 two teeth ewes from Ashburton sheep sale each year.

It seems rams were left with the ewes most of the year and often a lamb would arrive on Christmas day. To think a Whiteface sheep naturalised to the moor, usually lambing in March and April, can lamb in-country that early is revealing.

In the early '60s replacements were bred. A hogg ram was purchased at Ashburton Fair. Arthur said he was very protective towards the ewes. When the sheep came into the yard, 'the first thing to catch was the ram, and shut him in a shed', before as Arthur said 'he got you!' This bad behaviour progressed to the field after close encounters, the decision by Arthur was made to leave the breeding of 'Whitefaces' to the 'Moormen'!

Ewe lambs purchased amongst 'wethers' at Brent and Ashburton and ewe lambs bought in their own right, were used to replace the flock.

Rosemary's parents, Fred and Phyllis Bell, bought 'Wooder Farm', Widecombe-in-the-Moor in 1953. Rosemary's passion for the sheep started when as a young child she stayed with her grandparents near Bodmin in Cornwall (The Craze family), helping to care for their 'Cornwall Longwool sheep'.

She explained that her father, grandfather and the late David Skinner went to Chagford (first sale) in August 1960 and bought 20 closewool ewes and a ram – the families first sheep on 'Wooder'! Rosemary's love of sheep grew on her, and she did a shepherding course at Bicton College.

Her first experience of Whitefaced Dartmoors was working with Miss Needham's flock. She told her parents that the lambs just 'popped out', unlike the Devon Closewool.

Rosemary was to marry Arthur in 1971, and in so doing entered into three generations of Wrayford's.

This was an opportunity to have some Whitefaces again and in 2002 the Whitefaces were re-introduced to the Wrayford family having broken off back in 1976; ten six tooths from Patrick Coaker and one ram from T. Phipps formed a nucleus; as good mothers and docile in nature, Rosemary felt she had made the right choice!

Other Whitefaced Dartmoor Sheep Breeders and Keepers Stories

Bill Andrews

ZEMPSON, SOUTH BRENT

Bill Andrews now lives at Brent and his son Richard still farms at the family farm Zempson near Harberton between Dean Prior and South Brent.

Mr Andrews said he bought a lot of Whitefaces at Ashburton Sheep Sale in the 1960's or 70's. During the early years the Whitefaces were bred pure, but later a South Devon ram was used every so often to put a bit more size into the Whiteface and also the Greyface rams were used to a similar end. This was called 'an improvement' and the resulting sheep 'Improved Dartmoors'. Other breeds were used to this end too.

He recalls a lot of Whitefaces being sold in the old Ashburton Market with a lot of Whitefaces being brought in from the Widecombe area to the Annual sale.

When Mr Andrews recalled South Brent Sheep Sale he remarked that he thought it was Rendells who were the Auctioneers who sold Whitefaces at the Fair! The sheep were popular and could have several doubles. Other breeders around Zempson that he remembers keeping Whitefaces were the Steers at Dockwell and Thomas at Skerraton near Dean Prior.

The Norrish's now at Addislade he recalls sold Whitefaces at Widecombe Fair on the Green when they farmed Northway, Widecombe in the 1930's. Some of their sheep Mr Andrews remembers buying at Widecombe Fair.

Summarising the sheep, he said 'the wool would pay for the winter's keep. The sale of the wool was controlled during the second World War'.

He also said quite large flocks of Whitefaces were kept in the area in the past (70 plus ewes). However, the Whitefaces and other longwools needed 'roots' in winter to survive; this before the cake feeding of modern times. No Whitefaces are now kept at Zempson or very much around the area.

The closewool sheep (Devon), because of their ability to survive without roots, were the first breed to supersede the Whitefaces on many farms on the fringes of the moor under Brent Hill.

One particular story he remembers was that when he went to see the sheep of a night at lambing time, the wind would sometimes be driving across in front of him and would blow out his lantern light. Then Bill said he had to find a 'loo hedge', the side away from the wind, in order to light the lantern again.

Geoffrey French remembered Alfred Andrews that once farmed Owley Farm where Geoffrey's brother John once farmed. Alfred Andrews kept Whitefaces too and during the depression years of the 1930's he kept his wool until it finally made 1/- a lb. (One shilling a pound).

Antony Bolitho

WEST TREZELLAND FARM, BOLVENTOR, LAUNCESTON, CORNWALL

Antony Bolitho's father farmed Merrifield Farm, St Clear during the 1940's and '50s. His grandfather farmed Blackcombe Farm, Henwood, Launceston and Ashlake at Pensilva during the 1930's, and great grandfather farmed Sibleyback near St Clear in 1910.

Their story would have been one that was commonplace on many Cornish farms, and it involved the buying of 'Widecombes' from the big Tavistock Market Fairs of St John's, and especially 'Goose Fair' and driving these sheep into Cornwall to be crossed with Suffolk rams. This was a tradition with the Bolitho family. Antony recalled too that Dousland was a big sheep fair for Dartmoors. Hundreds of Dartmoors were purchased out of the sales by Cornish buyers. He remembered his father leaving home with a pony and trap at five o'clock in the morning from Merrifield, travelling via Gunnislake and Callington to get to Tavistock, a story presumably already repeated by his grandfather and great grandfather.

The sheep his father bought would remain near to the market in lairage for the first night. Then the next day with neighbouring farmers from Launceston who also bought sheep, they would all be driven together, with pony and traps behind the sheep via Greystone Bridge to Launceston, a journey of some 16 miles.

Very often, Antony explained that once the sheep reached Greystone Bridge they met up with 'paid drovers' who walked the sheep the rest of the journey, on what at that time were just 'gravelly roads and seemingly not too severe on the sheep's feet! Lorries really came during the 1940's and were open topped.

Antony also recalled his grandfather attending (South) 'Brent' Sheep Fair in 1930 and buying a prize Greyface Ram to put on the old Devon Longwools he kept at home.

He turned the ram out into the orchard when it arrived home. Later, to his astonishment he saw his workman's two sons riding this prize ram around the orchard. Fortunately it seems none came to any harm.

Some of the good Widecombe draft ewes bought out of Tavistock would be sold there in future sales in their latter breeding years.

The Whiteface rams were also crossed on Scotch Blackface ewes; Antony explained that this improved considerably the weight of the wool of the resulting cross sheep, and 'didn't kill the hardiness of the Scotch' in the resulting first cross sheep, more than likely improving hardiness.

Antony spoke of an absorbing story of the arrival of Scotch sheep on Dartmoor, and how a Lionel Palmer explained to him that when the sheep arrived on the trains, some of the people at the stations were afraid to unload the 'Scotties' because they didn't know what they were! No doubt their wildness and imposing black faces and horns made them quite intimidating, especially seeing them for the first time!

It's recorded that importations to Princehall in the early 1800's were transported down from Scotland by the ship load, and unloaded at Plymouth.

Paul Caunter

BOWDEN FARM, SHERFORD, KINGSBRIDGE

Ned Caunter (originally farming Sweaton) as well as being Cecil's father was a grandfather to Paul Caunter. Paul explained that two tooth ewes (sheep in their second year of life) during the mid fifties were making £50–£60 pounds a piece. When he moved to Bowden Farm some were crossed with the Devon Longwool and South Devon sheep. When first farming at Woodley, near Kingsbridge, he had Whitefaces but they were bought to cross with other breeds. They were to be found in Kingsbridge market in considerable numbers and breeders and dealers came from Cornwall to buy the Whitefaces.

Paul also recalled in detail a captivating story about the Whiteface sheep belonging to his great grandfather, Albert Caunter, at Sweaton, that were affected by the great blizzard of March 9th 1891.

The sheep at the time were at Chillington near Kingsbridge which had been driven there from Sweaton for winter grass and swede keep to over winter.

The snow on March 9th was sudden and severe. The blizzard even buried the train at Princetown. It was late for such a bad fall of snow and caught everyone by surprise and coinciding with the lambing peak time it meant there were considerable losses.

The story goes that Ned Caunter (Alberts son) came home late from courting that night of the blizzard and a message was left by his father to 'take the pony and ride to Chillington' many miles away to help his brother Abe who was staying at the farm to lamb their sheep. The orders also were to 'dig out the live and bury the dead sheep' from the snowdrifts where they could find them.

After some time in the South Hams Ned was took back to Kingsbridge and given 1 shilling to come home on the train via Brent Totnes and Ashburton, leaving his horse behind. From Ashburton Ned still had to walk back to Sweaton.

When Ned farmed the Ring o' Bells at Hexworthy Paul worked at the farm and used to help among other jobs brand* [*Hot iron brand owners names on hides or horns of the animals.] and drift back the moorland stock.

Tolls were a very old means of helping to pay for the markets use:-
KINGSBRIDGE U.D. COUNCIL. Its cattle market reveals:-

TABLE OF TOLLS (early 1900's)

For every	Bull 1/-	For every	calf 2p
	Bullock 6p		Lambs Jan 1st
	Ram 4p		To July 31st – 1p
	Sheep 3p		Aug 1st to Dec 31st – 3p
	Pig 3p		Ass or Mule 1/-

1 large Pig – per pen 6p
For every Horse 1/- Entire Horse 3/-
For every Carriage or Cart 1/-
Poultry 1p per head, prepaid Chicken per doz 3p

Suckling Pigs – 1p each
Stabling Carts, Wagons, Traps, Horses 4p each
Cars 6p
Washing Cart 6p

RP Clerk to the Council
Wheeler

The Chaffe Family

CORNDON FARM, WIDECOMBE-IN-THE-MOOR

Ena Smerdon's (nee Chaffe) great grandfather originally purchased Corndon Farm. John Chaffe was Ena's grandfather. Whiteface Dartmoor's would have been the first sheep during the mid-late 1800's at Corndon. A sort of marriage twixt farmer/breeder and sheep, together with horse and dog and the moor that surrounded them.

Herbert Chaffe, Ena and Walter's father continued to farm Corndon, but he was only seventeen when his father (John) died and he had to take on the farm at Corndon. Herbert was born in 1900.

Walter Chaffe worked for his father and the family later moved to Huccaby Farm, Hexworthy in 1948. Ena said her father always took sheep to Widecombe Fair and everybody had 'Dartmoors'!

Sheep keep in country was always taken at Kingsbridge and right down on the coast; bought through the winter keep auctions at Kingsbridge and Totnes. The sheep would have been walked and accompanied by a horse and dogs.

Later there were lorries and Tony Beard's uncle, Wilfred, supplied a lorry along with a Mr Prouse. Ena also recalls her father riding on horseback to Bovey Tracey and shearing sheep for her relations the Helliers and shearing with the Smiths at Hexworthy. No money changed hands, but in exchange for the work, he received turkey eggs to sit in July to rear turkeys for Christmas, and apples for cider making were also as part wages.

The use of the adjoining moor to Corndon was important to the Chaffe family. The Whiteface hoggs were the first of the sheep to be put on the common. The ewes and lambs were put up after shearing, but the first sheep to come off the moor. But during an open Autumn the hoggs could stay until November. Gerald Smerdon explained that the ear marking specific to the Chaffe's sheep was a top cut and a half penny underneath the ear and pitch marked on the wool as 'C' (no J).

The practice of ear notching, cutting or simply a hole was commonplace with moorland farmers to enable their own stock to be identified; the physical removal of a piece of flesh from the ear that soon healed over, but left a 'notch-mark' unique to each owners animals, that could be recognised on the moor.

The lear was quite an extensive one near to Yar Tor and 'Vaggie Hill' and over the top towards Dartmeet and around Sherwell Hill and Corndon Tor. The Turner Brothers' learing at North Tor outside Corndonford Gate. However, grids have replaced some of the 'gates' although in some cases just stone posts in various states of repair remain, but with no gate to be seen, yet with the metal gate hangings still on the stone posts.

During the 50's and 60's a change from Whiteface Dartmoor to closewools seem to take place at Corndon. This seemed to come about because the Whitefaces had a bad reputation for 'breaking out' from their pastures or maybe 'breaking in' from the moor and were called 'breakers'. Certainly they were lively sheep and bred very hard, they were inclined to roam. The Turners and Chaffes sourced their closewools at Blackmoor Gate.

Mrs Smerdon said wool used to 'fall in hand' (kept over) sometimes and not be sold. However, she said that the neighbours thought you were hard-up if you had to sell wool! However, the poor prices in 1930's didn't help the cause of the Whitefaces. She spoke of the Irish's at Grendon even having to store wool in two bedrooms of the farmhouse; waiting hopefully for a better price.

Mrs Smerdon also recalled the Leamons of Great Cator and Dury keeping Whitefaces in the past, and a Dick Norrish at Middle Cator and Irish's of Lower Cator (Cator).

Whitefaces were traded at Ashburton and rams sometimes bought at Brent Sheep Sale to help mix the breeding and avoid the family lines being too close.

Although mangolds and turnips were regularly grown Mrs Smerdon always remembers her father buying a ton of maize (whole grain) to feed to the sheep in galvanise troughs every winter to boost them before they lambed as it is a good energy feed.

Ena remembers two amusing stories; on one occasion her father happened to see their Whiteface ram break out from the fields at Corndon and he managed to follow it into Corndonford. However, before he could prevent an accident his ram started fighting with the Turner Brothers' Whiteface ram and promptly broke it's neck and it died! So there was no ill feeling, a ram was lent to the Turners! On another occasion a local 'Scotch' vet rented a cottage near Jordan, on the other side of the river Webburn from Corndon. The vet, however, had left his new V8 Ford outside the cottage and one of the Chaffe's rams, on seeing its reflection in the car, immediately started to bang at the car and caused a lot of dents to the car's doors.

Speaking of how the family coped with the bad snow winters, Ena said her father always made sure to buy an extra rick of hay as an insurance policy against running out of food. In particular March and April and even May it can be very hungry months for animals kept on moorland farms. The ricks were 'ricked thatched'; straw, ferns and rushes, tied in with Hazel spears and sisal!

Tom Greeves wrote in 'Red Tide – The Summer Pasturage of Cattle on Dartmoor' in the Dartmoor Magazine Summer 1996, that some cattle for the south quarter of the moor were also collected from Bovey Tracey by farmer, George Smith of Hexworthy the day after the east quarter beasts were gathered. Herbert Chaffe (born 1900) remembered once driving 187 cattle from Bovey to Hexworthy.

In an 1857 Devonshire parish history book, Chaffe is spelt Chaff without an e, recording farmers, masons and thatchers etc of that time.

Arthur Courtier

'THE MOORS', HAYTOR

Arthur Courtier, now in his 90th year, has been able to confirm a story told by Mrs Heather Bond relating to a sheep fair at Haytor Vale in the 1920's and early 1930's. Arthur Courtier's father came to Ludgate, Haytor, in 1897. A sale of ponies at Haytor Vale, before there was a sheep sale, took place in the early part of the century, so Arthur recalled. As far as the sheep sale was concerned, Arthur explained that all local people took sheep to be sold, some from the Manaton area.

He recalls Ted Sawdye (John Sawdye's father) was the auctioneer and the two prominent breeds at the time, the Greyface (which Arthur kept) and the Widecombe Whitefaces were offered for sale.

Whitefaces being sold under the scrutiny of Sawdye & Son (Post card series). (Courtesy John Harris).

A sale at Haytor Vale was in place it seems up until around 1934.

When Arthur's father was at 'The Moors' the sheep sale moved from the Vale to a field at 'The Moors' called 'Higher Rock Park'. At this time with land rented at Middlecott, the family were farming around 130 acres.

Arthur spoke of the success of crossing the Greyface and the Whitefaced sheep. However he insisted that Whiteface ewes should be crossed with a Greyface ram when crossed and not the other way round! This is possibly because the offspring could retain more of the Whiteface's agile characteristics!

Sheep keep was taken summer and winter by the Courtiers, at a field at Brixham in the winter and Bickington in summer and Preston Down. Sheep were often walked as far as Brixham and then drovers completed the sheep's journey.

The Haytor Vale and Widecombe Fair sales apparently took place at around the same time of year and Rendells were auctioneers at Widecombe. In the early years of sheep at Widecombe Fair, farmers would simply exchange rams during a day at the Fair, with no serious auction taking place. If a certain ram exchanged was better or younger than another, a farmer might give something like five shillings above the exchange of his ram to the other farmer.

Inevitably, as the farming memories flowed, Arthur Courtier talked of the 1947 snow-winter and how at 'The Moors' just outside the house seven or eight larch trees just snapped off and, cracking like gunfire, fell under the weight of the snow. Similarly telephone lines iced up like giant pipes and the wires from Haytor to Greenlane just collapsed.

Arthur confessed that he lost more sheep than ever before and lambs froze to the ground as soon as they were born.

Speaking of the 'moors burning', Arthur said further back in time swaling was universal in the spring and around Haytor the whole village would go up to the moor of an evening with a box of matches.

Arthur used rights around Smallacombe Rocks, a large cluster of granite masses, near the eastern side of Hound Tor Combe. Arthur remembered point to point racing taking place at Haytor before the 1930's.

Sheep identification on the moor remained almost as important as the wool itself. A big 'C' was placed on sheep going to the moor. However, the Wool Board started to resist pitch-staining of the wool fleeces and penalties were brought in to discourage its use.

Sadly, too, Arthur explained how his father stopped pitch-marking when a sheep kicked over a 'crock' (once used for cooking or boiling potatoes for example, with the larger crocks for pig feed) of heated tar and badly burnt his hand and arm. The origins of the 'crock' go back to 1750 and before on inventories.

When moving to 'The Moors' from Ludgate, Arthur's father had four years wool over and had to sell at 4½ pence a pound.

Heather Moor

So pleasing to the eyes,
Its colour regal and luminous where it les,
The heather surrounding hut circle, mire and cross,
Meeting wall and road covering the granite moss,
Wider than a carpet, seeming laid across a swathe of moor.

As if pinned from tor to tor,
Nourished near idling moorland streams,
Sun drenched during lazy summer days it seems,
Refreshed by drifting mist and rain,
Blanketing this wild terrain.

Like a sea-wave of colour embedded in this barren land,
But with peat and granite for its roots and not sand,
Camouflaging in purple, red and white, the wheatear and skylarks.
Yet, the beauty of summer peaks, before autumn darks,
Just one shower now, and the scene begins to fade.

Colin Pearse

Ruth and Graham Cundy

WIDSLADE LAMERTON, TAVISTOCK

Tavistock area does throw up an affiliation with Widecombe's on many farms. Ruth Cundy and Graham Cundy (brother and sister) farm at Widslade Lamerton and their farm was farmed in 1897 by the Brooks brothers.

In 1850 wool had been stored for several years to achieve a better price and the farm bought with the proceeds of wool over the years.

The Watkins, Ruth and Graham's grandparents, were originally butchers in Plymouth during the early 1900's and came to farm Higher Walreddon in 1914.

The Watkins family used to keep Greyfaces but they became too much trouble when lambing with so much wool around the udder, so it was felt a change of breed was needed. One day Ruth recalled a 'white horned ram' with longwool that arrived to cross on the

'Feeding tame lamb'.
Ruth Cundy's granny (Mrs Watkins) with Ruth's mother feeding lamb.

Greyfaces, which must have been a 'Widecombe', and it was a much hardier type of sheep. The results were excellent, with more vigour and cleaner woolled sheep on the legs and belly, but still shearing more wool than the pure Whiteface. These graded up sheep were found at Higher Walreddon farm and my Uncle farming at a later date, Lionel Pearse, also had 'Whitefaces' at Lower Walreddon farm, in a lovely farming area of West Devon just 3–4 miles from the market town of Tavistock.

Ruths mother (in both photographs) and her brother Fernley, in harmony with their sheep.

Summer grazing would also have been available on Whitchurch and West Down.

The change to a Whiteface sheep was also prompted by the fact that the Greyfaces readily suffered from the 'caw' (liver fluke rot) at Higher Walreddon.

The Watkins family became faithful to the Widecombes, because they said they had a lot more 'guts and go' than the big old Dartmoors of yester year.

As an example Graham explained how a Whiteface ewe had bite marks on its nose, trying to defend its lambs from a fox.

Fred Daw

CHEDISTON BUNGALOW, FORMERLY LOWER BROWNSWELL FARM, ASHBURTON

Fred's Grandfather was a miller at Cockingford, Widecombe, and so the family were born to be millers. Fred is now 86 years old and his father, who died in 1984, lived until he was 101 years old.

John (Jack) Daw was just eleven years old when he left school in 1894. Apparently he paid one penny a day to be schooled at Buckland-in-the-Moor, and he walked to school.

On leaving school he went to work for an Uncle Albert Norrish at Nor'way (Northway) Farm, not wanting to follow the family tradition of milling. Sheep from here were taken using horse and dog and on foot to Daccombe for grass keep, and to Bickington in winter to fold swedes. Fred remarked that there was always a 'leader' sheep that knew where it was going, taking the flock on at a pace. Fred said that hand shearing in summer was like a holiday for his father.

Sheep went from Barramoor to Brownswell for winter keep, driven on foot by Mr White and his daughter Hazel.

It seems that Jack Daw, at the tender age of nine, became involved in sheep rescue as a result of the blizzard of 1891 that started on March 9th. Mr Mann at Dunstone (Richard Mann's ancestors) handed to Jack Daw a number of sticks to pierce the snow where a terrier had marked where the sheep were buried in the snowdrifts. No doubt the terrier was aided by the breathe holes and could smell the sheep. The sheep could then be dug out! It is surprising how long sheep can live under snow, but equally how quickly they can suffocate and die if sheep pile on top of each other in the drifts.

The family moved to Hatchwell in 1912. John became very much a Whiteface man. Then between 1912 and 1918 they moved to Tunhill on a farm of 60 acres. Around 30–40

Whitefaces were kept and common rights on Venton and Blackslade went with the farm, and after shearing this proved a valuable lear for the Whitefaces.

In 1927 Fred's father moved to Brownswell, Ashburton and Whitefaces were gradually crossed out using the 'Blackface' as Fred called the Suffolk.

Fred recalled that when they attended Ashburton school there were *no* days off for Widecombe Fair. This privilege remained with the Widecombe school children, so Fred had little to do with the Fair and its animals.

Fred remembers cattle being 'trucked' from Ashburton. However when the 40 hour week came in, there was it seems no one to load animals after 5 o'clock! Also the streets of Ashburton used to be soiled by cattle and other animals when they were walked into town, and sold in the street. As soon as the streets became empty of livestock, they were washed down thoroughly and returned to normal. However, the advent of lorries meant animal excrement would drain out of the backs of lorries onto the streets, and if lorries had to park up for long, this would add to the problem for the residents. Windows and doorways would be boarded up down through the streets!

Fred thought the sheep sale moved across to Whistley Hill just after the Second World War because there were too many sheep for the old market pens to accommodate [see photo]. So as Fred said, 'they moved out into the field', so reflecting the faith in livestock farming, encouraged by the need to feed the nation *during* the War.

Remarking on the Moor's grazing, Fred's positive remark was that the number of stock grazed on the Moor by any one farmer was equivalent to what his holding would hold in the winter.

Part of the existing Car Park at Ashburton was used by Berry's the wool merchant in Kingsbridge Lane and all of Fred's father's wool used to go there from Brownswell (1930s).

This was mainly a storage depot, and linked with Buckfastleigh. The story goes that in Ashburton Berry's depot was a tall building and chain and pulley lifted the wool bags to an upper floor from the outside, to store the wool on a dry wooden surface.

The 'Buckfast Spinners' were linked with the Axminster carpet makers and rugs were made (and serge). It's been remarked on how noisy the machinery was, that deafened the working people. Also the fluff of wool filled the air and bronchial and skin disease was a common problem.

The Doidge Family

WILSETTON, WHITCHURCH, TAVISTOCK

Michael's father, John Doidge, tenanted Wilsetton in 1942 and bought the farm in 1955.

John's interest was in the Greyface Dartmoor. However, the Whiteface Dartmoor was also crossed with the Greyface and vice versa over the years.

As Michal Doidge said 'there was more milk than with the Greyface, more get up and go and one could keep more Whitefaces in a given area of land'; he said, 'a good sheep to work with'. (However, Albert Palmer on Michael's mother's side used to keep a lot of Scotch sheep).

Yet over the years I expected to always see Michael turn up at Tavistock Market Sheep Sales with Whitefaces; hardy, fit sheep!

From Wilsetton the sheep would use Plaster Down, Whitchurch Down and Pu Tor and near the Merrivale Road, south of Cox Tor and Beckamoor Combe, the Tavistock side of the Merrivale Road.

Leared to their areas, sometimes the ewes and lambs after shearing (from a March 10th onwards lambing) or just the weaned ewes in July, used the above moorland rights.

On one occasion, Michael's father, John Doidge, went to the sale of Bill Northmore at 'Fawnstone' part of the Maristow Estate, who was dispersing his Whitefaces and other stock on retirement. Mr Northmore recommended his broken-mouth Whiteface ram (twelve months as a broken-mouth). 'You buy him', Mr Northmore said, 'you'll like him', and they did! He was originally a Championship ram at the Ashburton Sale because, Michael explained 'that Mr Northmore was the sort of person if he liked a sheep he would stand back and go for it'. Also Michael said he bred a cracking lot of Whitefaces!

On occasions because John Doidge liked a heavier sort of sheep on their better soils, he would go back to using a Greyface ram on the Whiteface ewes and more wool resulted; when Michael said 'wool was wool, and wanted'! Michael has sheared by hand, and machine many Whiteface sheep over the years.

In partnership with his father around 1962 he had 150 Whitefaces on a commercial basis. He recalled how, at 'Dousland Sheep Fair', there used to be a double-sided row of sheep and a half side with 1000–2000 Whiteface Dartmoor Sheep in the sale field. Taking sandwiches and a shandy drink and with 'sheep sale weather' the characteristic sunshine, showers and clouds rushing across the sky, it was a day out everybody looked forward to.

Many sheep that were bought crossed the border into Cornwall and to North Devon and South Devon. Some crossed their sheep with the Suffolk rams. In South Devon the 'South Devon' rams were used to 'mix and match' with the Widecombe and maintain proliferacy and milk and also temper the size of the South Devon sheep and add spice to the wool!

John's Fair was really the sale for the Greyface registered sheep (Dawe, Ryall, Kingwill etc.)

Michael spoke with some feeling of the blizzard of February 18, 1978. He was at a dinner at the local Golf Club and was called home, driving his Austin Maxi car, because it was snowing so badly on the Saturday night. 'The Scotch sheep were "out to the moor" and somehow had found their safe shelter; with more room and less confined they had a choice, that the sheep around the farmyard fields did not'.

Thinking the storm looked bad, Michael fed his Whitefaces and Cheviots on the sheltered side of the hedge in the afternoon. However, the wind was so bad on that Saturday night it blew out over and buried 150 sheep, suffocating themselves under the snow against the hedge

The bare Rowan rooted to a moor's wall and the drifted snow make for a chilling, wintry scene. (Photo: Colin Pearse).

where he had fed them. The snow as it sometimes does in a bad blizzard, will form large drifts both sides of a hedge!

Talking of crossing Whitefaces to expand their bloodline, Michael mentioned that there is a bigger type of Welsh Mountain Sheep that would cross well to compound the Whiteface 'hill-type characteristics'.

There has been a crossing of these two breeds in the past, with notable success and the smaller Welsh Mountain Sheep has played a part in fixing breed traits most beneficial to both breeds that helps to maintain hardiness.

Dissected by the river Tavy and close to the Devon border with Cornwall, Tavistock has stood at the western gateway with Dartmoor for more than a thousand years.

As a former Stannary town, and still as a west Devon market town, Tavistock has strong links with its historical past and families, like the Doidge family who have used its market over many decades.

Although the birthplace of Sir Francis Drake, the community has its origins in the foundation of Tavistock Abbey built by Ordulph, the Earl of Devon in 974AD (a Benedictine Abbey).

From its early years the towns' economy centred around farming and later from its tin and woollen industry. The growing wool industry boosted the town economy to such an extent that it was granted a market charter early in the 12th century. It saddens the reader today to find we are losing markets nearly a thousand years old. In 2005 it celebrates 900 years as a market. Well done!

From wherever and whenever our native longwool sheep originated breeds like the Dartmoor would have been in demand and sheep with natural wool characteristics would have been prized as the towns industries grew.

From the beginning of the 14th century the medieval town became involved in the marketing of the tin mined on Dartmoor, making it an official Stannary town along with Ashburton, Plympton and Chagford, where weighing and stamping took place.

By the mid 19th century it was a booming market town. Profits from the mines were ploughed into the new buildings notably the Guildhall, Corn Market and the Town Hall and Pannier Market.

The Cistercian Monastery of Buckland Abbey above the river Tavy was home to Sir Francis Drake.

The centuries old tradition of Goose Fair is a much-loved tradition in Tavistock. Held on the second Wednesday of October every year since the mid 1500's it celebrates the era when farmers would drive their geese and other animals to market.

However, in the early 19th century Goose Fair was still a two day affair (Tuesday and

Wednesday). Animals were bought and sold in the open spaces around the churchyard railings as well as in the cattle and sheep markets, which then occupied Guildhall Square. The origins of the Goose Fair (also known as The Goosey or Goozey Fair) can be traced back to the 12th century and it was in 1105 that the Abbot of Tavistock (of a Benedictine Abbey) established a weekly market. In 1116 a market charter was officially confirmed by Henry 1st.

Perhaps the origins too of inns for market day merriment and sustenance sprang up from these appointed livestock and produce markets and so the many now named 'Market Inn's' all over Devon may have gained their names. 'The Jolly Farmer', 'The Dog and Duck' etc.

In the early days people would have travelled in on foot and later by horse and cart.

During the Fair rents and monies due to the Abbey were collected from tenants and farmers in kind and payment included many geese.

After the Abbey was dissolved by Henry VIII Goose Fair was held at Michalmas but in 1823 the date was changed to the 'second Wednesday in October.

However rent day on many tenanted farms today still falls on Michaelmas and Lady days, having its roots in these fairs and the Monasteries. Goose Fair was a typical country fair and livestock market serving the farming community surrounding Tavistock.

Before market carts and motorised vehicles farmers gathered their livestock and geese in the early hours of the morning and drove them across the moor on foot by the lantern light.

Geese were more plentiful then as many moorland folk possessed rights to graze their geese on the commons. It is said that geese were kept in the sheepfold at Postbridge and flew home to Widecombe.

The advent of the age of steam brought the Great Western Railway to Tavistock in 1859, and the London and Southwestern Railway in 1890 and the town was eventually served by two railway stations. The map attached to page xi in the preface of this book clearly marks these rail-lines (GWR and L&SWR).

Tavistock South had direct access to the cattle market at Whitchurch Road. This form of access to livestock markets was universal throughout Devon (e.g. Ashburton, Kingsbridge, Totnes, Moretonhampstead, Okehampton, South Brent etc.)

Easier transportation vastly increased the trade in livestock and their movement nationwide and especially on the occasions such as the Goosey Fair when lots of sheep and cattle were offered for sale.

Since 1996 and the emergence of BSE and Foot and Mouth stock numbers on the open market have 'took a dive'.

In Clive Gunnells 'To Tavistock Goosey Fair' written in the 1970's ('named') farmer John Doidge and auctioneer Tom Brown told of the days in the early decades of the 20th century when animal pens stretched from the cattle market along Down Road to Whitchurch Common in order to accomodate over 3000 head of stock brought to the fair for sale, many of the sheep were Greyface and Whiteface sheep.

Dartmoor the Country magazine:- All the Fun of Goosey Fair – Janet and Ossie Palmer. Issue No. 14.

Peter and Jane Dracup

BROADAFORD FARM, WIDECOMBE-IN-THE-MOOR

Peter Dracup explained that sheep have been at Broadaford for at least 400 years.

This is an outstanding record of the sheep's place on the farms of Widecombe documented in the late 1500's when Edward Gould might have started his farming at Broadaford. For in 1628 Edward Gould's Will said he had 18 cows valued in total at 54 pounds, 1 bull valued at 46 shillings and 8 pence and 143 sheepe valued at £47.13s.4d. in total.

It seems the farm was rented for most of the next three hundred years. On the break-up of the Sandridge Estate it passed into private hands, it was once used by 'Warreners' (rabbit farming).

In the mid-late fifties Miss Needham came here with her Whitefaced Dartmoors. In 1957 she employed a farm student, who stayed for the winter. They parted friends in the spring when he went to try and earn more money than agricultural wages (£7 per week). However, after the bad snow winter of 1963 she offered the farm to the said student, who agreed to come and try to put into practice what she had taught him.

So Peter's beginnings in farming are here revealed. His father-in-law said, 'buy what the locals have got!' So at the Ashburton Sheep Fair of 1964, Peter explained, he purchased 50 ewes from the 'Michelcombe-French's of Holne' and a £30 ram from Cecil Caunter of Ipplpen. Peter recalled at least six or seven lines (rows) of Whiteface Dartmoor Sheep for sale on the day.

To provide regular income eight Ayrshire and three South Devon cows were milked.

For the next fifteen years the flock was built up to nearly one hundred, keeping it pure, but not registered pedigree.

In the late seventies Peter said he co-operated with the Meat and Livestock Commission (MLC) to individually record the flock and its performance. Peter feels as a breed the Whiteface has a great ability to grow whilst young. They seem to plateau around mid-summer and then he said, make steady progress to finish as hoggets.

Peter said, 'he had the blessing of a black ewe lamb out of White parents', but this black lamb never recorded a black lamb herself.

However, the benefits of recording Peter said, proved useful, for it was found their daughters produced a black lamb. Peter explained it seems the genes miss a generation! This may be because it is a recessive gene and almost a form of mutation in breeding.

Peter felt that over the years he became concerned about the reducing size of the breed. However, their place on the moor in the past could be attributed to their small size and fitness. In an attempt to boost size and introduce new blood, Peter went to Lincolnshire and bought a Lincoln Longwool. Peter said he was a fine example of his breed and worked for two seasons leaving many well grown sheep. Peter then stabilized his breeding policy and increased the flock by buying in two-tooths. The Dracups now lamb about three hundred sheep; eighty to the Whiteface for breed replacements and the rest to Suffolks for prime lamb production.

The traditional day to start lambing in Widecombe was 1st March, but Peter said experience over the years has encouraged him to change. Early March weather in those days used to be a fortnight of good weather followed by 'the second winter' which meant extended feeding in an attempt to keep the ewes milking. Now lambing for Peter begins the first of

April and so by the time the lambs are looking to graze we hope to have grass in front of them. However, it has been said the last three Aprils have produced snow in quite considerable amounts resulting in a 'hungry-gap' and also making the foxes hungry too with unwanted lamb losses.

Recalling the quite considerable snow of February 1978, Peter said the hoggs were at home and seem to rise with and on the snow drifts, but some other sheep underneath died and were lost altogether.

As the snow melted Peter explained a hole could be seen and there was still a hogg under the snow. Peter said he found that it is often better to try and feed the sheep where it is and not to remove it from the drift as it becomes disoriented and feeding them too much too quickly can kill them. The food needs to be re-introduced slowly or they will die.

Scanning sheep at Broadaford has proved to be an effective management tool. It has enabled the different treatment of ewes that are known to be carrying twins or singles. The latter can be rationed before and after lambing, the former fed more energy.

The use of A.T.V. (quad bike) what Peter calls 'the mechanised zimmer frame' has appeared to help the ageing staff at Broadaford cope with the management of the flock. Through bringing in lambed ewes in a trailer Peter said twins and problems can receive special attention.

Over these many years of working on Dartmoor and with our local breeds of livestock, Peter said he has tried to understand the old ways of doing things and to compare it to modern farming practice. For example, Peter analysed why ewes were taken off the moor at different times of the year and kept in-country. Dartmoor is, he explained, very deficient in minerals and trace elements like cobalt and selenium due to, among other reasons, its high rainfall and porous granite derived soil.

However, today he says, these minerals can be provided using proprietary products.

The introduction of the Scotch (Blackface) to Dartmoor, the so-called Scotties that were to become known as the 'heather croppers' for their aggressive grazing of the heather moor is felt by Peter to have proved a reckless measure.

All this time ago Broadaford was spelt Bradaford and Devon Inventories of the 16th and 17th centuries, edited by Margaret Cash recorded the rest of Edward Gould's belongings; two colts £8; rye in the barne unthreshed and five bushells winded £9 (winnowed!) Oates winded and unwinded 14s; tenn acres of rye in the grounde praysed at £16-13s-4d; five acres of oates in the grounde £6-13s-4d; 'plough stuffe for tenn oxen performed 50s;' one payre of wheeles and a cart butt 40s; two newe hogsheades and one Pipe 7s; one old cupboard 6s-8d; one sellocke and a Lanthorne 2s; one winnowinge sheet and a canvas sheet 5s; one pecke and three seaves 10d; a sive 2s; one wheele barrowe 2s; one wheele barrowe 2s; thre shovels and three evells (prang forks) and two mattocks 4s-6d; one harrowe with Hamond and treases 6s-8d; a hammer a payre of pincers and a reape hook 12d (perhaps later a paring hook); a payre of ropes 12d; the hay in the lofte 12d; two ladders 3s-4d; one cheese wringe 3s; two iron barrs 6s-8d; two hundred and thirty one sheepe at Hole Parke £86-12s-6d; corne in the barne at Fursdon unthrested £7; A Ricke of Woode £5; tenn young bullocks £25; forty ews and lambs £16; sixteene Hoggettes at Predamsleigh £18; sixteene fat sheepe £8; two colts £4-13s-4d; thirteene younge bullocks £17; six acres of wheate in the grounde £15; an acre and halfe of oates in the ground 40s.

Also things in the house; in the Hall, the Parlour, the Buttery, the Parlor Chamber and in the Buttery Chamber and in the Cockloft! Wooll and yarne in the latter at £3. A foote of leather and a pigges skin 15s. Other examples: two brewinge chittles £6; one old brazen furnace 6s-8d (could be camp furnace or kettle!); a warminge pan 4s. In the buttery: five standerdes for butter and fower (also spelt fowre!) (four) saltinge tubbs 26s-8d; two hanging bordes and one plancke and seaven dozen of trenchers 3s. Two hogsheads and two halfe hogsheads 10s.

Other inventories:- one side saddle and furniture 30s; one grey nage 40s; woode trees rooted lyeinge in Long Parke £5; sixteen oxen £60. Oxen were formerly employed on the moor, working the moor on the roads they were shod ('Q' shoes). Five hogsheades of Syder at £5. One Steare 33s-4d; three nagges and one mare with packsaddles, hackney saddles, gerses bridles (other furniture) £13-16s-8d. Packsaddles used to carry ferns, peat and wool and crooks attached to them and truss ropes. Threescore and two sheepe and hoggetts £18-12s. Fowrescore ewes and lambes £32. Recorded in another inventory at the same time were thirty six other store sheep at £11. (total). Four acres of Barley and half an acre of Beanes at £8.

Bygones then were referred to as 'goodes or things forgotten'! Also recorded two brasen crockes, one yron Gridiron, 'Brandiron', pothangers and fryeing panne £2; one windinge sheete, with sackes and seeves 3s-6d.

Pot crokes (over the hearth fires) and tonges 3s; and interestingly three paier of 'Fullers Sheares' 20s. Possibly these were not for shearing the sheep but for preparing wool for the weavers!

It is interesting to find even within a small inventory like the above that the same word can be spelt differently, probably relating to the fact that dialect locally dominated the recordings and also at this time 'diction' would not have been set in stone! e.g. plough = plow!

Some of the flock in 1990 at Broadaford.

In 1990 the British Wool Marketing Board published 'British Sheep and Wool'. A photograph used as a representation of the ewes was at Broadaford. A brief description of the Whitefaced Dartmoor breed said Wool Classification, Longwood and Lustre, found in S.W. England. A description, said, white face and legs. No wool on face. Rams usually horned. Wool staple length 15–20 cm. Fleece weight 5½–7 kg. Quality 38's–44's. The Whiteface Dartmoor known to the moor since earliest records. It is hardy and thrives on meagre pastures at 1500 feet above sea level. The fleece is white and has a fairly strong 'crimp'. The wool is used for carpets. It also produces valuable lambswool.

Adrian Edmondson

TEIGNCOMBE MANOR, CHAGFORD

Adrian Edmondson's aspirations of keeping Whiteface Dartmoor sheep is obviously a well considered one, for these self-caring animals scavenge his land as their ancestors did, when the fields at Teigncombe were just part of the barren moor.

The farm at Teigncombe lies on the foothills of Dartmoor under Kes Tor Rock, Chagford. With the variation of dialect and diction Teigncombe was spelt 'Tincomb', pertaining to its tin mining and streaming and Chagfords stannary importance.

If one watches the entertainment on television provided by professional comedians it becomes obvious who is holding the obliging Whiteface Ram, and the owners face is a familiar one. Not however what you might expect from a hands-on entertainer, yet this relationship is no joke, and Adrian feels the sheep are now a special part of his life and deserve all the attention he can give them on his moorland manor retreat, where the fresh air and the attraction of Dartmoor has allowed him this opportunity to keep a few native breeds of animal.

The Whiteface Dartmoor sheep and Dexter cattle at Teigncombe Manor are a far cry from the filming studios of celebrity life in London. At Chagford his wife Jennifer Edmondson a distinguished celebrity comedienne on television as Jennifer Saunders, and their family, find peace and quiet and a different 'getaway from it all lifestyle'.

The Whitefaces have through their minority status of late attracted people with 'hobby' intentions and it is again a credit to the sheeps character and agility that all kinds of people in varying walks of life are adhered to this unique and ancient breed of sheep.

Adrians first crop of lambs from his small flock of sheep, bred locally, produced 5 ewe lambs and 5 ram lambs.

Adrian was surprised at the

ease of lambing of his Whitefaces. He said 'he was fully expecting to get his hands dirty during his spring lambing, yet they all popped out without any trouble, and just stood in the field to greet me on my rounds'!

So this is a new and proud Dartmoor sheep farmer already seeming weathered into the Moor's life and supported by a granite post, a rock, and a hard place, and grasping a Whiteface Dartmoor ram, that seems helpful and submissive, 'too ready to believe', but might think too, that life is not so bad on his new found farm at Teigncombe Manor!

Teigncombe Common Lane which it was once said was strewn with boulders and resembling more the bed of a stream than a track has been called wryly 'Featherbed lane'. So will Adrian Edmondson become a 'Featherbed farmer', a phrase once coined politically of farmers because of subsidies or perhaps the first of a new breed of 'wool-bedded' farmers, sleeping soundly on their sacks of wool, that has little value anywhere else!

When Adrian brought his ram over to me, something very interesting happened; for having placed him in the field with Suffolk rams as well as one Widecombe of mine, his ram immediately paired up with the Whiteface ram, that it had never seen in its life before! Perhaps some form of geneology is at play being of similar ancestry and lineage, (lineal descent), that distracted it from the Suffolks!

Mr Jack Geake

HAYE FARM, LAMERTON, TAVISTOCK

The Brent Sheep Fair (sale) was a big sheep sale in the past (a big market) Mr Geake recalled. (Bullocks were sold in the street, common in many towns in bygone days). Mr Jack Geake's uncle (the Martins) used to buy Whitefaces or 'Widecombes' as Mr Geake referred to the sheep. The sale field was a little square field in the village and near to the station. The sheep sales were often very close to the stations, as Brent was, in the past. This was convenient to load sheep on to the train after the sale. Mr Geake was probably only 12 years old when he first went to Brent Sheep Sale.

Large numbers of sheep were trucked to Cornwall from Brent in the past and the hundreds (600) Whitefaces that Mr Geake's uncles bought ended up in Saltash, purchased at one sale. He said there were many truck loads of sheep and it was not difficult to miss some of one's own sheep when checking the numbers and not be sure which truck they ended up on because the sheep were loaded so fast on to the train.

Apparently, the 'smeech' from the smoke of the train used to affect the eyes of cattle as the train drove forward, hitting a head wind and driving the smoke back over the trucks. The sheep often became lame and sore-footed; not only was there the ride on the train to their destination miles away, but also they may have already been walked many miles to the sheep fair. Also it was several miles by road to the Martin's farm after the sheep arrived at Saltash, so there were long journeys for man and beast. The trains smeech blow *over* the sheep!

The price paid for these sheep in the early thirties period was between 10s and 30s a piece, Mr Geake remembered quite clearly (he is now 80 years old himself).

South Down rams were used to cross with the Widecombes to produce early maturing fat lambs. One year the family decided to buy some South Down ewes and bring them down from Chichester where the South Down rams came from. This was a very big sheep fair of some 25,000 sheep Mr Geake explained. The rams and sheep were dear!

However, the ewes that came down to Saltash did not survive long. 'The change from the Chalk Hills and the rape was too great and they did not adjust to grazing in the West Country Mr Geake recalled. Their intention was to try and breed some South Down rams of their own from these ewes.' It was not uncommon to see 20,000 sheep at South Molton Fair, in Devon.

As an interesting foot note to Mr Geake's story there is a reference in the report of the 'Bureau of Animal Industry' and the chapter 'The sheep of Great Britain', it details the struggle between the Dorset Horn (improved Dorset) and the Southdowns for the occupancy of the chalk soils of Dorset (long and bitter) and explains how good the sheep were at the time. It says 'that the Southdowns finally supplanted the Dorsets, not because they were considered as so much the better sheep, but because they were better fitted to crop the close herbage of the chalk hills and being smaller many more could be supported on a given acreage'.

A prominent factor in the struggle for preference was the wool. This I am sure must have been realised by the Whiteface Dartmoor Breeders in adopting the Southdown to cross for fat lamb production with the Whiteface sheep. Any resulting crossbred ewe lambs kept to breed from in their own right would have had the added potential to improve the quality of wool.

The fleece of the Southdown in those days (-1850+) was held in great estimation.

During the April of 1957 important news to the market towns Kingsbridge and South Brent was the merging of two old firms of auctioneers: Messrs R.H. Luscombe & Sons of Kingsbridge and Messrs John Maye & Co. of South Brent, they were to become 'Luscombe, Maye & Co.'. Their offices were at Kingsbridge, South Brent and Plympton. Principals were Mr R.H. Luscombe and Mr J.H. Cockrem (Jack).

Quoting all this from Rowley's Page in the South Devon Journal; it went on to say:- 'The market town auctioneer is more than a voice; picking bids out of the blue, then chanting the climb with brisk monotony. He is a personality of the market, trusted by those who sell and buy. He must have that sense of timing which is highly rated among actors; for to risk a joke at the wrong time can kill the 'house', whereas the apt joke at the right time can put all in a merry mood with an ease as deceptive as it is important. A good auctioneer it is said, in good form can be as entertaining as an old music hall act, most of it impromptu and promptly answered. The important thing is to keep potential customers happy without slowing the business and some of the best auctioneers have made the joviality of one a parent of the other.'

Bob Kerswell

BEARSCOMBE, KINGSBRIDGE

An old adage 'that you need buyers as well as sellers' was one given by Bob Kerswell.

Bob remembered his first visit with his father to the old Ashburton Market in about 1949, buying Whitefaces and their crosses. The breed was recommended by a Mr Lane of Churchwards (Wool Depot at Buckfastleight). He said they were good for their wool.

It turned out that the Kerswell's bought some Whiteface ewes at the sale and then crossed them with a South Devon ram. This was 40 ewes at £6 7/6d each.

Bob himself hardly ever missed a sale at Ashburton Sheep Fair and bought hundreds of sheep out of Ashburton. Brent Sheep Fair was another popular sale for Bob and his father. Bob's grandfather also farmed, but he said 'out from Bigbury'.

Bob's son, Harry, buys Whitefaces and crosses them with the South Devon and more recently with the Teeswater which he said produces good sheep. He recalls making £70 a piece for two-tooth ewes sold at Kingsbridge Fair. They were Whiteface Dartmoor x South Devon sheep.

Bob had a preference, when buying, for Cecil Caunter's sheep and the Hext's (Wilfred) at Buckland and the Mann's. He also liked the 'ear character' of the French's, Michelcombe, sheep. However, he especially remembers the double H.H. (derived from Hermon Hext, Wildred's father) pitch black mark on a sheep. However, he said it did spoil the wool where marked.

Bob felt the South Devon crossed on the Whiteface ewes did harden up the wool. He never bought a Whiteface ram! Always crossing with a South Devon ram. It seems some good sheep were also bought from Joe Mortimore at Shallowford, Widecombe. Also from whom he referred to as 'two-sticks' Walter Irish, and he speaks of young John in the pen with his father when selling their sheep at Ashburton.

Bob said that over 30 years ago he received a letter from Sawydye & Harris 'Please go and buy some couples from Joe Mortimore' (on the last day of March).

Bob sent some mangels up in the cattle lorry because everything was so hungry at Joes. When he let the tail board of the lorry down on the dung heap in Joe's yard, geese, sheep everything came to eat the mangels. They were starving for food because it was snowing so badly.

It is interesting to find the use of the railway for transporting sheep being mentioned again and this time the connection from Brent to Kingsbridge. Many fairs seem to take place very near to the railway stations – South Brent, Kingsbridge, Totnes, Okehampton, Bovey Tracey, Ashburton, Moretonhampstead, Princetown etc., all for the convenience of moving animals to and from market, but it seems mostly from the markets and home to the buyers' farms here and to other parts of the country.

Jack Lewis

'HAYCROFT', MURCHINGTON, CHAGFORD

Jack Lewis was known and respected as a breeder of Greyface Dartmoor Sheep. He explained to me when I visited him at the age of 93, shortly before he died, that there were not many Whitefaces around Chagford. The photograph, however, does show very old fashioned 'Dartmoors' at Throwleigh around the 1920's with some Whiteface characteristics. Photo supplied by Chris Chapman. 'Looks like a bit of "raddling"* going on here'!

He said there was a lot of difference in having to graze around the slopes of Watern Tor north of Fernworthy, than even to graze Brent Moor with Whitefaces. So, the further south one went the better the moor, especially towards Brent and Ivybridge.

George Hutchings of Fernworthy Farm, before the land was flooded and before he moved to Teignhead Farm when the Fernworthy Reservoir was built, used to look after the sheep that came up to his part of the moor.

Jack could remember Greyface rams being sold below where the 'Spar' is now in Chagford and sheep penned in the street. Some of the very old photos show wooden hurdles placed upside down because of the hard cobbles and tied to form pens. Both Greyface and Whiteface sheep can be identified (late 1800's, early 1900's).

*Red Ochre used on the rams to see the sheep went to the ram!

Recalling the 1947 snow winter he said that telegraph wires on the ground tangled up in his horse. He also remembered icicles outside the windows and windows that could not even be opened because of so much ice. The wind was whistling all the time and trees were cracking off and telegraph poles were breaking, sounding like the war or something worse than war. Ponies were frozen stood up on the moor, dead where they stood, and similarly all out over Scorhill. There was snow all up through Murchington, Berry Down and Scorhill.

Stuart Baker at Lincombe, Chagford still keeps Whitefaces and uses the Chagford Common rights he has when appropriate. This he said, was a great asset in the dry summer of 1976 when grass in-country just burnt away. Stuart has been a regular buyer and seller at the Ashburton Sheep Sale. He has always spoken highly of the sheep's adaptability to a hard life and he takes them to Lapford in winter for a change of keep and minerals.

The Farmers Weekly April 25th 1947 explains how cobalt combats mineral deficiency. To highlight this there is a caption showing a very lively ewe and lamb chasing away an exhausted fox!

It explains the successful use of cobalt as a curative agent in the treatment of nutritional anaemias in sheep is largely due to research carried out in New Zealand and Australia. The result of this work has established beyond reasonable doubt that the prime cause of these diseases is cobalt deficiency in the pasture. In our own country excellent results have been obtained and sheep suffering from 'pining' and other anaemias have fully recovered after cobalt treatment.

As a footnote to Stuart Baker's story, it seems Mrs Baker could be seen in spring collecting bits of wool that the sheep left on thorn bushes or barbed wire; something to bring in a few pennies!

Francis Maddock

UGBOROUGH – THE FAMILY FORMERLY AT MOOR FARM, CORNWOOD

As far back as Francis Maddock's grandfather's days at Moor Farm, Cornwood (where a John Northmore farms now) in 1914, sheep were walked to and from Slapton for winter keep by the family.

Francis recalled a very old memory when in 1906 his father and grandfather and a Mr Luscombe of Hall Farm, Cornwood, went to Princetown Fair to buy Whiteface rams to bring back to Moor Farm, Cornwood. The rams were tied up in what Francis called a 'big market trap', such no doubt as are seen in a photograph of Princetown Fair published in 'Dartmoor Magazine (2001) where Whiteface rams are shown tied up to carts in the early part of the 1900's.

The family moved to Sharpham, Avonwick in 1914 from Moor Town Farm, Cornwood and then moved to Yalberton (Paignton) in 1920.

At the age of 14 years old he recalls his father renting keep at Stannon Newtake under Aldophus Coaker of Runnage. Francis Maddock's father, Edward Maddock, then paid £15 a year for the keep. Francis remembers this keep being taken in 1935 when keep at home was short. The sheep were kept on the moor until August or September.

On one occasion when Francis was just 14 years old and his father was too busy to go to Stannon and gather the sheep to bring them home to Paignton, he sent Francis and their workmen and 2 dogs (one called Scott) to walk the sheep home from Runnage, the normal gathering place for the moorland stock as they were put to moor in Spring and drifted ready to go home in Autumn. Francis was dropped by car at Runnage and the sheep were home in a day.

The journey proceeded to the top of Widecombe Hill, down to Cockington Ford, across country then on their way to Paignton at

Francis Maddock judging at Okehampton Show 1998.

Woodlands, having crossed the A38 to Smokey House and Marldon and Tweenaway and so finally to Yalberton.

Greyfaces and Whitefaces were kept at Yalberton and the respective rams crossed on the two Dartmoor breeds and some also kept pure.

Francis has his doubts about breeding too much wool on a Whiteface and giving it a 'Greyface fleece look'. He said the Whiteface Dartmoor needs to retain its own identity.

Clifford Mallett

ASH PARK FARM, STICKLEPATH, OKEHAMPTON

Previous to the sale of his flock at Chagford Market this summer (2003) Clifford kept around one hundred 'Widecombes' at Ash Park Farm. A sale of Whiteface sheep at Chagford is rare occurrence here on the northern boundary of our breed.

The lower border farms on this the north side of Dartmoor are certainly lying where the soil can be quite damp from heavy winter rains on the Moor's edge. One would naturally think not entirely suited to Whitefaced Dartmoor Sheep, used to hard standing granite and short pasture, such as the high rising land of the Moor above Ash Park, which is South Tawton common, backing away from the winter's sun. Here Clifford has forty-five acres of additional land that helps compensate his wetter land, which his father bought in the past and where Clifford and Derek Clark put the walls back up to stop the sheep coming in from Dartmoor, not an easy task! (On the wetter 'in-bye' land in summer the Whitefaces do well.)

These fern covered fields hug the Moor and are a good example of how desperate measures on these steep sided slopes took place to reclaim land for farming with livestock. These were probably the last of the newtakes allowed on the Moor (or 'intakes').

As the ferns encroach, the battle is never easily won to control or defeat its reversion from poor grazing back to bracken and stunted gorse or moorland on an acid base; for over Clifford's wall is real Dartmoor!

In the autumn as the bracken dies back to a rusty colour, many of the border field walls become visible that divide the 'patchwork quilt' of small individual fields that skirt the Moor's edge.

Rams from Runnage and Phil Coaker seem fit and lively, and not it seems concerned about damp feet or excessive rains overhead that can fall on Okehampton, for on Dartmoor the sheep have seen it all before!

Lambing takes place in April, as slowly warmth and grass return to the Moor.

On just one day Clifford and Derek Clarke sheared 300 sheep, many years ago now, as Clifford remarked, in summer.

One of the stoney stories on folklore of Dartmoor is about a 'menhir' known as the 'Honest Man' standing on a tiny grass patch at the top of Sticklepath Hill. Circles of upright stones invariably attract greater attention than does one lone menhir, unless particularly conspicuous.

However, the longstone on Shuggle, Shovel or Shuffle Down above Chagford, has impressed itself more. It is said to pivot around slowly at sunrise, warming each cold granite face in turn! Possibly this is in compliment to the 'Grey Wethers' who perform the same rite on Sittaford Tor overlooking Shuffle Down; but the imagination has to be vivid, although *time* judgement in the past might have relied on this!

The village of Sticklepath, tucked into the Taw Valley at the foot of Cosdon Beacon, possesses two smaller menhirs. One, the 'Honest Man', the other an 'incised menhir' placed at 'the foot of the school path behind the Ladywell'. It was knocked down and moved from its original position when the present main road was constructed in 1829. Two St Andrew's crosses and an hour glass figure may be traced, now very weathered.

The Honest Man's incisions are almost indecipherable as the old stone once showed more of itself above the ground, now sinks lower and lower. A St Andrew's Cross can be traced on one face, with faint markings resembling a circle and a crescent.

Ruth E. St Ledger-Gordon suggests in their original positions as ancient menhirs they later became 'signposts'.

The incised stone indicates where the track from Belstone joined the old highway. The Honest Man shows where the Mariner's Way branched off on its tortuous route to Sampford Courtenay and the North Devon coast.

The figure eight symbol on the incised stone is a mystic sign used in the Witches' religion and could have been cut in the Middle Ages! The St Andrews Cross could relate to Sticklepath's Chantry chapel, as an appendage of the Mother Church of St Andrew at Sampford Courtenay. The Honest Man began its life as a Bronze Age menhir of unknown purpose, then served as a signpost, and perhaps as Ruth E. St Ledger-Gordon thinks as a meeting place for pagan worshippers who placed the sun disc and crescent moon upon one side. Yet I believe the emblem of Ashburton has the sun and moon's crescent symbolising the tinner's importance on their economy, and where tin was stamped and weighed, starting its journey on the Moor.

Two different stories account for the Honest Man's complimentary name.

It is thought that only the most eccentric mariners would ever have chosen to journey from Plymouth to Bideford or Barnstaple by the circuitous and improbable path traditionally allotted to them and known as the Mariner's Way. In following it, a mariner would have had to walk the roughest open tracks of Dartmoor; cross rivers on precarious stepping stones, often submerged; wander through fields and churchyards and squelch through the mud of farmyards and rough lanes. No wonder that the traveller turned in at any alehouse that lay along the way for much needed refreshment!

According to legend, one of these mariners, having over-refreshed himself at the 'Sticklepath Inn' lost his way in the wilds of Sticklepath Hill above the village. Looking for the 'signpost' or someone to direct him, he peered through the darkness and to his joy (he thought) he espied a figure ahead. In his relief he threw his arms around it embracing what turned out to be the 'solid granite form of the menhir' and inquired, 'Be you an honest man?' and so the stone was named. Perhaps in the times of 'highwaymen' and rustlers and dishonesty, questions needed to be asked!

The second explanation of the Honest Man's name relates to how, in these same wilds, a traveller was set upon by thieves (as I speculated above) who robbed him of his purse.

Fortunately for him, at the crucial moment a good Samaritan happened to ride up, rendered first aid and restored his purse to the victim, after which this self effacing rescuer rode off without disclosing his identity. The traveller, impressed by such disinterestedness and presumably having recovered his strength, found and set up the stone on the spot, in commemoration of 'so honest a man'.

George Medland

WILMANSTONE, TAVISTOCK

George Medland's father came to 'Radge' in Peter Tavy parish in 1912. He was born at Lydford. He kept from 100 to 200 Whitefaces, and the rights on the moor attached to Radge were at Long Plantation, and beyond to Holming Beam, up over from Bear Down and North of Two Bridges opposite HM Prison Dartmoor, and on the prison farms' north and eastern boundary.

Several farmers around Radge drove their sheep along with George's father's own Whitefaces out to Holming Beam for their summer lear and the sheep were brought back to the home farms in September; again walked with horse and riders and dogs all following and alongside. (George would ride his own horse). Today his son James explained that their Whitefaces are now put out to 'VELLAKES' Newtake near Sourton, the Okehampton side of the moor, after the sheep are sheared.

Holming Beam, or as often said 'Omen Beam' is noted for the abundance of its whortleberry plants and has long been a favourite place with the gathers of that fruit says Crossing. Old mine workings exist here and much peat was formerly cut near the Blackabrook.

Southward of Bear Down Newtake Corner, the Devonport leat crosses the Blackabrook. With the leat and the river on the left and the prison enclosures on the right, the Tavistock road via which George brought his sheep to Holming Beam is reached west of Two Bridges near to Long Plantation.

George Medland's father died in 1948 and then George farmed Radge for a while himself. Then he bought 'Shillapark' and his first important farm was 'Week Barton' near Brent Tor. The grazing rights used from here were on the Merrivale tilt and back over again to the Forest of Dartmoor.

Brent Tor church in the far distance, as seen from Walkhampton Common.

Other farms that George works with at present are 'Crockern Tor' that holds a Duchy lease and 'Long Ash' the opposite side to Merrivale. George said the main rights are on the Forest and mostly shearling (two tooth) Whitefaces were put on the moor.

A homebred flock of Widecombes has always been kept along with other breeds like the Scotch, but George has kept up the family tradition of breeding Whiteface sheep. The home farm of Wilmanstone has no moorland rights. James Medland however, feels that for Dartmoor farming to succeed everybody has got to work together!

Reflecting a little on sheep prices, George remarked that in the 1940's rams could probably be bought for as little as £20 each. George, over many years has always attended Ashburton Sheep Sale to buy Whiteface rams. George's angled cap on his head, would easily distinguish him among the sales busy crowd.

He said 'over the years he always took Whiteface ewes to John's Fair at Tavistock and they were popular to buyers from far and wide, and Dousland Sheep Sale was regarded as a good market for sheep and buyers came up from the South Hams, such as John Symons, from Churchstow and buyers from Cornwall regularly came for Whiteface sheep to Dousland'. George remembers upwards of a 1000 Whitefaces at Dousland Sheep Fair in the past being offered for sale along with other breeds of sheep.

Recalling other Whiteface breeders, George mentioned Leonard Ball and John Repe of 'Nattor' Peter Tavy who was more commercial with his Whiteface.

The root sales and grass keep sales in the autumn and spring were an important time in the calendar of the 'moor' farmers, so George explained because they could buy keep for their sheep to winter or summer away. He remembers quite high prices being paid, for example, as much as £100 per acre during the 1950's. Grass, swede-turnips and mangold caves were purchased.

George said he went along in the 1940's and 50's to Totnes root sale with Leonard Ball to buy roots. Leonard Ball's home farm was Axna and George explained that Leonard used the moor up over the back of Mary Tavy where the village itself joins the moor.

The practice of dipping sheep has always been important to George and he has never missed in 29 years. He felt the quality of the longwool fleeces reflected attention to regular summer and especially autumn plunge dipping of sheep to keep the fleece healthy through the stress of

Whitefaced ewe hoggs enjoying a rub on an old horse pulled granite-roller, now converted to the tractor, for towing.

winter weather and by keeping the threat of sheep scab away. George, however, was despondent of today's wool prices. I remarked, 'perhaps we would be better burning the wool' and he candidly said, 'But it won't burn will it?'

Referring to modern breeds of sheep used for crossing, he is impressed by the potential of the Blue-faced Leicester. He said it provides an excellent cross with the Exmoor Horn sheep producing a stylish modern-type 'mule'. It has been tried on the Whiteface too with equally good results. There is extra vigour, milk and increased lambing percentage (>200%) and using terminal sires like the Suffolk to produce a top quality three-way cross.

Farming so close to Brent Tor it is probably appropriate to mention Brent Tor Church; the most curiously-placed church of any belonging to the moorland district, situated on the summit of a lofty hill. It was it seems erected by the monks of Tavistock Abbey. Mention is made of it in 1283, and it has been considered probable that it was standing at least half a century earlier, so Stephen Wood records in Dartmoor Farm.

The modern way of controlling ecto-parasites.
Here at Barramoor, North Bovey, Keith Morris of Cheriton Bishop, provides a 'mobile-spraying' set-up. Two hesitant Whitefaced Dartmoor rams await their fate! George though stresses the importance of 'dipping' or 'parasite' control on his farms. Like myself he was brought up to 'plunge dip' in summer. Today shearing and the timing of dipping or spraying still go hand in hand. To control scab effectively, autumn treatment is essential. Mobile equipment releases the farmer from the handling of sheep into plunge dips, where sheep become wise to the event and retreat from the dips smell!

Richard, Margaret and Sheila Norrish

RIDDON FARM (SPELT 'REDDEN' IN THE PAST)

Riddon is on the Wallabrook, not far above Babeny, and is one of the forest farms. It is one of Dartmoor's ancient Tenements recorded in 1344, with Pizwell and Babenay (Babeny) also recorded in 1260. It was then named 'Riddam', later 'Redden' and now Riddon. A mile north of Riddon is Pizwell Bridge.

In 1702 Thomas Bernaford, rector of Lydford, filed a bill in the Exchequer against John Hext and others claiming tithes, in the tithable places in the parish of Lydford in the 'waste of Dartmoor' from 35 ancient tenements, and the rector was successful.

The list of tenements in their old names (taken from Robert Burnard's Dartmoor Pictorial Records) reads:

Rennidge (Runnage) and Warner – one each.
Piswell (Pizwell) – three tenements.
Hartiland and Riddam (Riddon) – one each.
Barbary (Babeny) – three tenements.
Brimpson (Brimpts) – three tenements.
Lying in Huccaby – four tenements.
Dury – one tenement.
Hexworthy – three tenements.
Sherborne (Sherberton) – three tenements.
Dunabridge (Dunnabridge) – five tenements.
Princehall and Brownberry and Bellaford – one tenement each.
Another lying in Bellaford and the other called Lake – two tenements included here.
Lower Merripit is said to make up the 35.

The districts of these tenements consist of a comparatively rich upland with sheltered and fertile valleys, and are certainly sealed in the best and most favoured portions of the Forest of Dartmoor, and have been from pre-historic times down to the present occupied by succeeding races of 'moormen', and where Whiteface Dartmoor sheep have been recorded pasturing several of these tenements over many generations.

There is an account of the tenants of Dartmoor as early as 1344–5, and reference is given to such familiar names as William de Meriput, John French, Richard Dokwill, Richard Dury, William Northweye, William Hext, Robert de Hextenworth (Hexworthy), William Dunnybrigge, and others like Man and Northmore (Mann as of today).

They are recorded with our Whiteface breeders today, and here included in these stories are surnames which are even common on Dartmoor at the present time, or have survived in such place names as Merripit, Dury, Hexworthy and Dunnabridge.

'In 1346 the forty-four tenants depastured no less than 4,700 oxen and 37 steers and shows conclusively that the favoured spots in the Forest of Dartmoor, some 5½ centuries since, carried considerable herds of cattle', so says Robert Burnard.

Riddon's (Redden) farmhouse is relatively modern, but occupies the site of more ancient buildings. Jack (John) Norrish moved to Riddon in 1927 following a family called Snow. His family of Richard, Sheila and Margaret are still at Riddon. Margaret explained that there were 'no tractors in they days, just horses to get about.' Their mother was born at Leightor, Poundsgate.

Richard Norrish and John Irish shearing at Blackaton, Widecombe. A petrol engine giving power to the clippers (double-head). Blackaton Common is in the background.

Sadly Jack Norrish died in 1947 and was ill during the atrocious snow winter of that year. The family were young!

Sheep were being lambed and the work somehow had to go on.

Jack and Bill Norrish (of Northway) were brothers and also 'road menders', breaking stone for road improvements.

Whitefaces were farmed at Riddon, and common rights included Riddon Ridge, where sheep and lambs were summered. After buying some of Middle Cator land the Norrish's common rights now extend to Corndon Down and part of Spitchwick Manor. Wool went to Buckfastleigh and a Mr Lane was in charge of its grading.

The Walla Brook flows through Riddon farm and forms a boundary for all the tenement farms of which there are no other tenements on its eastern side.

A bumpy lane from Cator Green near to the farm's top road from Bellever leads for half a mile down to the farm, where new and old marry up with each other and where cow and person once entered the fifteenth century longhouse through the same door.

A no longer used milk churn standing at the drive entrance to Riddon is another relic to a past story when cows were milked by hand, before machines and bulk tanks. The concrete stand (some were just made of stone or sleepers) is built into the hedge opposite the drives end and boasts the farm sign of 'Wild Goose and Riddon' above it. The last churn was collected in December 1971. Milk had been collected by lorry and taken to Daw's Creameries at Totnes. The 'empties' or clean churns were left on collection of the full milk churns, to be taken back to Riddon to hold the next two milkings. Margaret recalled her father selling two cows at a 'special sale' at Ashburton Market for £30 each! Probably before the 2nd World War.

During the winter of 1947 Margaret explained that they were 'farm locked' for six weeks and *then* the blizzard didn't arrive until the end of January! Sledges were used behind the horse to move food and milk churns; but the horse's feet would clog up with snow and slow down its progress.

Food for the animals was stored in ricks and had to be cut out with hand-held 'hay knives' and there wasn't any machinery to move things around like today.

The 1962–63 snow winter arriving at Christmas also meant hardship.

Roots like swedes that were 'topped and tailed' of leaf and tap-root were 'pitted' (an earth pit in the field) in November before winter, in the field where they grew, and covered with rushes and earth, to give protection against frost, and they were set a good foot into the ground. Previously, potatoes were harvested in September and 'pitted' in the ground and protected with rushes and earth, often in the same field in which they grew. Mangolds were harvested in October, before autumn frosts, and stored often beside a hedge in long clamps. They were then covered liberally with hedge parings and bracken ('verns'). These clamps were also set a foot into the ground, and excavated earth would then be used to bank the sides and the top of the clamp to hold down the covering of vegetation and help repel the frost.

These were all somehow dug out as precious food during the 'snow hard' winters and during long 'hungry gaps' in the spring. The swede tops were given to bullocks that did well on them, but the mangold tops were left to rot in the field, because they were not good for animals!

Hayricks were raised on 'vuzz' (gorse bushes) in some cases, instead of 'ash faggots' (the branch wood of ash). Margaret said this discouraged the rats.

As the hay rick was used away, 'wood faggots' on other farms would be used to burn in the hearth fireplaces.

Cator Court and Babeny are farms on the Riddon boundary.

Field names at Riddon are still retained. Names like 'Barn Park' and 'Down Gate' are lovely countryside names that roll off the tongue. Here every field was just as important as the next, and everyone was to know its name, so a task was not performed in the wrong field, or a sheep or bullock accidentally placed to inappropriately graze the retained winter crop or the unstocked hay field, and where rail and hurdle were replaced by a 'Devon Gate' that latched onto the eye of a stone post, that might be etched with 'slot and L'.

At originally seventy acres, Riddon farm is almost the smallest of the Duke of Cornwall's twenty-two farms on Dartmoor.

High moorland tenements like these are special, and the way they have been cared for, humbling. They convey remoteness and self sufficiency created out of necessity, and where the shortcomings of the Moor are simply confronted and accepted.

Whitefaced Dartmoor sheep and South Devon cattle were breeds of stock that were common to the Moor and combined to help achieve the self-sufficiency, and kept the breed pure. They walked the commonland tracks to exercise the common grazing rights.

Their rights attached to the tenements meant the tenant had to fulfil duties like attendance at the Manor Court at Lydford, taking corn to be ground at the Duchy's Mill at Babeny, and helping in the annual drifts when the shedding of offspring in pounds like Dunnabridge, and in farm lanes and yards like Yardworthy took place (especially pony colts for weaning and autumn sale).

An independence of spirit has been bred that the family at Riddon epitomises, and is still engrained in generations that may succeed their families on these high moorland farms, mostly rising above 1000 feet above sea level. Butter and cream were made through milk separation. Pork and lamb provided meat for the house and surpluses sold in local markets. South Devon cows were hand milked (rich creamy milk) and sheep flocks were small, sometimes only 20 sheep. Horses pulled binders, later converted to be attached to the tractor, to cut oats ('Black oats' were also grown) that were 'stooked' in the field and ricked when ripe. 'Thrashing' (threshing) took place late autumn, early winter, and corn saved was milled for stock. However, whole oats were preferred by sheep, and 'oaten sheaves' were placed in cattle racks for young 'yarlings' to munch whole, as a common energy feed used in the wintering yards.

The Duchy is Dartmoor's biggest landowner with 70,000 acres, of which 50,000 is common land. Yet farms the size of Riddon that make up the rest could become increasingly rare, where families fail to succeed, and amalgamation takes place.

The redundant milking parlour where cows were milked abreast of each other now reveals the glass milk jars opaque with dust, that's undisturbed (outside now the cows are suckling their calf) and where the Norrishs just have memories of where milk flashed through on one of those unforgiving cold winter mornings, but when home based food was much greater valued than today. Keith Jackson read 'churn label addresses' to find farms when an apprentice mechanic with E. Bowden & Sons!

Margaret also spoke of local pronunciations, and how Widecombe was known as 'Wide-combe' (wide valley). But Crossing writes of snow on Dartmoor and says 'Widecombe folks are picking their geese faster, faster, faster, as observed by the people lower down at Ashburton'. A writer in Notes and Queries has suggested that the name of the moorland village in the saying is merely a corruption of the word 'widdicote', an old Devonshire term for 'the sky'. When the snow was falling we can imagine it would be playfully observed that the 'widdicote folks', or 'sky folks' were picking their geese. As the word Widdicote fell into disuse and its meaning became forgotten, it is easy to see how in South Devon the transition to Widecombe would take place. Widdicote would then make no sense, whereas they had all heard of Widecombe and knew it to be somewhere on Dartmoor, a place where much snow fell.

The families around about Widecombe are all interwoven among themselves and Colin Irish's Grandmother at Grendon and Grandmother Norrish were two sisters, and with Whiteface sheep as much part of their family too as the people.

The Leamons farmed Dury and Cator together at one point and with Whitefaces too, so Margaret explained.

Richard Norrish.

Richard Norrish's son Philip also farms Foxworthy (Widecombe) where sheep and farm over time have been inseparable (the Chaffe family in the past among others lived there, an Arthur Chaffe).

Hext and French, Beard, Hodge, Northmore and Mann are recalled farming ancient tenements in centuries past, their names present on Dartmoor today.

There were four ancient tenements at Huccaby, or lying in Huccaby where Richard Norris (Norrish), John Hext, Anna Norris, and Thomas Leaman are all very well established Dartmoor names.

The Forest Inn at Hexworthy overlooks the valley of the West Dart with a background of Yar Tor and Dartmeet Hill.

Newtakes cut off the northern portion of the Forest from the southern, by a broad belt running from Princetown to Dartmeet.

Huccaby is probably Celtic 'Ock' or

water, and may mean 'the abode by the water'. The moormen still pronounce it Ockaby, with the accent on the last syllable.

Hexworthy, close by, another ancient tenement is mentioned as early as 1379 when John Browning rented an acre of its land for three half-pence per annum, whilst at Bysouthexworthi John Holrig paid threepence for two acres. Traces of ancient enclosures can still be seen around about the hamlet.

Margaret recalls how hundreds of animals came up to pasture these Dartmoor lears from in-country.

In the combes and valleys around the Moor where as at Riddon, some shelter is afforded, the settler no doubt in Saxon and mediaeval times found a home. More than one ancient farmhouse remains today, reared on the site of a still older dwelling and inhabited by the descendants of those who in far away times chose to live here. They have each their own story to tell, as with the Norrish family. Their customs, folk tales and supersititions still live on and carry one back to a yet earlier period.

Norman Perryman

FORMERLY OF WEST STOKE, HOLNE

Norman Perryman farmed at West Stoke, Holne for 35 years moving there in 1952. His grandfather introduced their first Widecombes to Bowden Farm, Buckfastleigh (near Cross Furze's) around 1942. This was after the Pearse family moved out.

Norman's father (Charles Perryman) farmed Mill Leat in 1941. The 117 acres cost in total £100 a year to rent. Three to four years before Norman's father gave up farming he used the Whiteface ram on his Greyface Dartmoor flock. Norman said the resulting 'improved Dartmoor' were super sheep. Some of these sheep were bought to be farmed in Cornwall.

Roy Tucker (an uncle to Norman) bought Whitefaces to cross with Suffolk rams. Similarly, Norman bought older ewes at Tavistock and crossed them with the Suffolk to produce fat lamb.

Norman recalls sheep being taken to Torpoint to swedes for the winter. The journey could take three days. Appointments had been made to stay with different farmers on the way via Ivybridge. On another journey to Torpoint, someone would have to stay 'digging turnip shells' that the sheep had left behind in the ground, for them to eat and clear up more easily.

Speaking broadly about the moor, Norman mentioned the Venville rights, secured by paying just a few shillings. Because there was no physical boundary of the moors and no fence, the Forestry Commission could not impound your stock if they strayed and these rights were paid up. A lot of farmers had rights to Holne moor and the Forest beyond.

The Browns at Staddicombe had sheep that originated from Harry Norrish and these leared near to Huntingdon Warren; Harry's old rights. Also John Coaker's father had Scotch sheep on Holne and Buckfastleigh moor and 'French' Webber (David's father) put cattle and sheep into Brimpts and Holne.

Norman explained that Caunter's sheep were pitch branded to put in the forest with their owner's initials stamped clearly on the sheep's wool. Other owners would have done this as well to help identify their animals in the Autumn drifts.

Norman recalled that Harry, i.e. William Henry Norrish, was missing a sheep on the Forest at Greenhill towards the clay pits. Harry had an elder brother called 'Farge' near Ivybridge-Brent, so he sent him a postcard – 'missing one ewe'. His brother received the message and they were to meet at Redlake (claypits) very early one morning. Harry arrived back at 'Cumpson' (Combstone) in time for breakfast leading the ewe up the track and back to its lear on the pre-arranged day.

Radmore's Hernspitt

MEAVY

A very old story of Whitefaces with the Pearse Brothers is already recorded at Hernspitt. Roger Radmore, whose father Derek (Dicker) Radmore farmed Hernspitt from the mid-fifties, said he was about seven years old when his family moved to Hernspitt. His grandfather was a wheelwright.

Derek Radmore farmed at Parklands previous to this time, near Cornwood and Lee Moor under Penmoor.

Roger remembers his father telling him 'to get the pony', to help bring sheep back from Parklands. His father stood in a cart with the sheep and dogs ahead of him. They came to Hernspitt via Cadover Bridge with the pony and trap. Roger was attending Meavy school and was only 7 years old.

Closewool sheep were purchased from John Northmore's sale some thirty-five years ago. Derek took an interest in Whitefaces later in life, when into his sixties and nearly retirement age.

When Roger moved to Cornwall to farm between Truro and St Austell, flocks were swapped and Roger took the 'Dartmoor flock'; he said they were small Widecombe Dartmoors with no wool down their legs and clean-faced. However, they would get on their back and it was not really a sheep farm.

Farms do differ in their preference for sheep or cattle and in Cornwall just one and a half miles across the road the geography would favour sheep immensely, and yet not the other side of the road.

Sixty Whitefaces was a regular flock number and one held by the Radmores. Roger is knowledgeable and engrossed in 'sheep learing'. Rights of common grazing on the Moor from Hernspitt Farm were 'running the Plym' the width of the river either side, up around Ringmoor Cot and Ringmoor Down. Sheeps Tor is placed at the North Eastern corner of the Ringmoor Down. It is one of the largest of the Dartmoor tors.

Sheepstor is a small moorland village and takes its name from the huge pile that rises from the hill above it, but this, as an early form of the name proves, has nothing to do with sheep, so says William Crossing! An earlier name used for Ringmoor Down is 'Rydemoor'. The Reverend H. Hugh Breton M.A. in his book Beautiful Dartmoor also says the name Sheep's Tor has no reference to sheep, although flocks of sheep often browse on its breezy slopes, but means 'steep'. The old names of the Tor are Shittes Tor, Schittes Tor and Shepiftor (1611). Also according to Breton, who was born in 1873, writing the above book first printed in 1911 and republished in facsimile in 1990 by Forest Publishing, he explained that Sheepstor is one of the few parishes still in Venville.

In return for a 'fine' paid to the Duchy, there are certain rights. On the Duchy lands ponies and cattle can be pastured, peat cut for fires and take away from the Moor anything that 'may do us good, except green oak and venison'.

The Venville rights originated many hundreds of years ago. Breton says several of the explanations of their origin are incorrect. They were originally granted to the farmers, in return for the services they rendered to the Forester, in assisting him in exterminating the wolves which infested the forest long after they were extinct in other parts of England. As evidence that wolves infested English forests later than is generally supposed, there is an interesting tomb of a Bishop of Wells in Wells Cathedral, dated about 1200, on which are recorded the noble deeds of the prelate. One of his exploits recorded was the material assistance which he rendered in exterminating the wolves in the great 'forest of Mendip' by hunting.

The old tradition of buried treasure which is related to so many places is attached to Ringmoor Down. It used to be said that if this could be discovered, 'all England might plough with a golden share'!

From Ringmore Cot one can descend to Lynch Down and then to Meavy and Yelverton and Dousland up the hill!

Sheeps Tor brook rises at Gutter Tor mire. Learing sheep and stock for Roger was a personal experience and he remarked that 'before he could hardly remember things', he recalls pony trips on Dartmoor 'living in the saddle'! Sheep he said 'actually going home was not a regular occurrence'! This did happen as other breeders experienced. Roger explained that 'it is difficult to drive sheep off their lear in a different direction'. But going out to their lear across the Plym the front sheep couldn't be held back and didn't look to go back. A few sheep at the rear of the flock may try to turn for home, because they weren't familiar with the lear. Roger spoke of the sheep counts and how farmers had to run and run across Ringmore Common.

Swaling too was a planned issue one in ten years to a place to break the cycle, and pieces of moorland were burnt for stock 'to move onto' and gain young grazing from regrowth of gorse, heather and moorland grass shoots.

Roger's memories extend to the special pony sales at Princetown and 'trains up the Princetown line' loaded with ponies for Princetown Fair. He said 'some 2000 ponies could be seen in the area years back'!

Roger returned to his learing story and he said one particular sheep insisted on going to Okehampton every year. He picked her up three times. To put a stop to this one day Roger marked her head. He took her to near Lee Moor and let her out the tail of the van. He explained that if stock run out of a lorry or other vehicle with the tail board down they think it's home. She never strayed again and ran between tors at Penmoor. The explanation seems to be that they don't know their way home if taken in a vehicle, and 'the lear becomes their home.'

Sheep, it seems, don't easily mix well and the Moor is a prime example, and so 'learing' too can be controlled; Roger said, sheep can 'only go to the hedge-wall' from any moorland patch. A lovely expression of Dartmoor's newtake and moorland boundary walls, as the latter are a form of 'stone hedge'!

Albert and Robert Rogers

COOMBE FARM, ASHPRINGTON

The Rogers family farmed Whitefaced Dartmoors at Modbury.

A move was made to Cornworthy Court, Cornworthy, later to farm Frogmore in the parish of Ashprington. Coombe Farm became the home of 400–500 Whitefaces when Albert Rogers took on the farm, when the 'Sharpham Estate' was split and sold. This was a sizeable flock of pure breeding Whitefaces maintained solely on the root and pasture fields of the South Hams.

Sheep were walked from Coombe Farm to swedes grown at Stoke Gabriel. These 'roots' were probably purchased in the Autumn, when sold as winter keep along with 'grass runs' and hay and straw at places like Totnes, under the auspices of auctioneers such as Rendells at winter keep sales. The swedes were folded or fenced for the sheep to eat and the walk to Stoke Gabriel was about ten miles. The back lanes of Totnes would have been a quieter route to Stoke Gabriel to drive the sheep away to keep.

The Whitefaces that Robert Rogers remembers were not, he said, 'what you would call big sheep'. Robert explained that his father Bert frequently sold sheep at Totnes and the Ashburton show and sale.

Robert's father later crossed his Widecombes with the Border Leicester to produce a bigger sheep, resulting in more lambs. She was also clean bellied, and on the face and head and legs, there was also no wool.

This change took place some twenty years ago at Coombe and the Suffolk acted as a three way cross. The Border Leicester cross sheep was described by Robert as a super sheep produced by the Whiteface mother and not far away from the character of the latter, with plenty of milk and clean legged.

Shearing and dipping were both contracted out. At Totnes where their farm runs steeply down to the banks of the River Dart, the late Jim Widecombe and his father found favour with Whiteface sheep, no doubt greatly advantaged by the fact that a sheep getting on its back would soon roll on and over on the steep grassy slopes of their farm to get back on its' feet, and try and stay upright, for a different reason than an itching back, when arriving at the field's bottom.

Jim could regularly be seen attending the association sale to buy Whiteface ewes and rams. His wife Helen and two sons Ian and Michael continue to farm at Totnes.

The Shinner Family

STRETCHFORD FARM, BUCKFASTLEIGH

Shinners were recorded at Stretchford in 1858. They had the first herd of South Devon cattle entered in the Foundation Herd Book in 1891. Robert Shinner still farms at Stretchford with his family, following his father Jim Shinner, who sadly died in 2003. Another son, Mervyn, farms South Devon cattle at Coyton Barton Farm, Ermington near Yealmpton in the heart of traditional livestock country. Previously Coyton was the home of Richard and George Pearse.

Robert and Mervyn's great grandfather was Edwin Shinner, and their grandfather Robert Shinner founded a flock of South Devon *sheep*; these were ewes selected from Edwin Shinner's flock that was registered in 1915, and these had been entered into the 1916 flock book.

Obviously along with the formation of the Greyface flock book in 1907–8 these sheep excited great interest, in respect of wool and docility! Robert's grandfather achieved best pen of ewes in 1920 with a pen of twenty ewes of South Devons at Totnes Sheep Sale (now no longer held!). Prices were so poor that the Auctioneers allowed farmers to keep their prize money if they didn't sell their prize winning sheep. Six tooths were usually offered for sale.

However, although pure breeding flocks of Whitefaced Dartmoors were not kept at Stretchford it is interesting to find that Whitefaced Dartmoor rams were used over many, many years, bought from Ashburton sheep sale by Jim Shinner to cross on his South Devon sheep. Jim's face was a regular one to be seen at the Association sale, as too was Edward Caunters in the photo shown. The Greyface had been tried before but not for long, and was found to be a sleepy sort of sheep, and demanding in shepherding skill, which failed to achieve satisfactory results for the Shinners!

The Whiteface, Robert explained, 'got lambs on their legs'. The udders of the first cross ewes were much neater and lambs could suck the smaller teats; an altogether livelier sheep was bred. The South Devon rams at a later date could be crossed

Jim Shinner seen on the left with Edward Caunter at Ashburton Sheep Sale.

back for a while on these first cross ewes to improve again the size of the South Devon crossed sheep, and maintain the wool clip.

Jim Shinner used to ride to Totnes Grammar School on a horse, and tie it up behind his uncle's butcher shop, and it stayed there until school ended each day. He rode his horse home to Stretchford and Jim recalled passing a car with his horse; things were slower back then on four wheels!

Recalling a recent comment which revolved around the crisis in farming and the drift of labour from the land, Robert explained that a farmer from 'up North' remarked on the 'hefting of sheep' and that as a result of foot and mouth many hefted (attached to their own area of commonland grazing) sheep were removed, but more importantly said Robert, with them went many 'hefted shepherds' and the knowledge that goes with them, compounded over generations from family to family and the latter may never return.

At Stretchford sheep tended to stay on the farm and cattle were more likely to go away to keep in summer.

The Smerdon Family

SMALLCOMBE FARM, RATTERY (ERIC, JOY AND PETER)

The Smerdon Involvement with Whiteface Dartmoors

The Smerdon family all embracing a Whiteface ewe and her triplets (Eric, Kay, Peter and Andrew).

It is unclear where the Smerdon Family originated from, but it is undeniable that they have been moorland farmers for many generations. Smeardon Down near Peter Tavy probably has a connection with the family, but it is well documented by Mike Brown in his 'Elliotts Hill News' or 'Smerdon Newsletter' that in 1639 Richard and Christine Smerdon were in residence at Elliotts Hill Farm in the parish of Buckland-in-the-Moor. From them a dynasty grew which was to reign supreme as the senior tenant occupiers in that parish for nearly two and a half centuries. The entire parish, much prized for its productive woodlands, extending to 1,500 acres owned by the Bastards of Gerston and Kitley, Lords of the Manor, from 1614 to 1926.

Given the importance of sheep in the economy of the whole country in days gone by and especially in that area of Devon, it is almost certain that the Smerdons would have kept the ancient moorland breed of sheep, the Whiteface Dartmoor. Details of leases and household inventories in the 17th century list as many as 100 'sheepe' (in one such document valued at £13 6s 8d with 'wolle' 20s). A transcript of the auction sale of William Smerdon at Bowdley in 1810 includes 52 couples, 10 barren ewes, 80 young wethers and 40 hoggets. The significance of many wethers, kept over many years for their wool, is seen here yet again!

In the early 1830's, Elijah Smerdon, Eric's great grandfather moved from Buckland to Bullhornstone in South Brent along with two other brothers, all of whom would have kept Whitefaces. Eric's grandfather, Albert Andrews, who farmed at Owley was a regular supplier of sheep to South Brent's sheep fair and Albert was renowned for the fact that when the price of wool dropped to an all time low in the 1920's he vowed not to sell his wool until the price rose to 6d per lb. He was true to his word and when the great day came there were great celebrations within the Andrews family. He would find the price of wool 80 years on as unreal!

A South Devon ram (much woollier about the head and legs).

All Eric's family continued to keep Whitefaces, most notably his uncle Owen, who was at Higher Downstow and later, when he married widow Emmie Andrews, at Zempson. A great stockman, Owen never joined the flock book, preferring to be free to use South Devon rams when he felt there was a need to improve the size of the flock. This practise was also adopted by Eric, and Joy Smerdon well remembers one particular ram of that breed that they always had to watch (he was very protective of his harem). The use of the South Devon was probably responsible for Eric proudly coming home from Brent Sheep Sale having topped the market for ewe lambs at £10 a piece around 1960. Our son, Peter, continued to keep sheep until Eric retired from the business, lambing up to 200 ewes, although the predominance of the Whitefaces was somewhat diluted by the introduction of Suffolks.

It is unusual now to find many breeding Whitefaces away from the fringes of the moor. However, here at Smallcombe, Rattery they are well suited to quite 'hard climate' farms in sight of Brent Hill to be seen to the west-northwest of Rattery village 4 or 5 miles away.

The foreword photo to this story is a truly telling picture, that demonstrates a great depth of love for the Whiteface sheep right down to the youngest member of the family, that wants to hold a lamb.

C. I. Stevens

KENDON, NORTH BOVEY

Christian farms in the shadow of Kings Tor and Hameldown, on its north side. Here the afternoon sun soon disappears behind the moor in winter and his heavy land stays wet and cold for longer than most farms. Not entirely suited to sheep farming, hence Christian favours his South Devon cattle. The farmhouse is dated 1675 but surely conceals an older settlement site, that was afforded shelter and plenty of water.

However, Christian still has memories of sheep and shepherding. He recalls Jack Sprague, a well known Greyface Dartmoor sheep breeder, inspecting and approving sheep. Rams, probably mostly Greyface sheep, were marked with a green 'A' on the rump if they were approved for use on flocks that used the nearby commons like Easdon. If a ram was rejected, an 'R' was placed on each shoulder indicating the ram should not be used as a stock ram, and that it hadn't passed this test!

Christian still has the homemade marking iron with the 'A' initial forged on it.

Speaking of farming practices in general and Christian's farming family in Essex, he said his father, like farmers on Dartmoor, liked to keep one year's hay in hand in the past, to have some food to take into the following winter for the animals in case of dry or wet summers.

In fact, Christian explained that to preserve one rick on the farm where his father worked, it was thatched three times before it was fed and that in a county with an average rainfall of 20 inches (Essex).

In the drought year of 1921, trees were cut down to feed the cattle and sheep and, when the harvest was collected, men walked in front of the wagons to prevent wagon wheels getting stuck in the large cracks that opened up because of the drought.

Form B. 18.
In quadruplicate
1st copy to Farmer
2nd & 3rd to Regional Office
4th retained by Merchant

BRITISH WOOL BWMB MARKETING BOARD

REGION South Western

WOOL PURCHASE INVOICE No.

11th October, 1960

Census No. SW 19318.

Merchant's Name Co-operative Wholesale Society Limited

Address Fellmongering & Wool-Combing Works, Buckfastleigh, Devon.

REGISTERED PRODUCER'S FULL NAME AND ADDRESS C.I. Stevens Esq., Kendon, North Bovey, Newton Abbot, Devon.

Received Weights					Grading Particulars					
Bale No.	Sheet Tare	cwts.	qrs.	lbs.	Grade No.	Net lbs.	Price per lb.	£	s.	d.
223	7	2	0	9	514A.Gsy.Deep ½Bd.Fs.No.2.	7	50½d	1	9	6
6616	7	0	2	10	604A. " Lt.XBd.Flc.No.2.	57	49¼d	11	13	11
43	7	0	2	4	603. " Ex.Horn Flc.No.1.	115	57½d	27	11	0
	21	3	0	23	603A. " " " " No.2.	39	54¼d	8	16	4
				21	536. " XBred Grey Flcs.	8	38d	1	5	4
		3	0	2	616H/HA. " Lamb 1&2.	59	45d	11	1	3
					θ " Dags.	53	4d		17	8
		= 338 lbs.				338		62	15	0
					B.109 Addition.				9	11
					S.J.G.S.			63	4	11

British Wool Marketing Board, South Western region:-
11th October 1960. The merchants name is interesting and descriptive of its company's business:- Cooperative Wholesale Society Ltd, Fellmongering (hides) and Wool-combing Works, Buckfastleigh, Devon.
The wool is not Whiteface but the grading and price per pound reflects prices of wool in 1960. Even 'dags' (tail-dockings) commanded a payment 4d a lb. Three hundred and thirty-eight pounds of wool with a B.109 addition was valued at £63-4s-11d. This equates with around 44 pence a pound in old currency (18.6 decimal pence per pound!).

The Turner Family

CORNDONFORD, WIDECOMBE-IN-THE-MOOR

The Turner Brothers were Richard and Edwin. Edwin was Alec Turner and Bessie French's father.

The three generations of Turner/French's were Bessie French's father, Edwin, Alec Turner, Bessie's brother, and Terry French, Bessie's son.

Corndonford is another very old farmstead and settlement, and on its farmhouse entrance arch is the date 1718. The Turner family moved to Cordonford from Higher Sherril in 1909.

Left to right: Alec, Edwin; and Ronald Hill is pictured holding a 'Widecombe' in the courtyard at Corndonford. Here in the 1930's the Whiteface finds pride of place!

The 'courtyard' in the above photograph is partly circled by the stone remains of the 'old round house', whose beams decayed over time, and collapsed, bringing down the old thatched roof. The large slabs and 'cobbles' (rounded stone) form the yard's floor. The tall granite pillars were evidence as to how important these roundhouse structures would have been when first built with 'horse wheels' attached to drive other simple cogged or belt driven machinery, and so transfer motion!

Here in this patchwork quilt of little moorland fields, every field has its own name:- Corndon Close, Square Park, Rock Park, Daisy's Park, Big Field, Shoot Park, Higher and Lower Long Close, and the familiar name of Barn Park, no doubt adjacent to some hay or fodder barn, and there were other names too!

Shire horses belonging to Annie Williams who owns Corndonford now, still grace the fields, but their work is mainly confined to competition ploughing with the old horse ploughs (balance 'saracuse'), and for towing the old wagons. It is now their clanging hooves that plod across the hard cobbled yard at Cordonford and announce the arrival of a far different dawn today! For they are no longer used to farm the fields at Corndonford.

Not uncommonly on many Devon and Cornwall farms, it was apparent that two or more brothers were responsible for different jobs on the farms, Edwin being the sheep man in this instance, and Richard was the horseman, but he also sheared and everyone seemed to be able to turn their hand to many farm jobs.

Alec too sheared and used to help out at the Leamons. Alec and his father Edwin could shear both left and right-handed with hand shears. (left, as seen in photograph with Edwin). No doubt the loss of part of Edwin's right index finger in a mangold-turnip root-cutter, encouraged him to work with his left hand too.

Alec also sheared with Henry Nosworthy at George Smith's Hexworthy Farm.

Sheep taken out into the field from the shearing shed for Bessie to photograph, using a box camera saved up for with 'cocoa tokens'!

Edwin and Alec Turner hand shearing at Cordonford – 'The shears clearly visible'!

Again it is interesting to see how the interest in sheep has been passed on to Bessie French's son, Terry. He is an excellent sheep shearer, and contract shears for many farmers (6000 sheep sheared in the year 2000) through the summer. Many hundreds of these sheep are still Whiteface Dartmoors, but Terry has to admit their numbers are dwindling in favour of Suffolk, Mule and Crossbred sheep and he doesn't shear so many Whitefaces as in the past.

Terry French starting the 'long blows' on a Whiteface ram, using electric clippers, at Barramoor Farm, North Bovey.

Edwin Turner worked for a while with Mr Edmund John Irish, Lower Cator. Mr Irish, (grandfather) allowed Mr Turner to pick his Whitefaces to start his own flock. These sheep were kept pure until 1950. So there were Whitefaces at Corndonford before Closewools.

The rounded hill of Jordan Ball and Shallowford Ball with its barren moorland pasture and gorse, is clear to see in the background in the spring sunshine of March, behind Bessie's tame ewe and her lamb.

The ewe is seen foraging under a feed pan, so she was still having preferential treatment!

Bessie too was very much part of the farmlife and she reared tame, this ewe that is now rearing her own two lambs.

This 'dipping' is thought to be at Hexworthy (Ring 'O Bells). Richard Turner is holding the sheep. A wooden crook holds up the second sheep – Whitefaces.

Bessie is full of wise and old sayings, and at a wonderful age of 87 years they are still clear to her.

I remarked that it is said, 'if there's shade in May there will be shelter in June'. She was quick to remark that Jan Leamon used to say 'if you grow hay, you grow a lot to rot'! and this she said, relates to the uncertain weather in summer. However, just two or three days good weather with silage will secure a harvest in these days of modern machinery!

The taking of sheep keep away was common practice to people like George Mills, Langford Harberton and to Chudleighs at East Leigh and Foale's Leigh, Reg Eveleigh, Rolsters Bridge. Edwin walked these sheep to and fro and on the way home he was always relieved to get back to Hembury behind Codd's of Stoodley, and be able to put the 'stragglers' in a field near Hembury. This drift was often only days before lambing when the sheep were walked home from their winter keep. In this case they came home to roots in the form of mangolds and swedes.

The wether hoggs were sold after shearing in June (15 months old).

Sheep dipping took place at Southcombe under John Hannaford and at the Leamons, Great Cator and at Sweaton (Harry Axford and Bill Caunter).

Gyp French, Stan French and Ralph Bamsey, 1930s. At 'Town Wood' (Gyp's farm). Clearly a Whiteface sheep being held (an identity mark: 'chock-cut' off left ear), about to enter a galvanise tub, set in the ground; water carried from nearby! A 'faggot' of wood 'stops a gap'!

'The dip in action'. The high netting says 'they are not meant to escape' (poultry wire)!
I, and I'm sure many other folk, remember being 'bathed' in one of these; before or after dipping, I wonder?

This must have been an extraordinary lot of work, carrying each sheep to the dip, and dipping one at a time; 'mobile-sheep', rather than a 'mobile dip'! There is little evidence of 'Safety First'! (Gloves or masks).

Bessie vaguely remembers sheep being taken to Widecombe Fair to be sold in the 1920's.

Terry explained that his Grandfather would not keep Whitefaces unless they had a 'top knot' (wool on their head), that is '*not* bare-polled', as Bessie called them.

Sheep picking is obviously still in progress, and a long line of hurdles is made available for the sheep sale in a field at Town Wood.

Bessie explained that a lot of Whitefaces were not replaced on farms that 'sold-up' especially during the 2nd World War, and this contributed to their decline, whereas previously everyone had Whitefaces and shared the commons grazing.

'One of the said sales'. Gyp French's sale on August 27th 1959 at 'Town Wood' (Widecombe). Terry French is seen centre as a small lad. John Sawdye just from the right. Gyp French second from the right. The sale was conducted by Sawdye and Harris.

She named Harry Axford at Sweaton, Len Hill, Gyp French at Town Wood, Stan French at Lowertown, Frank Norrish at Torr, Fern Langdon (Bill Langdon's father), Edred Langdon, Town Farm, in the hamlet of Lowertown, Chaffe at Corndon, and so on!

It must have been 1976 when one of the worst droughts in living memory occurred and affected many parts of the country and Dartmoor too. Little hay was saved because the grass lacked moisture and was burnt back, and the 'roots' grown away from the moor's edge, that were still relied on for winter food, came, but fizzled away with the soaring heat, that gave hardly any rain from February to September.

However, on visiting Cordonford Alec took me on a farm walk and across from the farmyard a moist meadow had been ploughed for kale, and the little plants had emerged, and here were doing well!

With moor all around Cordonford, it's home to Bog Cotton, Ragged Robin, Sundew and Red Shank, and others that are the moors wetland plants, and therefore would have been no surprise to a moorland farmer like Alec, that crops grown here would not be adversely affected by drought. As a wise old moorman quoted by Val Doone in 'We see Devon', said, 'You can't leave the bogs out of Dartymoor, nor the devil, nor the weather, they'm everywheres'.

Cordonford is very near to the common and the lear is used above the Newtake on Corndon Tor (North Tor) towards Cator Gate and on to Sherril (Sherwell).

Hoggs were put up on to the common in April–May, before the ewes. The hoggs became charcoal grey from rubbing the 'black sticks' of gorse and heather left standing amongst the rocks as a result of the swaling; the soots clinging to their faces and legs. They seemed very fit and their wool was a blue-grey colour.

As animals searched for the young shoots of gorse, grass and heather, which is encouraged to grow as a result of the burning, they rub against the burnt sticks, and some snap off making a cracking noise, as animals push through these stark black areas. Black sticks ('light sticks') were collected to light fires in winter!

The sheep especially find the new shoots very nourishing and quite soon after swaling are seen browsing what appear to be 'black deserts', staying for hours on these newly swaled patches finding the emerging shoots sweeter, and softer on the mouth.

Bog-cotton.

Sheep among the swaled (burnt) 'black sticks'.

The practice of swaling is a very old moorland tradition and when thousands of animals pastured the moor in the past, pasture quality was also controlled by systematic burning, and the animals excrement also dressed the acid peat.

Bessie said, 'everybody seemed to drop a match in March, and it might get into a hedge a bit'!

She remembers her father and brother saying from the farm, 'that fire is still going out there,' ('out auver').

Terry said 'Hameldown could be burning two days and two nights lighting up the night-time sky on the moor, towards the direction of Kings Tor, creeping over a big area.

Herbert and Reaney Vallance

LOWER WHIDDON FARM, ASHBURTON

Another farm with its history carefully presented and preserved behind framed glass on the writing desk, recording its tenants back to 1886 and updated to 1919 and 1956 and its purchase in 1962 by Herbert and Reaney Vallance, the present owners of Lower Whiddon.

Herbert recalled a Smerdon family farmed it in 1741. A document on the sideboard reads:

'The Western Daily Mercury (provided by the Western Morning News) printed on Saturday May 28th 1886:

'In the "Parish of Ashburton" let by Tender for a term of 14 years "all that desirable farm" called Lower Whiddon containing about 86 acres of good pasture, orchard, and arable land (17 acres of which are unenclosed and which was part of "Ashburton Down" which in total was once around 170–180 acres.'

This picture tuly records a different 'era'! Roy Tucker stood in a wain, bringing 'flatpolls' (cabbage) to the Whiteface sheep (1936).

Gathering here another story on Whiteface sheep produced an old breeders photo at Lower Whiddon with Reaney's Uncle Roy Tucker stood in a wain that brought flatpoll cabbages to the sheep (and lambs) that they can be seen eating in a grass field nearby. The photo was taken in springtime in 1936. Looking more closely at the photo, mud can be seen clinging to the horses hairy legs, no doubt coming from the muddy root field that grew the flatpoll cabbages. Also a brass can be seen drooping down over the lovely white blaze of the blinkered horse's head attached to a brow band. The Whitefaces had been brought up from Blackawton in 1919 when Uncle Roy Tucker moved to Lower Whiddon. The farm had been advertised as

57 acres 1 rod and 28 poles in size. His first rent in 1919 was £90 a year. The tithe rent was £9-2s-8d.

The sheep's previous territory at Blackawton was frequented by Whitefaces and their breeders; a finger of country in the South Hams which in itself is quite hard and uncompromising to man and stock. The land at Whiddon suited the Whitefaces too. Roy Tucker was the tenant at Lower Whiddon until 1956.

Speaking of defining the origins of the Dartmoor and different breed type, Herbert remembered specifically seeing at Dousland Sheep Sale on one occasion, big Whitefaced Longwools, a sort of improved Greyface or Devon Longwool cross, or maybe just big Whitefaces that had been crossed!

Herbert also passionately remarked that the fact that you could breed almost any sheep away from a Whiteface spoke highly of its constitution.

He also reminisced as he saw the old photos collected for this book. He spoke of the desperate snow winter of 1947; the wind and the cold and the 'ammil ice' and the incredible prism like colours that showed up in the 'tilley lamps'. These tilley lamps were pressure lamps that didn't 'blow out' like hurricane lamps! The light of the lamp reflected off the ice that was rock hard down the lane at Whiddon.

Herbert spoke of digging out turnip shells embedded in the root fields, that the sheep found too awkward to eat.

He reminisced of 'Prince and Smart' names also given to faithful shires on other farms. Also of seeing six horses drawing a thresher (used to separate the corn from the sheaf) in his younger days and of reapers and binders!

Field names too, unchanged over generations, have a romantic ring about them. Long Close, Middle Meadow, Gratnar (forever granite and stone also defined as Green Tor!) and Laney Brake; a dialect habit of adding a 'y' or some other letter to bring emphasis to a particular word.

Herbert remembers the farm and market carts, and pig nets used to cover carts to help keep in animals on their journey home, and to market; the carts pulled by 'cob horses'.

The farm is without Moor rights. William Whitley seemed to control the rights as part of Buckland Manor. However, during 1976's very dry summer and severe drought when little rain fell between February and September, Herbert rented off the Waite family at East Dart grass keep in 'Archerton Newtake', but even there in the heart of the moor some sheep didn't survive the drought.

Whitefaces did frequent the area near to Lower Whiddon, and Albert Hamlyn nearby bred Whitefaces.

Mike Voisey

BUCKFASTLEIGH WOOLLEN MILL

John Hannaford's daughter, Pam (her father worked at Furzeleigh as the monks' shepherd), said it is perhaps important to distinguish between the 'Buckfast Mill' (and the monks) where a lot of wool was imported and was not all from local fleeces, but associated with the making of Axminster carpets and woollen trade; and in contrast the 'Buckfastleigh Mill' and associated Tan Yard (hides), also known as fells. Once trading as the Cooperative Wholesale Society Limited, Fellmongering and Wool-Combing Works, Buckfastleigh, Devon. In the South Western region of the British Wool Marketing Board.

Mike Voisey previously at Buckfastleigh Mill and before his untimely death whilst still working at the Devon and Cornwall Wool Depot at Liskeard, told me of Churchwards Grading Depot and the Co-op and of establishement dates such as 1843. Also, quite graphically, he talked of Old Buckfastleigh and how the Old Mill was the length of Chapel Street. Then he said the industry was a big thriving chain of production in about the 1920's (Wollen cottages for the workers at the Mill).

There was strong wool for carpets from a longwool base. Blankets were made through people's own wool being taken back. Also rugs and carpets were made at home using different types of wool. However, the complete processing story was recorded in the factory.

Probably the industries success revolved around two great assets, sheep and water. The sheep we know about! The water in abundance running off the granite is of the right hardness for scouring the wool. The leats leading to the factory were directed to come right into the factory to drive the turbines. The wool was then washed with chemicals and then oil actually put back in using cones of vegetable oil.

Mike Voisey said, 'If no oil is added the wool becomes very static and would crack'.

Freda Wilkinson writes that sheep washing just before shearing to clean the wool of foreign matters (to protect hand shears) and of a proportion of the 'yoak' or lanolin grease, is not practiced here now nor has been in living memory. She goes on to say that Vancouver mentions that sheep are normally shorn 'in the yoak' (greasy) here, and adds that, 'It is advantageous to wash closewool sheep before shearing, but to sell the long and coarse stapled fleeces in the yoak'.

However, at Blackaton 'Newtake' in the Forest against Babeny is what appears to be the remains of a sheep washing place with a crush pen and a narrow gate opening on to a wide flat-bottomed ford in the Dart. The narrows Freda says could easily have been partially dammed to increase the depth and the animals passed from man to man. Standing thigh deep across the stream, turned up and 'dunked' by each in turn and let out into Babeny Pitt on the other side. The ruins look ancient she says and may date from the days when the Dartmoor sheep was still a relatively short woolled breed.

Returning to Mike's story and some reasons for the woollen industry's decline, he says that recently worldwide the production of natural fibre has been high and wool plentiful. Our type of wool has had a specific use, especially in carpets, and the demand for the latter in woollen form have been substituted with synthetic fibres.

However, in a very partisan manner, Mike explained, '*It is still difficult to substitute the quality of fineness of the longwool*'.

However, the amalgamation of the South Devon and the Devon Longwools to form the Devon and Cornwall Longwools and also because the grading of wools in relation to breed was stopped, the special definition of the original fine longwool ceased. All wools now make the same product from many different breeds all lumped in together, so Michael explained!

Roger Whale

WILD GOOSE, WIDECOMBE-IN-THE-MOOR

Roger's first introduction to farming was at the age of just over 17 when he went to work for Richard Coaker at 'Runnage'. Roger said, 'Richard ran sheep from "Darthead to Dartmouth". Sheep were summered up the West bank of the East Dart around Lower White-Tor and to near Cuthill'. Sheep were brought back and their lambs weaned around early August; ewes (mainly six-tooth) were picked to sell at Ashburton Fair. The hoggs went back to the moor for a month or so and all sheep were cleared from the moor by the 1st October.

The sheep then stayed on Runnage until November and then keep in lots of 4 acres of swedes and 10 acres 'grass run-backs' was taken away from Runnage as the winter's keep.

Richard, he said, would go back year after year to the same keep farms and other farmers sheep might be lambed away to keep.

Roger said John Andrews taught him to shear alongside Roger Hutchings. Roger Whale's first test of shearing was to just belly out the sheep with hand shears. Wif Irish and Joe Mortimore sheared at Runnage. Owen White also sheared around the area and at Widecombe. Rams could shear around 20 lbs a fleece and ewes 10–12 lbs.

Roger said of Richard Coaker, 'that he was a showman selling excellent six-tooths at Ashburton Sheep Sale and gaining many prizes in the Show and Sale'. Lionel Foster, Paul Caunter and Bob Kerswell were the buyers who liked his sheep. They were big strong sheep with at least two years breeding left in them.

Roger said he was trained by a Dartmoor farmer who was cautious, but gave him a good knowledge of farming life. Also his emphasis on showing his sheep was a good advert for the markets at Ashburton. Roger also recalled that rams were making around 100 gns during the early 1960s. Black sheep sometimes turned up and were sold to John Sawdye.

Mr J. Savery and Mr Roger Whale with two of Mr Savery's prizewinning rams. Ashburton Fair 1967, Roger on the right of the picture

For the first dinner and dance at the Ashburton Motel (for the Association) Roger wrote the 'Whiteface Anthem'. Roger remembered he was out in the field 'pitting swedes' and because it was peaceful, the idea came to him for the Anthem and he felt it was an honour to put the song to music. (See preface to this book).

After 1955 the dinner started to become a regular event for the handing out of Cups for the year's achievements including the flock competition winners that showed their sheep on the farm and a social evening too, and in latter years auctioning crabs as well! The dinner was held in earlier years at the Green Café, Widecombe.

Roger became chairman of the association in 1969 and remarked 'that he must have been the only chairman who didn't keep sheep'!

The snow winter of 1962–3 also brings back memories when Roger remembered seeing around 60 sheep that had been buried in the Quarry area up Merripit Hill and had died, but were being ripped apart by hungry foxes hunting in packs of at least 6.

A postcard lent by Roger Whale of Tavistock Inn and Whitefaces, in the early 1900s, showing the old lamp-lit trap and horse and perhaps the farmer/shepherd beside the wall and sheep! (Courtesy of Roger Whale).

John Hamlyn White (Joe)

LOWER BATWORTHY, CHAGFORD

Joe White's Grandfather lived at Sherril (Sherwell) Widecombe-in-the-Moor in 1857; William Hamlyn White; in 1502 the hamlet is spelt 'Shirwyll'.

Sue Booty has a poster of Sherwell detailing its auction in 1874 by Sawdye and Son; this would have been Ted Sawdye (the son) (John Sawdye's father) and John's Grandfather was Sawdye, well before the business became known as Sawdye and Rendell, or even Sawdye and Harris in the late thirties of the nineteen hundreds!

A Richard French tenanted 'Sherwell' in 1874, before its sale. The Whites were at Middle Sherril in 1909 and Joe's eldest brother William Hamlyn White, was born here. As you wind your way down to 'Sherwell' (pronounced Sher'ell) under Yar Tor and Corndon Tor, this place seems carved out of the Moor's granite and is protected and over-shadowed by the high tors that surrounds this moorland hamlet. William White is recorded driving cows into the 'Longhouse' at 'Sherwell', for milking!

The White family then moved to Langworthy Farm, following in the footsteps of a John Hannaford, who it is recorded in a history of Devonshire (1857), also farmed neighbouring Hatchwell Farm. These farms lie on the lower slopes of Hameldon and Grimspound, and at the south-eastern entrance to the Challacombe valley.

Whiteface sheep were always kept, and in 1921 the family of John Hamlyn White, his wife Ivy (nee Hannaford) and three sons, William, Owen and Joe, and daughter Annie, moved in-country to Batworthy Farm, Chagford. Joe was about one year old and has remained at Batworthy ever since, and his niece's Whiteface ewe hoggs still graze the fields in winter at Batworthy.

With their few wain and/or wagon loads of possessions, they also walked their South Devon cattle and Whitefaced Dartmoor sheep to their new farm.

Joe explained that the 'Widecombe' was regarded as being the real Dartmoor breed, the 'MOTHER OF ALL DARTMOORS', was the expression he used, the Greyface he said having been

July 1940. The Warren House Inn can just be seen on the middle right edge of this picture. Joe Mortimore, William White and Owen White riding out with sheep ahead to the Moor; Stats bridge side of the Warren (Stats also spelt 'statts').

A Whiteface ewe and her lamb at Batworthy. The photograph was taken in the summer of 1946 and the sender said 'just to wish you all a very happy Christmas and all the best in 1947'. The bad snow blizzard came at the end of January 1947!

'improved' several times using other breeds, with which they have been crossed. A well known Greyface Dartmoor breeder, Jack Sprague of the past, who lived next door at 'Stiniel Farm', near to the White family, put a very special prize-winning Greyface ram, on one occasion, in fields next to Batworthy with some of his Greyface ewes (his flock was registered with the Greyface Dartmoor Association). Owen and Joe White spotted this good ram, so they decided to put some of their ewes near to the boundary. Of course the ram got in over the boundary hedge and served several sheep; they were quietly hoping this would happen!

So the following spring, Jack Sprague saw some lambs that looked like his over the hedge in the Batworthy fields. He retorted, 'you artful Whites' you must have had my ram last autumn!' The resulting Whiteface cross Greyface sheep were lovely sheep; hardy, and sheared more wool than the pure Whitefaces.

It was not unknown for Whiteface rams to be used on the Greyface also, to maintain a degree of white in their mottled faces, to help emphasise the grey and black of their noses when shown at local shows.

Jack Sprague used to do a lot of showing with his Greyfaces (along with Jim Cole, Olive Luce and Norman Mortimore etc). Owen White would shear them with hand shears; Jack would say to Owen, 'Shear 'um rough boy, shear 'um rough'. If the wool was not cut off too tight it would re-grow a lot quicker and enhance the fleece for showing the sheep at different shows through the summer.

Mary Kirkham (nee Northway) at 'Broadhalls' Chagford used to hand shear sheep for showing too, and she explained that shearing down the sides from the back to the belly could achieve this rough-cut line, keeping the shears well off the skins of the sheep.

Talking to Joe about sheep in general, he recalled Tony Stanbury of Teigncombe Farm, Chagford, keeping 'closewool sheep', (Devon Closewools) in grass keep at Horselake, Chagford, just a stone's throw up the road from Batworthy. The Closewool ewes were crossed with a Whiteface ram and the resulting first cross sheep, Joe explained, were 'cracking ewes'. The Devon Closewool used to have a popular niche in and around Chagford.

Joe's memories of specific happenings on the farm are still very clear. He said that on one occasion the mangolds had been 'hand-hoed', (thinned out and cleaned of weed using a turnip hoe), but the sheep at Batworthy at the time somehow 'got in the root field', and were eating the young plants! Joe's father was so annoyed he told the 'boys' to drive the sheep out to Teignhead (on the Moor) out the way, (a newtake with common grazing rights).

During the very severe blizzard winter of 1947 at Batworthy, somehow the White's sheep were not buried and food such as caved mangolds and a hayrick were available, the latter thatched with ferns and then covered with rushes cut from around the farm, formed the outer layer of thatch. The rushes were placed cut end looking to the sky and so the sharp pointed ends of the rushes were placed downwards to shed the water more easily off the rick. The sheep burrowed in under the rick to pull out the sweet smelling hay. They were very hungry as ice and snow covered all else; and after some time the rick nearly collapsed on top of the sheep. Posts had to be used to prop the rick and prevent the sheep being buried and suffocated.

Joe explained that his father and brother shovelled a path up the road at Batworthy to the second gate where, inside the field the rick was placed, and they then made a track across two fields to the stream and eventually to the 'ricks plat' (plot) where the mangolds were caved (or 'pitted' as Joe might say, an expression used when swedes and potatoes were dug into the ground and covered with rushes and earth in the field they were grown in to protect them from frost).

The sheep travelled from stream and mangolds to the hay rick. Joe said this was important to the sheep to make them exercise. He said, 'it was difficult to keep the mangold cave from freezing.' As soon as it was opened to take out the mangolds, straw had to be taken over to cover up the front and protect the cave from the hard frost. Frozen mangolds could cause abortion and scouring in sheep and cows, so 'safe keeping' this valuable root crop was not guaranteed, despite being covered with first ferns, earth, rushes and earth again, when clamped in the autumn.

Joe explained with his Devonshire humour 'that the 1947 winter was so bad that bird life suffered too, and pigeons weren't worth shooting, because they were so thin!'

Under the holly trees planted so precisely on hedges, or as hedges, to become weather breaks in their own right, there was a vital protection for stock, keeping them away from the chilling wind (loo-side) and the worst of the drifting snow that often swirled away from the

Owen White ahead of his sheep coming through New Street, Chagford (late 1950s) (Copyright Frith Ltd).

hollies on the sheltered side, but had been known to blow through the holly hedges and trap animals either side.

Always watching for signs in nature that might help forecast the weather, Joe said a neighbour had said to Joe's father 'that as there were a lot of holly berries around one Christmas, that it was going to be a hard winter.' Joe's father said, 'it will be an even harder winter if there are no berries on the trees for the likes of the birdlife!'

Selling their sheep and cattle at Chagford Market from 1921 up until the late nineties was a regular occurrence for the Whites.

The animals most times walked through the back roads past Broadhalls (Broadells or Broom Park) and via Nattadon, or through New Street, nowadays lined with cars, after coming down from Meldon to the market's old site behind the Globe and Ring 'O' Bells inns. Also via Middlecott and through Weeke to Chagford past Orchard Meadow. Also via Adley Lane to the new market. Rented fields at Orchard Meadow and the top of Meldon help them to place animals closer to the market before the sales and as a form of lairage overnight.

Sheep sales at 'Rushford Mill', under the permission of Lord Hayter-Hames took place for many years after sheep were stopped from being sold behind the Globe and Chagford's old market, when the farm was managed by Chris Askew and his father.

Back in time sheep were penned in the street to be sold, when wooden hurdles formed the pens, and 'bowler hatted' country folk in time-honoured fashion presented a sense of pride and timelessness to a very basic way of selling their sheep.

The fashion of creep holes was very evident when Mr Joe White, his father and mother, and brothers and sister went to Batworthy in 1921. Their Widecombe sheep would have been kept on folded roots and this valuable food accessed by the 'sheep creep holes' at Batworthy in the early part of the 20th century. Sheep holes originally were a way of changing fields where there wasn't sufficient food or space, or an access between a field and the commons.

Mr Joe White standing near his 'sheep creep hole', at Lower Batworthy, (66" long, 15" wide and 30-40" high, with stone lintels and sides).

The social well-being of the Moor's people and the welfare of their animals over the centuries has relied to a great extent on the use of granite.

The building of homes from hut circles to longhouses; the stone pounds and folds protecting and controlling livestock; stone gateposts, high and strong walls and stone-based hedges seen all around the Moor; the building of churches and carving of crosses. Granite was used to shape their tin ingots in the form of moulds, and to grind and mill corn and crush apples.

The granite-built 'sheep hole' (or 'creep', or 'sheep creep hole') is a good example of ingenuity. However, it can only be speculation as to exactly when these lovely granite stone-built holes and tunnels may have been included in the plan of the fields and newtake management, in the late 1700s perhaps!

In the early to mid 1800s the term 'to fold-on' was used in respect of root crop folding (hurdled flocks), that is the eating of turnips, swedes and kale in situ (in the ground) during the winter and especially in the spring. The term sheep creep could well have been adopted at this time. An old Saxon word 'crype' meant to tunnel under.

The fields adjoining the sheep creep hole would usually have been grass leys and provided a 'dry lie' for the moving sheep coming and going from the roots, which in winter could be very muddied! The sheep creep holes gave sheep alone access to these crops. The 'runback' grass field may also have guaranteed access to running water from the root field, where folding may have commenced at the drier access point of the sheep creep hole in the root field.

In attempting to keep sheep's feet dry during wet long winters on peaty, high rainfall soil, especially on the folded areas of root crops, meant burnt lime was conveniently placed on the sloping floor of the creep holes, and in the stone tunnels it kept dry and when picked up on the sheep's feet helped to avoid feet problems through hardening of the feet. Outwintering of sheep was the only choice for their potential survival and breeding in days gone by, and serves to highlight the 'Widecombes' popularity in this situation with their inherent hardiness.

Those creep holes that remain on the Moors farms may well be tucked away in hedges and not known to their owners. In some cases they have been blocked with stone and only a few are still in use today. Many others were taken with hedge removal! However, to name but a few, in North Bovey and Chagford parishes, some uncovered creep holes can be seen. A good example exists at Gratnar Farm at North Bovey in one of the smallest field walled banks. Another survives in the newtake wall at Liapra (Moorgate Farm) accessing the common beyond, also within the North Bovey parish. Others can be seen at Stiniel, Yardworthy and Batworthy farms.

Whitefaced hoggs seen emerging on the north isde of the 'sheep hole' at Mr Joe Whites, coming out from Barn Hill field.

One at Batworthy has been re-opened. The stone in this instance seems especially selected and hand dressed to achieve a smooth passage for the sheep; the roof lintels are especially level and evenly cut. Further afield at Huccaby, Hexworthy, Michael Mudge still uses his creep hole to allow his sheep to be kept in a particular field near to the house during lambing time at night, and to allow access to a daytime field.

There is still evidence of sheep holes in newtake walls bordering common land, as well as from 'in-bye-land' to newtake. So the learing of stock from controlled grazing to the Moor was assisted through the use of these holes. Through this the sheep's own spot on the Moor could be established, achieving the separation of different owners' stock. The ewe and her lamb together going forward meant the lamb also knew its lear the following year.

How this apparently simple yet clever idea advanced to become commercially used with animals in general today is clear to see. It could have been the forerunner of intensively creep feeding animals in modern times. The pig, lamb and calf creep allowed the feeding of offspring away from parents, economising feed where needed most, and has gained in popularity.

So forward creeping and the novel idea of the sheep creep holes probably gave rise to the small beginnings of livestock intensification on and around the Moor and further afield, assisting in the controlled stocking and management of farm animals.

However, when the woollen industry thrived on Dartmoor and brought wealth to England and was the backbone of its economy and culture, the golden hoof was so important in the fertility of Dartmoor's light and hungry soils. Then the sound of many sheeps feet treading through numerous sheep holes on and around the Moor would have been heard. Any means of rotating sheep easily around the farm would have been welcome, as it was said that sheep shouldn't hear the church bells in the same field twice in any week. From Batworthy the peal of North Bovey church bells can still be heard, albeit not now as often as twice a week.

Many commoners who owned no sheep or cattle could at least get their fuel from the Moor, a right of Turbary (cutting of turf and peat).

Joe said the 'vags' were just heather 'moors' (roots) and were taken just a foot or so off the top surface (turfs). He said the heather recovered wonderfully well where the peat was cut and the animals loved it, and lied over it and dressed the scarred areas.

Tractors were used sometimes to plough off some of the peat. The surface 'turves or vags' were cut in flat blocks, rather than bricks, and set up to dry in pairs. Long 'trains' of horse drawn turf (peat) carts were used to carry the *fuel* off the Moor. Wheel tracks to the 'turf and peat ties', (the latter is the larger and deeper cut areas of peat) and the more remote peat cuttings led from every entrance to the Moor.

Owen White (Joe's brother) and Cyril Wonnacott supplied the Warren Inn (for their historic fire that never goes out), with peat, but their business became, it seems, too big and they were stopped by the National Park!

The resulting 'vags' burnt slowly on the hearth fires all around the Moor, and a pungent but pleasant smell of peat-smoke prevailed in the villages around Belstone and Postbridge etc. But the horses are no longer used, and the carts were used for firewood; gone says Widgery is the 'dusty' moorland vags!

An ancient Longhouse, housing a wonderful horse wheel and cider press still survives at Batworthy. Also Owen, Joe and Annie were noted for the ritual of pig killing on the farm, made famous in Chris Chapman's photography of Dartmoor people.

Not without coincidence it is said in Dartmoor Folklore and Quaint Customs that 'a quart of cider for every inch of the pig's tail' was a rule strictly adhered to until quite recent times on pig killing days.

As Dartmoor pigs have tails of abnormal length it is needless to say that in 'ye olden dayes' pig killing was not conducive to sobriety, so wrote the Rev. H. Hugh Breton M.A. in 'Beautiful Dartmoor' (and its interesting antiquities).

With the ancient apple orchard and cider press at Batworthy being in close proximity to the farmhouse, the occasion of pig killing was always celebrated with home-made cider siphoned from the old wooden barrels, some of which still remain in the old cider house today! No doubt there was a wish that the pigs tail during the latter weeks of its life would grow just that little bit longer!

A final memory of the love of nature that comes from Batworthy is about birdlife nesting regularly in farmed fields in the past.

When cutting fields for hay Owen would be seen driving young peasant chicks with a big stick away to the relative safety of a hedge. The gentle speed of the mowing and turning meant the chicks would be seen, and their hatching have taken place as harvest was later.

When hoeing potatoes in the early part of the year, and on coming across, commonly a Lapwings nest and eggs Owen would mark the nest with a stick. This was to show Joe where the nest site lay, so he would avoid burying the eggs when he came to 'bank-up' (make into earth ridges to protect the growing 'spuds' and help their harvest) the potatoes at a later date.

Cyril Wonnacott

RETIRED ORCHARD MEADOW, CHAGFORD – BORN AT VENTON, DREWSTEIGNTON

Shapley is also pronounced 'Sheepley' in local dialect. A 'sheep-lay'; their place!

The family moved to Shapley in 1923. Cyril remembers the old speckly-faced Dartmoors with top knots. They seem to get woollier as time went on, and this would change with the keep.

When Cyril was a boy of 11–12 years old (now 85 years old) he remembers his father buying Widecombes and taking them back to Shapley, where the farm hugs the moor near to Fernworthy.

The dozen Whitefaces were crossed with the more popular Greyface Dartmoor kept in the area as 'in-bye' sheep, that were not put on the moor. However, at Princetown Prison Farm the Greyface still does well, and was farmed there at a high altitude in the past. The resulting Greyface crossed sheep at Shapley were to produce more wool than their pure Whiteface sheep.

Cyril recalls a farm sale next door at Yardworthy in 1928 when 6 tooth sheep made twenty eight shillings a piece.

Maurice Hill at 'Coombe' Chagford near Kestor, used to put the Widecombe ram on some of his Scotch Blackface ewes. This produced an excellent 'beautiful sheep', that was improved and bigger, and as Cyril said, 'it cut a good fleece.'

The fleeces of the Whitefaces did change over the years and were at one point a lot straighter in their wool, and some of the ewes were 'snag-horned', (a short stub of horn). However, at Shapley the Widecombe was replaced by the Closewool sheep and the Widecombes 'ran themselves out', as Cyril remarked. Rams with no horn were called 'Nat'.

Chagford was the northern limit for the Whiteface, and Closewools were popular. Cyril and his family drove sheep miles to keep; to Hatherleigh, Spreyton and Bow. Cyril said on leaving Spreyton for home the first sheep would already be crossing at 'Hollycombe Cross' not far from Whiddon Down, as they left Spreyton with the last of the flock. 600 sheep (ewes and lambs) were taken home for shearing or weaning.

Sheep were again drifted away after weaning. Swedes were taken in winter at a Mr Hills at Hittisleigh. Some sheep were put on clover seeds so the sheep could tread them, to help establish the seeds.

Carts followed the sheep to and fro keep, and Cyril used to ride on the shafts that were attached to the horse's harness!

The cart was used to load exhausted sheep and some that died on the journey. Sometimes it might be a cartload of sheep by the time they arrived home to Shapley. Cyril recalled that when his Grandfather rode on one occasion, two sheep died and ended up in the cart, and he told Cyril he wasn't going again to help drove the sheep!

Cyril reflected that the family was always on the road moving animals. However, you might only meet the butcher or the baker with their vehicles and little else. Today it's everyone *other* than the butcher and the baker!

Sheep were also taken to near Hatherleigh Moor to grass keep, and on arrival in the spring it would be very wet and the grass just peeping through standing water. The end of May they returned for shearing.

The steep climb back up to Shapley from Chagford was a 'killer' Cyril remarked, but was helped by 'Bob' the dog (and others) who barked all day and would run along the backs of the sheep. At this time of year the sheep were heavy with their wool and this slowed their journey home, and tired them!

Cyril enjoyed handshearing and remembered shearing at French's Merripit. He also said he sheared sheep that were pitch marked 'H' which belonged to the Hext family, and he sheared on many other moorland farms.

For George and Ernest Dicker at Drewston Farm, Cyril said he sheared 38lb of wool off a Greyface Ram.

During the bitter cold winter of 1947 on a field hedge near to the lane at Shapley, Cyril recalls there was a 'maister' holly hedge! and he remembers heaps of it was cut down in desperation to feed the starving sheep. Leaves were eaten and the trees debarked by the animals. Sheep were kept moving to keep walking down the snow, and to try and stop them being drifted into the snow.

At Tawton Gate near to Yardworthy and Shapley a telephone post, due to the weight of ice on the wires became bent in the shape of a bow, touching the ground, and others just snapped off like the noise of gunfire.

River water splashed up onto trees, and produced icicles 'as large as church organ pipes', said Cyril, and ice and lumps of snow the size of 'skittle balls' were seen hanging from ponies tails! A really chilling story of the 1947 bad winter came from Cyril. He remembers a pony being found near 'Caroline Wheal' behind the Warren House Inn, and somehow it survived the very cold weather by eating a hard thorn bush to the ground, and nothing was left of the bush, when the pony was found alive.

The high roads that now cross Dartmoor follow the line of old tracks. Part of an ancient way from Bideford to Dartmouth (Mariners Way) once used by sailors passing from one port (Bideford) to another (Dartmouth) is still in use. It ran between Yardworthy and Shapley farms, and crossed the Two Bridges track near Yardworthy.

In Owens Britannica published in 1720 the road from Exeter to Tavistock is shown as passing over the Moor from 'Yadrey' (Yardworthy). It ran by the enclosures of Willandhead (Willuhede) where Cyril dipped sheep (the sheep dip was built by Cyril's father), and along a wall; and a stone near Metheral Farm gate probably marked its course towards Hurston Ridge over which it passed to a point near the present Statsbrook Bridge. When the present road across Dartmoor was made (1772) although it mainly followed the line of the ancient track, it was not carried from Statsbrook over Hurston Ridge to *Chagford*, but found another old path that ran across Bush Down to Beetor Cross and to Moretonhampstead.

A person living at Willandhead, it is said, burnt the doors of his house to keep warm; it could have proved rather counter-productive when the fire went out.

Reliving again his past years Cyril remembers his father asking him to keep an eye on two rams that were fighting. However, as they are inclined to do when confronting each other, one ram came back a distance and raced towards the other ram and broke its neck before Cyril could stop it!

Also a vist to Fernworthy to see the old bridges that were showing in the dry Autumn of 2003 Cyril said he worked for the forestry and used a large cart horse and farm cart to carry wood and chippings across the old bridge that originally led to Fernworthy Farm. He explained he was the *last to cross* the bridge with a *horse and cart* before the newtake was flooded to become a reservoir.

Jean Wonnacott explained how little life changed in her younger days; there were she said, 'the same old farmers back then'!

For example; Frank Endacott and Arthur Endacott at Middle and Lower Corndon's.

Cyril said Frank Endacotts sheep would lear near Assacombe from Corndon Farm and would stay there for two or three months and remain in the same area almost to an inch! Yet inbye Widecombes might as Cyril put it, 'be always "scrawling" about the hedges'!

A. Wotton, Stirt Farm, Cornwood

Andrew Wotton's father kept Whitefaces at Cornwood. However, all around Brent and the moor there were Greyface, Whiteface and Closewool around the 1950's. Mr Wootton said the Whiteface reared a good lamb and the Down rams, notably the South Down cross were put on them and they were good mothers.

They were put on the 'stall' by going through Cornwood and up through Watercombe to the moor. Mr Wootton used to dip at Sherrell and the Abbot's farm at Lee Mill before John Norrish built his own dip.

Rams were bought out of Ashburton, but the Devon Closewool seemed to take over and was used on the Whitefaces and the latter were crossed out.

Remembering Brent Sheep Sale, Mr Wootton referred to John Pearse in 1952 and he also said John Maye (of Luscombe & Maye) was the main Whiteface Auctioneer and recalls 3½–10½ gns paid for Whiteface rams at Brent. Whitefaces were also shown by other breeders at Brent Show.

Greg Wotton near Kingsbridge told me his father kept Whitefaces and on one occasion he kept a Whiteface ram and Greg said, 'it banged hell out of the caravans nearby and caused £300's worth of damage and the ram had to be sold'.

Conclusion

So it is not without good reason that the Whitefaced Dartmoor sheep is one of England's most ancient breeds of sheep. Probably shaped 2,500 years ago which characterised its breeding then, but with its origins possibly rooted even deeper in a prehistoric past and known to hunter-gatherers. A partnership forged and born with man's domestication of livestock in the Bronze Age. Here pounded and shepherded on the harsh southern slopes of Dartmoor by a peoples using an unwritten law, where remnants and shadows of this history can still be seen today in the form of fold, pound, reave and hut circle, witnessing to a bygone era.

Sustained in farming and industry by a need for skin, wool and meat, influenced by culture, plague and fashion, responding with productivity and to the economy, throughout the centuries, up to modern times. Nurtured during medieval times and enclosed as agriculture gradually changed to accommodate industrial revolution with more mouths to feed, and people to clothe. Yet still pasturing the Moor in a custom of shepherds long since gone. Native to only Devon and especially Dartmoor it has acclimatised naturally to one of the Southern England's original Forest landscapes; challenged by and tolerating extremes of weather in the form of heavy rains (peaking on the high Moor at 80"–100") and snow blizzard.

Looking towards Haytor (left of centre) from near to Hemsworthy Gate. (Photo Colin Pearse).

Their hardiness and adaptability to this terrain must have been key players in their survival up until this day.

'They and the impressive grandeur of their environment insensibly carries back the mind to an earlier and ruder age'. Yet the sheep can still accommodate today's landscape, and the landscape needs the sheep.

Many a captivated artist of Devon has painted our sheep onto canvas and recorded their presence in history, encouraged by the natural beauty of the uncultivated wilderness that gave our sheep a sense of home, and thereby animating the mood, and aestheticism of a painter's subject.

Jasper Wilson captures mist and sheep and Lether Tor, Yelverton.

Wm Morrish painted Kestor Rock and an horizon of moor and contented sheep.

Almost unknowingly the timeless occupation of Whiteface management has spanned the centuries. Quiet pride, dedication, disappointments and rewards, with working alongside these wonderful sheep handed down in families. Their family succession seeming not to be questioned, treated as something that was expected to continue and succeed through its ability to give satisfactory results over the years. Leared (leired) and agisted to the Moor, walked to, and folded on roots and grass in-country, trucked (train) away when purchased at the fairs and markets; always on the move! But change away from tradition was slow in that well tried and tested cycle of events.

Writing in the late 1st Century B.C. a Greek historian said, 'Britain was inhabited by tribes that preserve OLD WAYS'! This story truly is a piece of ancient England that still survives in modern times, possibly for that very reason! To think that those antediluvian sheep that were smaller and hairier than today's Dartmoors were taken along by the tide of events and contributed through their 'birthright' to such a huge industry up to the end of the 19th century.

In the past natural selection would have helped to eliminate harmful genes, and contributed to the evolution of the breed. In the wild there is strong dominance on the part of the male, where one male controls the all year round mating, and is the sire passing on the strongest 'gene matrix'. Having to fight for the flock's control and succeeding, should mean the strongest male's inheritance traits suppress recessive weaknesses!

Way back in history our sheep can be seen to have evolved in a similar way. The Moor though has changed or its practices diluted, and agistment that once related to pasturing of sheep, cattle and pony is even more extensively driven as environmentally senstive area schemes demand stock removal at certain times of the year and overall lower stocking rates.

The sounds and scents once commonplace have all but disappeared; the ring of hammer on stone, swaling of the Moor's vegetation, bird song, and the echo of the ringing horn. The preparation of stone gateposts and the patient chiselling out of granite troughs is now rare.

Swaling near Hound Tor. (Photo Colin Pearse).

The practice of swaling is not so well planned, permissible or meaningful, for it was once essential to rejuvenate the Moor and replace with ash, (ash-sweeten) and kill ticks that carried life-threatening diseases (red-water in cattle) and bring back new young shoots for stock to summer graze. 'The fire amongst the ling', used to light up the night-time sky, an honest natural aroma drifting off the hill, from the burning of bracken, heather and molinia and gorse. It was helped by one of those brisk easterly March winds, halted perhaps by bog, road or the 'hedge-wall'; 'creeping lines of fire arrested by the mire!'

The sound of Lapwing and Curlew is now becoming rare, not anymore masters of their own destiny and confined in small numbers to pockets of Moorland; vermin, people intrusion, and a scarce food source all contributing to their decline.

No longer either the 'echo of the ringing horn' summoning man to beast, and beast to man, to begin the 'big droves' off the Moor, and signalling 'the drift'; the horn blown against a rock to achieve an echo! Known as the 'blowing stone'. On one side the stone was concave and the 'horn of a bullock' blown against this was supposed to give forth a louder sound at a lofty point on the moor!

The Whiteface sheep fitted into this complex jigsaw, influenced by time, nature and man. Let's hope its presence remains in the new order of things! Yet they have seen oxen, still recorded working in the 1600's, replaced by the horse, and the latter replaced by the tractor. It has been challenged by the Scotch sheep, by land (wall) enclosure in the past, denying access to the high Moor, by the decline in demand for wool.

The final doubt is fragmented flocks, and a lack of unrelated bloodlines; but natural selection, and careful breeding has brought them this far, as the stories here bear witness and vividly reveal. The Whitefaced Dartmoor's 'genetic constitution' is firmly written into its own unique DNA matrix.

Acknowledgements

Whitefaced Dartmoor Sheep Breeder's Association (photographs and text).
Short Run Press Ltd (Mark Couch); the printers of this book.
Alison and Phil Abel.
Sue Booty.
Buckfast Abbey for allowing the use of some of their farms history.
Simon Butler's greatly valued support in compiling images.
Chris Chapman for his photography used in this book. He has recorded some of the most inspired images of Dartmoor's people and landscape over many years.
Jenny Codling.
Bridget Cole.
Doctor Tom Greeves.
Jean Hutchinson.
Charlotte Kingsmill.
Pippa Sellwood. Agribusiness Communications Ltd, Shropshire.
Elizabeth Stanbrook.
John Weir. Head of Communications, D.N.P.A.

Bibliography

Breton, Revd. H. Hugh. *Beautiful Dartmoor and its Interesting Antiquities* (Hoyten & Cole, Plymouth, 1911 and 1912).
Burnard, Robert. *Dartmoor Pictorial Records.*
Cornwall County Council and Library Service.
Crossing, William. *Guide to Dartmoor* (W.M. News).
—*One Hundred Years of Crossing on Dartmoor* (W.M. News).
Dartmoor Country Magazine.
Dartmoor Magazine.
Devon Library Services.
Devon Life.
Farmers Guardian.
Farming News.
Farmer and Stockbreeder (letter by R. Trow-Smith).
Farmers Weekly. Editor Stephen Howe.
Gill, Crispin. *Edited Dartmoor: A New Study* (David and Charles, Newton Abbot, 1970).
D. St. Leger Gordon. *Devon.*
Ruth E. St. Leger Gordon. *The Witchcraft and Folklore of Dartmoor.*
L.A. Harvey and St. Leger Gordon. *Dartmoor* (Collins, London, 1953).
Hemery, Eric. *High Dartmoor. Land and People* (Robert Hale, London, 1992).
King, Anne Randall. *Dyed in the Wool.*
Lacey and Danziger, Robert and Danny. *The Year 1000.* (First Millennium).
Love, Labour and Loss – 300 years of British Livestock Farming in Art. Patron: HRH The Prince of Wales.
Martin, Clement. *The Devonshire Dialect.*
Mudd, David. *Dartmoor Reflections.*
Page, John Lloyd Warden. *An Exploration of Dartmoor and its Antiquities* (Sealy and Co, Essex Street, Strand, London, 1889).
Place Names of Devon. Gower Mawer and Stenton.
Rural History Centre. University of Reading.
Seymour, John. *Rural Life.* (Promotional reprint Co. Ltd. for Selecta Books Ltd, 1993 edition).
Smith, Vian. *Portrait of Dartmoor* (Robert Hale Ltd, reprinted 1976).
South West Farmer.
Stanbrook, Elizabeth. Dartmoor Forest Farms. *A social history from enclosure tio abandonment.* (Devon Books, 1994).
Trow-Smith, Robert. *Farming Through the Ages.*
Vancouver, Charles. *General Views of the Agriculture of the County of Devon.* (Commissioned by the Board of Agriculture, London, 1808).
Western Morning News.
Widgery, Frederick, J. (illustrated). *Devon, Its Moorlands, Streams and Coasts* by Lady Rosalind Northcote. (Cammin Exeter, Chatto and Windus, London, 1930).
Woodman, Marian. *Cotswolds to Calais.*
Yesterdays Villages. A Dartington Rural Archive Publication.